CW00828609

In 1953, Dr. Dean Wooldridge le[ft]
where he was vice president for re[search and,]
with Dr. Simon Ramo, created T[he Ramo-Wooldridge Corporation.]
Upon its merger with Thompson [Products, Inc., he]
became president of the enlarged c[ompany. In 1962]
he resigned the presidency of Tho[mpson Ramo Wooldridge,]
Inc. to devote himself to scientific pursuits and writing. He is
especially interested in certain modern fields coupling the physical
and life sciences, in which there is a need for translating the
results obtained by the scientists of one discipline into language
that is understandable to those of the other. This book is an attempt
to provide a readable introduction to some of the recent developments
in brain research.

Martina Pickin.

McGRAW-HILL BOOK COMPANY, INC.

New York   San Francisco   Toronto   London

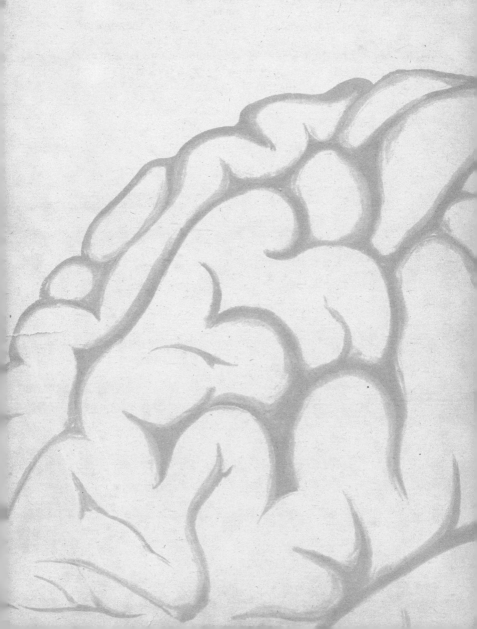

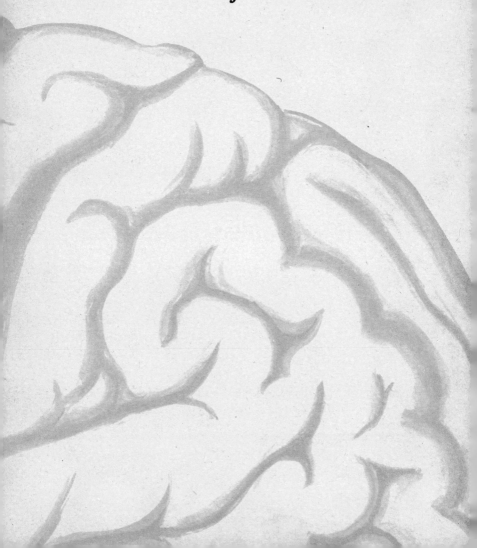

DEAN E. WOOLDRIDGE

Research Associate
California Institute of Technology

The MACHINERY
of the BRAIN

The Machinery of the Brain

Library of Congress Catalog Card Number 63–13940

151617181920 MUMU 7

ISBN 07-071841-5

This book is not for the expert. It contains few, if any, original ideas. It sets forth no new theories of memory mechanisms, of learning processes, or of higher mental activity. Instead, it is only a description of some of the past discoveries and present hypotheses of the brain-research scientists. It is intended to be easily comprehensible and, hopefully, interesting to the reader with little if any training in biology.

With the possible exception of Chapters 1 and 3, which can be skipped without doing excessive violence to the continuity of the treatment, I believe that the book is easily readable by those with no technical background of any kind, biological or physical. Such readers should only occasionally feel that the treatment is not really designed for them when they encounter the analogies between biological processes and the properties of electronic systems that are scattered throughout the book. I have used these physical analogies, and I have included Chapters 1 and 3, because it is really my intention to address myself to a narrower audience than that comprising all "general readers." My primary target is the large body of physical scientists and engineers who may suspect there are matters of interest to them in current research on the nervous system, but who feel that their lack of background in biology makes it prohibitively difficult for them to explore the field. It is my hope that the occasional physical science analogy, together with the elementary nature of the treatment, may make it easier for those with this kind of technical background to read and enjoy the book.

It is not my intention to claim credit for a pioneering effort in interesting physical scientists in brain mechanisms. In recent years a number of mathematicians, physicists, and engineers have seriously concerned themselves with attempts to apply their experimental and theoretical techniques to brain-related biological processes. Such terms as "bionics," "neural networks," "perceptrons," and even "information theory" owe their origins, in whole or in part, to a growing belief in the similarity between the adaptive and intelligent processes of natural organisms and the operational principles of modern man-made devices. There seems little doubt that the resulting interdisciplinary teamwork between the biologist and the physical scientist holds a potential for important future developments. It is likely that a competent theory of intellectual processes will come from the physical scientist, with the aid of clues supplied by natural organisms. The machinery for practical conduct of intelligent activities today resides preeminently in the domain of the life scientist but, with the aid of improved theoretical understanding, may ultimately be translatable into component and circuit designs suitable for synthetic fabrication by man. The practical implications are tremendous—both for man's improved management of the naturally provided strengths and weaknesses of his own nervous system and for the injection into all aspects of life of intelligent machines to increase productivity, diminish routine, and generally enhance the capabilities of the race.

Although these thoughts are not new, and although biologists and physical scientists are increasingly forming liaisons for cooperative research, the amount and variety of such joint work are still small, compared with the potential of the field. Considerable expansion of the effort is highly desirable, and very likely to occur. For such expansion, there is presently not enough written material to make it easy for the specialist in one field to acquire the information he needs about the other. There are, of course, language difficulties. There is also a requirement for selection of the material from one field that is likely to be found most pertinent by the collaborator from the other field. These needs will be satisfied in time. Meanwhile, there are gaps to be filled.

In starting work on this book, I had hoped to help fill a small part of one of these gaps. It was my original intention to produce a primer about the operation of the brain and central nervous system that might serve a physical scientist as a point of departure for more intensive studies. Eighteen months and three hundred pages later, I realize that even this modest goal was too ambitious. To be worthy of the name, a "primer" needs to be a collection of material so skillfully selected that it comprises the real essentials of the subject. I learned that a better expert than myself is needed to discriminate with certainty between what is likely to be fundamental and lasting and what is superficial and transient in the dynamic field of brain research. Therefore I gave up my original notion of calling my book a "primer for the nonbiologist."

In retrospect, I believe this treatment is less like a textbook and more like a travelogue—a description of an exotic land by one who visits it for the first time. There is no assurance that the naïve visitor is going to understand the strange land he is visiting well enough to focus his reporting on the elements of greatest importance, but he may nevertheless manage to convey to some of his equally uninformed countrymen the excitement and enthusiasm he feels for the things he sees. This may inspire others to pay their own visits to this new land or to consult more expert sources for elaboration of the matters that have caught their fancy.

What follows must therefore be recognized as only a recital of what appeared important and interesting to one former physical scientist as he was exposed for the first time to what has been going on in the field of brain research. To be sure, I have done my best not to omit matters that the biologist considers of first importance, or to place undue emphasis on aspects that seem trivial to workers in the field, but I can provide the reader with no assurance that I have succeeded. However, the material presented here is certainly a significant part of the current storehouse of information about the brain. In addition, it should be easier for those with a physical science background to read than the original papers, most of which are couched in the technical language of the biologist. And if I am very successful in meeting my objectives, some of the fascination that is held for me by the modern discoveries on how the brain seems to work may convey itself to a few readers with physical science background and thereby help them decide to seek opportunities for collaborative work with the life scientists. This is the real object of the exercise.

Many people have helped in the preparation of this book. Heading the list is Duane Roller, my former physics professor and my close personal friend of thirty years' standing. He has devoted many hours to detailed editorial analysis and polishing of my literary efforts. If the subjects and predicates are in their proper places and the meanings are expressed clearly, it is largely his doing. The passages that fail to achieve literary adequacy are most likely those in which I rejected his improvements in favor of some mode of expression that seemed more natural to me.

In addition, I have profited greatly from the willingness of experts in the field, many of whom I have never met, to read parts of my material and provide corrections and suggestions for changes. All of their comments have been thoughtful, pertinent, and helpful. Almost all their suggestions have been used, and the accuracy and quality of the treatment has thereby been much enhanced. Without implying that these men necessarily endorse my book, but only for the purpose of gratefully acknowledging their assistance, I list their names here: W. R. Adey, University of California at Los Angeles; J. B. Angell, Stanford University; Maitland Baldwin, National Institutes of Health; Reginald G. Bickford, Mayo Clinic; James Bonner, California Institute of Technology; J. V. Brady, Walter Reed Army Institute of Research; R. W. Doty, University of Rochester; D. H. Fender, California Institute of Technology; Robert Galambos, Yale University; D. O. Hebb, McGill University; W. R. Hess, Zurich; E. Roy John, University of Rochester; G. D. McCann, California Institute of Technology; Donald Michie, University of Edinburgh; H. Q. North, Thompson Ramo Wooldridge, Inc.; Wilder Penfield, Montreal Neurological Institute; Werner Reichardt, Max Planck Institut für Biologie; W. Ritchie Russell, United Oxford Hospitals; J. P. Segundo, University of California at Los Angeles; R. W. Sperry, California Institute of Technology; and A. van Harreveld, California Institute of Technology.

Dean E. Wooldridge

contents

The Electrical Properties of Nerves

In the preface, this book has been characterized as a sort of travelogue or description of an exotic land by one who, like the reader, has never been there before. As is not unusual in travelogues, we shall start with a brief consideration of the circumstances of original discovery of the territory we are about to visit.

There is general agreement that the modern science of neurology had its origin in the discovery of the electrical properties of nerves. Much less certain is which of several eighteenth-century scientist-philosophers should be credited with the discovery. Actually, like so many scientific developments, the important new concept that nerve action is electrical grew out of a number of different observations. As early as 1750 several investigators had published reports on muscular convulsions observed in recently deceased animals and humans when they were brought into contact with a discharging electrostatic generator or Leyden jar. Not much later, in the 1770s, two or three writers suggested that the shocks received from the *Torpedo* fish were electric in nature.

Despite the possible merit of the claims of some of these early investigators, the title "father of modern neurology" appears to have been bestowed by biologists on Luigi Galvani, public lecturer in anatomy at the University of Bologna from 1762 until his death in 1798. Some time before 1780 Galvani appears to have developed what was to be for him an abiding interest in the interaction of electricity and frogs' legs. One version of the story has it that he was initially intrigued by something he saw in a butchershop. The shop was featuring frogs' legs, and the carcasses of the frogs were suspended from copper hooks that projected from an iron railing. What Galvani was supposed to have noticed was that when a dangling carcass touched the iron railing there occurred a lifelike twitching in the muscles of the frog's legs.

Apocryphal though this story may be, there is no doubt that Galvani combined dead frogs with copper hooks and iron supports in his laboratory and in fact spent many years on a wide variety of experiments seeking to improve his understanding of the phenomenon of "animal electricity," as he chose to call it. His publications, commencing in 1791, created a great stir in the civilized world. The possibility of "restoring life" to a dead animal caught the public fancy and inspired a kind of unrestrained speculation based on insufficient scientific knowledge that is not unheard of even in the twentieth century.

Much of Galvani's theory as to what went on when a combination of copper, iron, and a dead frog produced a muscular reaction was later learned to be unsound, but that need not concern us here; it is easy to redescribe the Galvani experiment in accurate modern terms.

First of all, Galvani's results depended upon the electrical fact, just being discovered in his day, that a combination of dissimilar metals such as copper and iron can under suitable circumstances produce an electric current. Also pertinent was the anatomical fact, known to Galvani, that muscular actions are controlled by nerves: that, for example, a frog's muscle will contract if the main nerve leading to it is pinched. These pieces of scientific knowledge were enough to permit the proper connection to be made between the twitching of frogs' legs suspended from copper hooks against an iron railing and one of the most important facts in the science of life—the electrical basis of nerve action.

The deduction that the twitching of Galvani's frogs' legs was caused by electric currents in the attached nerves was verified in many laboratories in the early part of the nineteenth century. It was discovered that not just frogs, but all animals tested, including humans, exhibited the effect: electricity sent into the nerve controlling a particular muscle would cause that muscle to contract. By performance of these experiments on live animals, it was ultimately established that a property of living tissue was being dealt with. The existence of the phenomenon in dead animals was simply a consequence of the fact that nerve and muscle tissues, particularly when suitable efforts are made to preserve them, remain alive and relatively healthy for considerable periods after the expiration of the animal itself.

But there are two types of nerves that connect to muscles in animals. In addition to the nerves that control the response of the muscles, there are other nerves connecting the muscles with the brain of the animal that are passive, in the sense that physical deformation of such nerves does not produce muscular reaction. For these nerves, it was found that electric excitation would not produce an observable effect. As measuring techniques improved, however, it was ultimately found that stretching the attached muscle would cause a current to appear in this type of nerve, presumably thereby sending to the brain of the organism information, in electrical form, about the degree of elongation or contraction of the muscle.

In this way, investigators early in the nineteenth century succeeded in establishing the electrical nature of the action, both of the *efferent,* or *motor,* nerves, by means of which signals are sent from the spinal cord or the brain to cause muscles to contract, and of the *afferent,* or *sensory* nerves, by means of which the muscles send information to the higher nervous centers as to their state of elongation or contraction. More generally, it was found that this electrical property of nerve action is not limited to nerves attached to muscles but is a characteristic of the entire nervous system. The afferent nerves were always found to transmit their signals by electrical means, whether their function was to indicate muscle stretch, touch, pain, warmth, sound, smell, sight, pressure, chemical composition, or the reports of any of the many other "senses" that supply the information needed for the regulation of the health and well-being of the animal. Similarly, all nerve signals sent out along the efferent nerves to the effector mechanisms were found to be electric, whether these effectors were of mechanical nature such as muscles or of chemical nature such as glands.

Important though the establishment of the basic electrical character of nerve action was, the techniques available to the research workers of the nineteenth century did not permit the answering of many obvious questions about the details of the phenomenon. For example, when a touch receptor in the external skin of a test animal is stimulated, how fast does the electric signal travel toward the brain? How long does the nerve continue to generate current after the stimulus is removed? Answers to questions such as these had to await the development of improved measuring techniques. In particular, the advent of the technology of electronics was required to make practical the detection and measurement of tiny electrical effects that had previously fallen outside the range of the instruments available. Of special importance was the development of the cathode-ray oscilloscope, to provide laboratory workers with a tool for the precise observation and measurement of short-duration electrical phenomena. By means of the new electronic tools, research workers of recent years have been able to make many significant discoveries about the workings of the nervous system.

The "All-or-Nothing" Nature of Nerve Signals

Let us now look more deeply into the electrical phenomena produced in the afferent nerve that sends information to the brain of the frog about the amount of elongation of a muscle when that muscle is artificially stretched. Let us imagine that we have assembled a suitable arrangment of electronic equipment so that, at some point up the nerve from its connection to the muscle, we are able to observe precisely any electrical effects that are produced by our manipulations. Starting our experiment with the muscle in its relaxed condition, we observe that no electrical effects are indicated by our instruments.* Next, we proceed very cautiously to stretch the muscle. For a while, nothing happens; for a small amount of stretch, no effects are indicated by our circuits, even though this stretched condition is maintained indefinitely. In other words, there is a lower limit, or *threshold,* that must be exceeded by the amount of the elongation of the muscle before the attached nerve takes notice of it. When this threshold level of stretch is reached, however, the circuits begin to indicate a flow of electricity in the nerve. This current, however, is of a curious kind. It is not a steady flow, but instead consists of a series of pulses. Starting from zero, the current at the point in the nerve adjacent to the measuring terminal rises quickly to a maximum value during an interval of a few ten-thousandths of a second, and then drops more gradually back to zero, the entire process requiring approximately one-thousandth of a second. A fraction of a second later another identical package of electricity passes the point of measurement. This pulse is followed by a third, then a fourth, and so on. The train of pulses continues as long as the muscle is stretched.

This is the kind of electric signal that is produced by an amount of muscle stretch just slightly greater than the threshold value. What happens when the muscle is stretched still farther? The result is most interesting: the individual pulses are identical with those produced by a small stretch; the only difference is that they come more often. As the muscle is stretched more and more, the rate of generation of the pulses increases until a maximum is reached that represents saturation signal for the nerve under test; no amount of additional stretching of the muscle can further increase the frequency.

Although, for the sake of concreteness, a specific experiment on a frog's muscle has been described, the basic electrical properties of the

---

* This is not always quite correct. Nerves occasionally "fire" spontaneously in the absence of an applied stimulus. However, such "noise" in the circuit does not affect the essential validity of the description given here.

signal transported by the attached afferent nerve are found to be common to all afferent nerves of all animals tested. Whether the nerve is one that indicates stretch, touch, chemical composition, warmth, cold, sight, or sound, it transmits its information by means of a train of pulses of electricity, all of approximately the same magnitude and duration, regardless of the intensity of the stimulus, with only the rate of generation of the pulses indicating whether the sensation is trivial or intense. The properties of threshold and saturation are also commonly possessed by the afferent nerves: they will not respond at all until the strength of the stimulus exceeds a certain minimum value, and as the stimulus becomes very strong, a point is ultimately reached beyond which further increase produces no further change in the signal propagated upward in the nervous system.

By this time, the reader will not be surprised to learn that similar properties are possessed by the efferent nerves—those that conduct action signals to the muscles and glands. Thus, an essential property of the whole nervous system is that it transmits information by electrical means and that the type of electric conduction it employs is of an all-or-nothing nature. It is as though the basic mechanism of nervous conduction consisted of some form of electric on/off switch!

Nature's On/Off Switch: The Neuron

For many years it has been known that nerve tissue is largely composed of special types of cells, called *neurons,* not found in other structures of the body. If on/off switches are essential components of the nervous system, they would be expected to occur in these fundamental neuronal building blocks.

Figure 1-1 is a schematic drawing of a neuron. The bulbous portion is the *body* of the cell, the twisted rootlike projections from the body are called *dendrites,* and the long fiber extending away from one side of the body is called the *axon,* or simply *nerve fiber.* While all neurons have these general features, they vary greatly in their constructional details and dimensions. In the long pathways from the extremities of man's body to his brain there may be, in some instance, no more than three neurons in series in the complete communication channel between the periphery and the "central data processor," or brain. In such instances, the axon of a single nerve cell may be 2 or 3 feet in length, even though the cell body is less than $\frac{1}{100}$ inch in diameter. In other cases, particularly in the brain, the maximum dimension covered by all of the processes of a single neuron may be only a few thousandths of an inch.

Functionally, there are three general classes of nerve cells. These

Fig. 1-1. Schematic drawing of a neuron, or nerve cell.

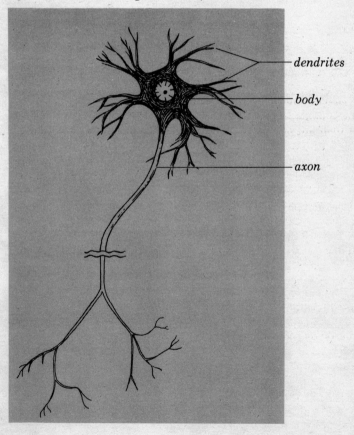

— dendrites

— body

— axon

are *sensory*, or *receptor*, *neurons*; *motor*, or *effector*, *neurons*; and *internuncial neurons*, or *interneurons*. These three classes may be thought of as input devices, output devices, and everything in between. Apart from variations in size and shape, the most conspicuous constructional anomalies are exhibited by some of the receptor neurons, whose terminations are provided with a variety of attachments—"transducers" to the physical scientist—by means of which the pressure, chemical composition, temperature, or other physical quantity that the neuron must measure can be converted into the kind of electrochemical signal that neurons are designed to handle. In a later section we shall take note of some of the ingenious methods that nature has devised to accomplish this conversion of environmental data into the standard form required by the nervous system, as well as the method employed to translate the standard nerve signal of the effector neurons into the chemical form needed to activate the muscles. In the present discussion we shall simply bear in mind the existence of these specialized input and output mechanisms and choose the somewhat simpler but basically similar interneuron as the model for our study. There is another justification for this choice. A much larger number of nerve cells are needed to accomplish the difficult communication and data-processing chores of the nervous system than are needed for the relatively simpler input and output tasks. Of the approximately ten billion nerve cells in the human body, over nine billion are of the interneuron type.

Let us see how a neuron works. Different parts have different functions. The axon is just what it appears to be—the means of conducting the nerve impulse generated in the body of the cell to some other location, usually to another neuron. The axon is nature's analog to the interconnecting wire of an electric circuit. When the axon gets to where it is going, it divides into smaller branches that make contact with the "input terminals" of a number of other neurons. The input terminals of a neuron consist of its dendrites and its cell body. Microscopic observation shows that the axonal branches of one cell normally terminate on these portions of the receiving cells, and not on other axons. Each connection between an axon of one neuron and a dendrite or the body of the next is called a *synapse*. We shall see later that the properties of the synapses are basic to some of the most important activities of the nervous system.

The all-or-nothing character of nerve conduction stems from an interesting general property of living cells. The protoplasm of any cell is held together by a very thin, transparent membrane. Because this membrane is not equally permeable to the different types of electrically charged molecular fragments (ions) that normally float around in the protoplasm of the cell and in the watery liquid that surrounds it, the material of the cell is negatively charged with respect to the surrounding fluid. In the nerve cell of an animal, this internal potential is approximately 70 millivolts *negative* with respect to the outside. However, a similar property is possessed by all cells, whether from plants, fish, or men, regardless of what part of the organism they come from; so far as is known, every cell possesses a membrane across which a potential difference exists. This is an interesting example of the extensive similarities among living organisms, without which the task of the life scientist would be even more difficult than it is now.

Nerve conduction is achieved by a specialization of this membrane-potential property of living cells. Signals coming in over the input terminals of the neuron produce effects (to be discussed later) that lower the magnitude of the electric potential of the protoplasm in the cell body below its normal 70-millivolt value. This reduced potential extends a short distance into the base of the axon. If this potential reduction, or *depolarization,* becomes large enough, the axon displays a curious property of its own: it suffers an electrical breakdown. In more precise terms, decrease of the internal potential from 70 to about 60 millivolts triggers an abrupt change in the permeability properties of the membrane that separates the protoplasm of the axon from the surrounding fluid. This change is such as to allow sodium ions from the outside, which previously had not been able to penetrate the membrane, to surge into the axon, while a smaller excess of internal potassium ions moves out. The net electrical effect of this ion flow is an abrupt change in the internal potential at the segment of the axon where the breakdown is occurring, from the normal -70-millivolt value to a value slightly positive with respect to the surrounding fluid. This is initially highly localized, occurring just at the base of the axon. However, the resulting potential (voltage) difference between the breakdown region and the adjacent protoplasm causes a flow of ions that quickly produces enough depolarization in the neighboring segment of axon to cause it to break down; this provides depolarizing current for the next segment of axon, and so on. In this way a pulse of voltage breakdown, or *action potential,* is propagated along the axon. This is the all-or-nothing nerve impulse that has, from the time of its discovery, intrigued the neurophysiologist.

Some of the detailed properties of the action potential are of first importance. Its speed of propagation is such a detail. This depends in a complex way on the dimensional, chemical, and electrical properties of the axon and surrounding fluid. In general, nerve impulses move rapidly in large-diameter axons and slowly in small ones. In the human body, some messages move no faster than we can walk, whereas others are speedier than a racing car. The measured range is approximately 2 to 200 miles per hour.

Another important characteristic of axonal transmission is the complete absence of degradation of the nerve impulse as it travels along the axon. When this property was first discovered, it was a source of considerable surprise that, after traveling distances that were thousands of times greater than the diameter of the conducting fiber, the nerve impulse arrived at its destination with as much strength and vigor as it had when it left the body of the generating neuron. This is now seen to be a natural consequence of the phenomenon of traveling electrical breakdown, wherein the impulse is effectively triggered anew into existence at each stage of its progress. The energy required for such successive regeneration is initially derived from the differences in concentration of sodium and potassium ions inside and outside of the neuron; these differences, in turn, result from the chemical metabolic processes that steadily operate along the axon, to restore and maintain the electrochemical conditions normal to a resting cell.

The return of the axonal material to its normal condition of equilibrium after the passage of a pulse of action potential is of basic importance to the neural mechanisms. The anomalous membrane permeability that underlies the passage of the pulse through the axon is a highly transient phenomenon; the membrane recovers its normal permeability characteristics and the electric polarization its usual value in only one or two thousandths of a second. By the time the axonal segment is capable of firing again, the pulse of action potential has traveled many axon diameters away, and is too remote to stimulate the newly recovered protoplasm into fresh breakdown. As a result, the neuronal impulse always travels in one direction—away from the body of the cell.

When the material at the base of the axon recovers its normal properties, it can then be stimulated into the generation of a second neuronal pulse. This occurs as soon as the electrical effects of the nerve impulses coming into the neuron over its input terminals can once again develop a degree of depolarization in the cell body that is adequate to trigger a new breakdown at the base of the axon. If the incoming signals are strong, this will not take long; successive pulses of action potential will follow one another at brief intervals, and the nerve signal may attain a frequency as high as several hundred pulses per second. If, on the other hand, only weak signals are coming in over the input terminals, a relatively long period may be required to reestablish the threshold level of depolarization in the neuron body after the discharging effect of each impulse; in such case, the signal propagated along the axon may have a frequency of only a few pulses per second.

Entirely different kinds of events occur when the pulses of action potential reach a synapse of the axon with the body or one of the dendrites of a following cell. The arriving electric signal finds itself blocked at the synapse. Electron-microscope measurements show why: the axon of the transmitting neuron does not quite touch the dendrite or body of the receiving cell. There is always a gap of about a millionth of an inch. By ingenious and careful experiments, it has been determined that the nerve impulse rides across the gap on chemical carriers. Each arriving pulse triggers the release of a tiny amount of a transmitter substance, which floats through the liquid of the synaptic gap to the other side. There it modifies the permeability of the membrane of the receiving neuron in such a way as to cause an ionic redistribution with an attendant net change in the electric charge content of the body protoplasm. In about one millisecond the resulting "pulse" of electric charge distributes itself throughout the body of the receiving cell and thereby modifies the degree of polarization that determines whether the base of the axon will fire. It is important to note that the phenomena occurring at the input terminals of the neuron are not of an all-or-nothing character. In fact, from the point of view of the computer engineer, they are more like a sort of digital-to-analog conversion. With each arriving axonal pulse there is deposited on the next cell body a quantity of charge that decays relatively slowly. While all arriving pulses may be of the same magnitude, an incoming signal of high frequency, resulting from a large upstream generating signal, is converted at the synapse into a proportionally large depolarization effect. This in turn can generate a pulse signal of relatively high frequency in the outgoing axon of the second cell.

The foregoing picture is too simple in one important respect. Rarely if ever is a neuron inspired into action by the input from just one other neuron. Just as each axon synapses on the dendrites and bodies of a number of downstream neurons, so is each downstream neuron connected to the axons of a number of upstream neurons. The body of the receiving neuron acts as a sort of "summing amplifier" for the depolarizing effects of the various arriving input signals. To be sure, the depolarizing effect produced in the body of the neuron by an arriving pulse decays after 5 or 10 milliseconds, so that approximate time coincidence must exist among the various input signals if they are to sum to produce a common effect. But with this limitation, summation can occur. In fact, the evidence is that it *must* occur: signals must arrive over a number of inputs in order to generate enough depolarization in the body of the cell to fire its axon. Although in neurological literature there are frequently diagrams that show operating subsystems consisting of discrete chains of a few neurons, these diagrams are usually purely schematic. In the higher animals at least, it is only the scientist who deals with one neuron at a time. In nature the sensory stimuli usually come in over a large number of adjacent neuronal fibers; when interneurons are required there are many of them, and each has input connections with the axons of a number of sensory neurons; similarly, any data-processing output of the nervous system is sent over a number of axons for the activation of the many muscle fibers involved in the response. This employment by the nervous system of parallel communication channels provides relative invulnerability to the damage of a few nerve cells. It can also lead to a more nearly proportional relationship between the operation of the muscles and the activating stimulus. This is a consequence of the differences that always exist in the threshold for stimulation of the various parallel neurons. Because of such differences, a few axons may be activated by weak input stimuli, more for somewhat stronger stimuli, and all of them only for intense stimuli. Finally, the scrambling of the connections between the incoming axons and ongoing neurons at the various relay points offers opportunities for certain kinds of spatial integration effects that provide at one and the same time a possible explanation of some of the more complex behavioral properties of the nervous system and a source of difficulty to the scientist who attempts to trace out the detailed paths followed by the nerve impulses.

The integrating characteristics of the neuron are not completely described by the assertion that incoming signals produce depolarizing effects which are summed in the body of the cell. For arrangements have been provided by means of which some incoming signals can diminish, rather than enhance, the over-all effect. Certain kinds of neurons are of such an "inhibiting" nature. They have such a chemical structure that, where their axon synapses with the dendrite or body of another cell, the arriving nerve impulse causes a kind of chemical substance to be emitted that affects the permeability of the membrane of the receiving cell so as to make it harder, rather than easier, for its axon to fire. This electrical effect is referred to as an *inhibitory post-synaptic potential,* in contrast to the *excitatory post-synaptic potential* resulting from the arrival of nerve impulses over the more usual depolarizing type of synapse. A typical interneuron receives input signals from a number of inhibitory as well as from a number of excitatory upstream neurons. At any time, its axon will fire or not in accordance with whether the integrated effects of all relatively time-coincident inputs do or do not provide an above-threshold depolarization of the interior of the cell. And if firing occurs, the rate at which the axon emits pulses of action potential will depend on the amount by which the depolarization exceeds the threshold value for firing.

One final property of the neuron needs to be mentioned. In some circumstances it displays the characteristics of a variable-threshold device. If a number of excitatory input signals sum to a value that is just under the threshold for firing, a very weak additional signal over other input terminals may be adequate to trigger the action potential of the neuron. Conversely, the presence of inhibitory signals on some terminals can render the neuron insensitive to other excitatory inputs that would otherwise be adequate for firing. Variation of the threshold can also be produced by changes in chemical composition or electric current distribution in the surrounding fluids that modify the ionic or electric potential relationships normally existing between the outside and the inside of the neuron. In coming pages we shall have cause to refer to these variable-threshold effects.

Through all this the neuron looks a good deal like an electronic computer component. If hooked up in the right way, it could certainly be caused to display attributes similar to those of the computer designer's electrically operated on/off switches. If the multiple dendritic inputs of a neuron were grouped in parallel and connected to only two or three sources, and if input pulse signals were employed of some one specified frequency and amplitude, as is customary in digital-computer circuits, the neuron could be caused to fire or not to fire in accordance with the nature of the pattern of applied inputs. The equivalent of the computer designer's "and," "or," and "not" gates could be achieved in this way; by including suitable feedback connections, flip-flop and other switching elements could also be obtained. These are the properties required for the construction of a general-purpose digital computer.

But the neuron has other properties also. The increase of its output frequency with input amplitude, the ability to add and subtract different inputs, the effects of time coincidence on the summing properties, the variable-threshold characteristic, and other properties too complex for this treatment—all indicate that the neuron is a considerably more sophisticated component than the electronically activated switch of the computer designer. A competent engineer, presented with such components for the construction of a data-processing or computer/control system, would find ways to make use of their versatile properties to simplify the equipment and increase the capability of his system. In the coming chapters we shall see much evidence that nature does this too.

Nature's Input/Output Devices: Receptor and Effector Neurons

An electronic computer can operate only in terms of its own machine language or code; all information that it uses in its computations must be translated into this particular code before it is inserted into the machine, and all results of the machine's computations must finally be translated out of machine language into some other form that is useful in the outside world. Nature encounters the same problem and solves it in the same way. Just as the designer of an industrial process-control computer employs a variety of input devices to convert the critical measurements of pressures, temperatures, chemical compositions, and the like in the controlled process into the patterns of on/off voltages required by the computer, so does nature employ a variety of specialized receptor neurons that convert pressures, temperatures, chemical compositions, and the like into the patterns of on/off voltages that constitute the only language that is meaningful to the central nervous system. Similarly, the conversion of the output results of the electronic computer into control action, such as the opening and closing of valves or increasing and decreasing of temperatures, finds its analog in the effector neurons that translate the instructions received from the central nervous system in standardized on/off voltage code into suitable muscular or glandular responses.

While an extensive treatment is beyond the scope of this book, nature's ingenuity in these matters is well worth a little of our attention. Figure 1-2 shows some of the commoner types of nerve endings in the human body. A *touch receptor* (Fig. 1-2a) consists of a hair follicle and an associated nerve structure. When an object is touched, the external displacement of the hair transmits a motion along its length and stretches and compresses the tiny terminations of the neuron that are wrapped around the base of the hair follicle. The structure of these nerve endings is such that mechanical distortion produces an electric potential, which is converted by the axon of the neuron into the standardized train of pulses constituting the "machine language" of the nervous system.

A *Meissner corpuscle* (Fig. 1-2b) is a different kind of touch receptor that occurs extensively in the areas of maximum tactile sensitivity, such as fingers and lips. The mechanical distortion of its endings is conveyed, in this case, through the displacement of the surrounding skin tissue.

A *Pacinian corpuscle* (Fig. 1-2c), with the general construction of an onion, is a so-called "pressure receptor." An increase in the forces that normally bear on the outer skin causes the successive concentric layers of the corpuscle to slide on one another; this squeezes and twists the internal nerve endings in such a way as to depolarize the membrane and produce pulses of action potential. Pacinian corpuscles are found not only just under the external skin, but also in internal organs of the body.

Other specialized receptors measure pain, warmth, and cold. In each case, the microscopic structure of the end of the receptor neuron is specialized to produce the standard electric output when changes occur in the particular physical property that the receptor is intended to detect.

In addition to receptor neurons which measure such physical properties as pressure and temperature, the body contains many chemically activated receptors. The surface of the tongue and the membranes of the nose are lined with tiny nerve endings (Fig. 1-2d), each of which is a full-fledged chemical analyzer that produces its standard electric output only when it comes into physical contact with some particular class of molecules.

Remarkably extensive use is made by nature of the two basic types of neurons—touch-sensitive and chemically sensitive—by associating these neurons with other ingenious physical structures. For example, there are no nerve cells that respond directly to sound waves. Since nature decided that we must hear, she has gone to the trouble of building into our inner ear a structure that analyzes incoming sound vibrations into a spectrum of mechanical displacements that can be detected by touch neurons. Specifically, the cochlea of the inner ear contains a long stretched membrane so designed that different spots on the membrane vibrate in response to different tones. Touch-sensitive neurons are then arranged along this membrane so that the tiny hairs to which they are attached are distorted by the local vibration. The resulting pattern of standard action-potential pulses traveling along the axons of these touch receptors is what the brain interprets as speech, a symphony, or a baby's cry.

While we hear by means of touch, we see by means of chemicals. Everyone has heard of the rods and cones of the retina of the human eye and knows that these are receptor nerve cells that somehow translate the pattern of light and shadow produced on the retina by the focusing action of the lens into the kind of signals required by the brain for implementation of the sense of vision. In view of the discussion to this point, it will not surprise anyone to learn that the retinal neurons generate the standard electric-signal output in response to incoming light. What may seem surprising, however, is that the rods and cones do not appear to employ a direct photoelectric principle in their conversion of light to electricity. Instead, they are essentially chemical detectors. They depend for their action upon substances that are decomposed by light, in much the same way as the silver compounds of a photographic plate are decomposed. It is the substances resulting from this decomposition, not the light itself, that depolarize the neuron and produce its electrical effects.

The use of a chemical substance as a mediating agent appears to be especially common in the case of nature's output devices, the effector neurons. The final result of the extremely complex sequence of interrelated activities, by means of which the data-processing, regulatory, and decision-making functions of the central nervous system

Fig. 1-2. Some of the receptor cells of the nervous system. (*a*) Hair cell, for touch; (*b*) Meissner corpuscle, for touch; (*c*) Pacinian corpuscle, for pressure; (*d*) chemical detector, for smell.

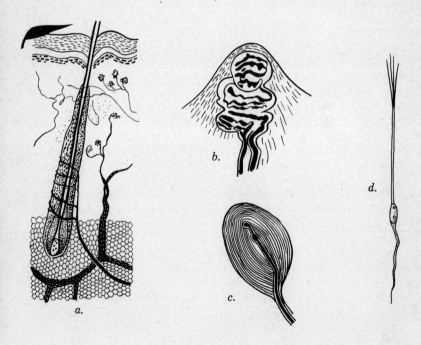

are brought to bear on the input data provided by the receptor neurons, is a change in the state of elongation of a muscle or the modulation of the action of a gland. The first of these is clearly a mechanical process, and the second may be also, since gland action is sometimes controlled by the muscular dilation or constriction of the associated blood vessels.

Such output action, exactly as in the output action of a man-made computer, is characterized by the employment of a feeble signal to control the application of a much more powerful source of energy to perform a useful result. In an electronic computer control system, the controlling signal might be used to operate a relay so as to close contacts that energize a powerful electric motor, which finally performs the desired task. For the actuation of a muscle by an effector neuron, nature's analog to the control relay lies in a certain property of muscular tissue: it changes from limpness to tautness as a result of the release of special chemical substances by the effects of invading pulses of action potential. Actually, muscles consist of bundles of long, thin fibers that are very similar to neurons. In fact, the axons of the effector neurons are connected to the muscle fibers by means of synapses that are very similar to purely neuronal interconnections. A chemical transmitter, in this case known to be acetylcholine, conveys the incoming nerve signal across the synapse and there generates pulses of action potential that are propagated throughout the muscle fiber by an axonlike process involving membrane-permeability changes of the same kind as those that travel along an axon. The special property that results in a muscular response, rather than a purely passive transmission of a communication signal, is the fiber-contracting effect of the action potential.

An interesting variation of the muscular structure is found in the electric eel. A healthy eel can emit 1 ampere of current at 600 volts, to stun or kill its prey. The source of the electric discharge lies in an evolutionary modification of some of the nerve/muscle junctions; muscular contraction has been eliminated, but the 60-millivolt action-potential change produced by the acetylcholine squirted out by the nerve impulses has been preserved. Additionally, the anatomical arrangement stacks a large number of these specialized cells end to end under the outer skin of the eel. When all are simultaneously discharged, the desired effect is produced.

In other fish the same principle operates, in a more modest way, to send out periodic pulses of electric current that are used for navigational purposes. Receptor neurons in the skin of the fish are sensitive to the pattern of electric field strength resulting from the interaction of the emitted pulses with surrounding objects. Field changes of only one-millionth of a volt per foot can be detected. Therefore even small nearby objects, which slightly distort the electric field in the water, can be avoided or sought out by the fish.

Thus, the receptor and effector organs, which at first glance appear to be so different from one another, under analysis are all seen to be variations on a single theme—the achievement of highly specialized properties by the employment of small modifications of and additions to the same basic neuron. While the principles of organic evolution make such a situation understandable, it is good, at this early stage of our treatment, to see concrete evidence of the existence of at least some simplifying factors to ease the task of understanding that we have set ourselves.

BIBLIOGRAPHY

Brazier, M. A. B., *The Electrical Activity of the Nervous System* (ed. 2, The Macmillan Company, New York, 1960).

Buchanan, A. R., *Functional Neuro-Anatomy* (ed. 4, Lea & Febiger, Philadelphia, 1961), chap. 3, "Receptors and Methods of Testing Sensibility."

Cox, R. T., "Electric Fish," *American Journal of Physics,* vol. 11 (1943), p. 13.

Fulton, J. F., *Muscular Contraction and the Reflex Control of Movement* (The Williams & Wilkins Company, 1926), pp. 34–37.

Galambos, R., *Nerves and Muscles* (Anchor Books, Doubleday & Company, Inc., Garden City, N.Y., 1962).

Wells, H. G., J. S. Huxley, and G. P. Wells, *The Science of Life* (Doubleday & Company, Inc., Garden City, N.Y., 1938), book 1, chap. 3, sec. 5, "Sensation and the Senses," pp. 111–127.

The "Schematic Diagram" of the Nervous System

The Input/Output Cable: The Spinal Cord

Nature's cabling arrangement is an orderly one. Starting from the periphery of the body, fibers from neighboring individual neurons are first grouped together as a *nerve*. In man and the other vertebrates the fibers of the nerves are sorted out on arriving at the backbone, entering the spinal column at various levels, where they join with many thousands of fibers from other levels, forming together the main cable between the input/output devices and the brain. In the human body, this main cable of the spinal cord reaches the brain with an accumulation of several million separate conducting nerve fibers. About half of these fibers are busy bringing information to the brain while the other half are busy transmitting to the muscles and glands the instructions that constitute the results of the brain's data-processing and computing activities. Each fiber is a few ten-thousandths of an inch in diameter. Many possess a thin covering of *myelin*—a kind of loading and insulating material that increases the speed of the nerve impulse and also helps prevent "cross talk" among the signals of the neighboring nerve fibers.

It is unlikely that the spinal cord would have been defined as part of the "central" nervous system if its function were purely that of a passive carrier of messages. In Chapter 3 we shall see examples of another function of the spinal cord: it interconnects the fibers of related afferent neurons so as to rearrange the data from the input receptors into a form more convenient for use by the central data processor, the brain. And in Chapter 4 we shall learn that the spinal cord interconnects sensory and motor neurons to achieve various kinds of simple reflex actions. Furthermore, there is a plasticity in the properties of the spinal cord that has no analog in the inter-communicating cable of the electrical engineer. If some of the conductors are blocked by disease or cut by the surgeon's knife, new interconnecting pathways are frequently formed by the nerve fibers in such a way as to restore completely or partially the communication or control function that had been interrupted. These interconnecting and adaptive functions are exercised by neurons whose cell bodies and axons reside in what is usually referred to as the *gray matter* of the cord, the abundant cell bodies providing a darker coloration than that of the *white matter,* which contains only axons. Together with the bodies of some of the motor cells whose long axons travel out through the effector nerve bundles to innervate muscles and glands, these interneurons appear in cross section as an H-shaped area symmetrically disposed around the center of the spinal cord and occupying about one-third of its sectional area. The remaining two-thirds is occupied by the message-carrying fibers, which are the principal interest of this chapter.

Keeping the Wires Straight

In electric communication systems, there are two ways of transmitting a large amount of input and output information over a single cable. In one method, which has been most extensively employed in telephone circuits, the cable consists of a large number of separate insulated conductors, and the various conversations that must be separately transmitted are individually assigned to these conductors. This is a straightforward technique and works well, provided that scrupulous care is taken to sort out the conductors of the cable and make sure that the right telephone transmitter is always connected to the right receiver. In the second method, all the telephone conversations are transmitted simultaneously over a single conductor of special physical design. In this case, confusion is avoided by tagging each conversation at the transmission end with a separate electrical property which is utilized at the reception end for sorting purposes. This is done in practice by sending each conversation along the single conductor on its own carrier frequency and then separating out the various conversations at the receiving point by means of a set of filters, with each filter tuned to one, and only one, of the frequencies involved.

It would seem possible for the nervous system to operate on either of these two principles of communication. Each has its own advantages and disadvantages. A nervous-system analog of the single-conductor method of telephone transmission would be simple in so far as interconnection of the neurons is concerned, but would be very complex in its output and input devices. Such a system would require qualitatively different kinds of signals to represent pain, touch, sight, and all the other input and output messages transmitted by the nervous system.

It is, of course, clear that the material so far presented is most consistent with the conclusion that information is transmitted in living organisms by the first method, whereby all input and output devices are standardized to work on the same basic type of signal. This means that we can tell the difference between a symphony concert, a colorful sunset, or an upset stomach only on the basis of the particular terminals in our brain to which the incoming nerve fibers are connected. But there are millions of these fibers, and according to the present line of argument each fiber in the process of the development of the embryo had to search out and connect with the proper terminal of the brain. This is impressive enough as to justify us in a desire for objective proof that the nervous system actually develops in this way before we finally accept the "standard signal, common machine language" theory that has so far been set forth.

There is interesting evidence that bears on this point. For example, R. W. Sperry, Professor of Biology at California Institute of Technology, has performed an experiment in which a patch of skin was removed from the belly of a tadpole and transplanted to its back. After the tadpole had developed into a frog, it was found that tickling the transplanted patch on its back would cause the animal to scratch its belly with its hind leg. Apparently, in spite of the strange location of the patch on the surface of the frog's body, the regenerated neurons connecting it with the spinal cord established connections with the system of ascending nerves that terminated in the portion of the frog's brain assigned to the detection of sensations from the belly.

A more spectacular demonstration of the same basic principle was also described by Professor Sperry. This time a toad was the subject. An operation was performed wherein the optic nerves were cut and reconnected inversely—that is, the right eye was connected to the nerve from the brain that previously had gone to the left eye, and vice versa. Of course, in such an operation, "reconnection" consisted only of butting the cut ends of the nerves together and waiting for natural processes to reestablish connections from the many tens of thousands of cut fibers to the brain. (Many lower animals possess this regenerative capability. Humans, unfortunately, do not.) Even in an uncut optic nerve, these fibers cross and twist in what appears to be a highly random fashion. In view of such twistings and turnings (which are also characteristic of the human optic nerve), it had always been a mystery how the electric impulses arising from the illumination of the various points of the retina get sorted out in an orderly fashion in the brain, which appears to be required to explain the fact that relatively clear vision is possible. Even granting that nature has some way to accomplish this feat during the development of the toad from the embryo, it seemed an unwarranted extrapolation to imagine that the many tens of thousands of cut fibers in its optic nerve could reestablish connections in the adult animal in such a way as to restore any kind of useful vision.

Yet, after a few weeks, the toad was able to see again! Apparently, as well as before. Certainly, the presence of a moving fly within its normal range of vision caused it to react in toadlike manner by darting out its tongue for the food. This and other tests led to the conclusion that, somehow, the fibers in each nerve proceeding from the eye had managed to seek out and reconnect themselves, one by one, with neurons in the brain in such a way as to reestablish there a clear image, with normal topological properties of up/down and right/left continuity. There was only one difference: if a fly appeared opposite the toad's right eye, it darted its tongue out to the left to attempt to capture it; if the food appeared to the left, the toad would always strike to the right. To the animal, since the optic nerve of the right eye was connected to the part of the brain designed to be used with the left eye and vice versa, the image formed in the right eye always appeared to be coming from the left and the image formed in the left eye always appeared to be coming from the right. No amount of experience ever caused the toad to learn to correct its mistake. It was obvious that the leftness and rightness of the vision were "wired-in" and not learned concepts.

This experiment on the visual system of the toad provides convincing evidence that the lower vertebrates and probably, by inference, the higher vertebrates including man possess means for meeting the stringent interconnection requirements resulting from the employment of standard electric signals to represent all input and output neural phenomena. In other words, nature has provided a way whereby the many millions of receptor and effector neurons are automatically connected to the specific terminals that the design blueprint of the brain allocates for communication with this vast aggregate of input/output devices.

Of course, the experiments described answer one mystery by the substitution of another. What kind of mechanism makes it possible, in the normal growth of an organism from the embryonic stage, for tangled masses of nerve fibers to extend their axons from the peripheral neurons to the precise spots in the brain called for by the "wiring diagram" of the central nervous system? The regeneration of the tens of thousands of separate fibers of the optic nerve of the toad is impressive enough; but when we consider that a similar process must account for the proper connection of the more than one million fibers of each optic nerve of the human eye, the matter becomes truly spectacular.

As yet, there has been no actual experimental determination of how nature accomplishes this impressive feat of bringing order out of chaos, but there does exist a reasonable hypothesis. The receptor neurons in the retina of the eye are assumed to contain two separate chemical ingredients that vary in concentration in accordance with the position of the neuron on the retina. One of these chemical ingredients might appear in very small concentration in the rods and cones located at the extreme left-hand side of the retinal field, with the concentration of this ingredient increasing steadily across the retina to reach a maximum at the extreme right-hand side of the field. Similarly, the other chemical ingredient might show concentration increasing progressively from the bottom to the top of the retina. With such an arrangement, the relative proportions of these two chemical ingredients in a given receptor neuron would provide an accurate indication of the position of the neuron on the retina, both left and right and up and down. Similar concentration gradients are presumed to exist in the interneurons and the neurons in the brain with which the retinal receptors need to be ultimately connected. Finally, it is assumed that there is some element in the dynamics of the embryonic growth process that causes the axons of transmitting neurons to seek out and make connection with receiving neurons of similar composition of the two key chemical ingredients.

Remarkable though the process just described appears, some such mechanism is required, not only to account for the specificity of interconnection of the nervous system, but also to explain many other aspects of the embryonic growth processes wherein two- or three-dimensional differentiation is achieved in evolving structures. It seems likely that research eventually will yield confirmation of the existence of this or a similar mechanism.

The Equipment Organization of the Central Data Processor

A medical student in an examination once defined the human brain as "the spinal cord with knobs on." The brain is in fact a grotesque enlargement of the top end of the spinal cord. Although when viewed from the side or above it has the appearance of a single cohesive organ (Fig. 2-1), a view from below (Fig. 2-2) reveals an arrange-

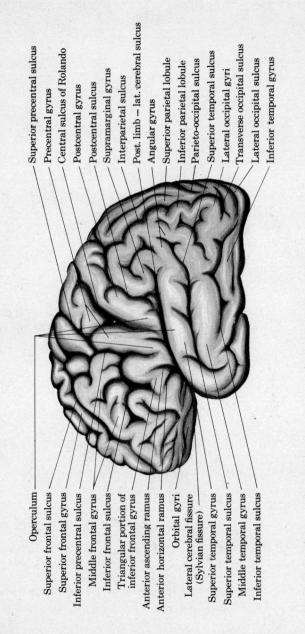

Labels (top, reading down):
Superior precentral sulcus
Precentral gyrus
Central sulcus of Rolando
Postcentral gyrus
Postcentral sulcus
Supramarginal gyrus
Interparietal sulcus
Post. limb – lat. cerebral sulcus
Angular gyrus
Superior parietal lobule
Inferior parietal lobule
Parieto-occipital sulcus
Superior temporal sulcus
Lateral occipital gyri
Transverse occipital sulcus
Lateral occipital sulcus
Inferior temporal gyrus

Labels (bottom, reading down):
Operculum
Superior frontal sulcus
Superior frontal gyrus
Inferior precentral sulcus
Middle frontal gyrus
Inferior frontal sulcus
Triangular portion of inferior frontal gyrus
Anterior ascending ramus
Anterior horizontal ramus
Orbital gyri
Lateral cerebral fissure (Sylvian fissure)
Superior temporal gyrus
Superior temporal sulcus
Middle temporal gyrus
Inferior temporal sulcus

Fig. 2-1. The brain, viewed from the left. *(From Raymond H. Houser, Graphic Aids to Neurology, Series 1, Scientific Illustrators, Long Beach, California, 1957. By permission of the publishers.)*

The "Schematic Diagram" of the Nervous System 23

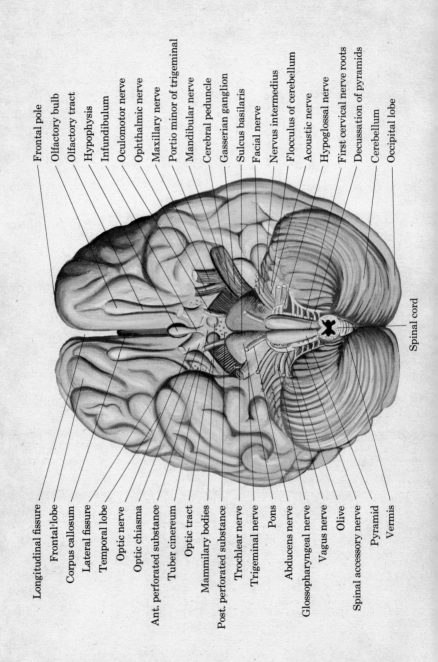

Frontal pole
Olfactory bulb
Olfactory tract
Hypophysis
Infundibulum
Oculomotor nerve
Ophthalmic nerve
Maxillary nerve
Portio minor of trigeminal
Mandibular nerve
Cerebral peduncle
Gasserian ganglion
Sulcus basilaris
Facial nerve
Nervus intermedius
Flocculus of cerebellum
Acoustic nerve
Hypoglossal nerve
First cervical nerve roots
Decussation of pyramids
Cerebellum
Occipital lobe

Spinal cord

Longitudinal fissure
Frontal lobe
Corpus callosum
Lateral fissure
Temporal lobe
Optic nerve
Optic chiasma
Ant. perforated substance
Tuber cinereum
Optic tract
Mammillary bodies
Post. perforated substance
Trochlear nerve
Trigeminal nerve
Pons
Abducens nerve
Glossopharyngeal nerve
Vagus nerve
Olive
Spinal accessory nerve
Pyramid
Vermis

ment of lumps and protuberances that suggest that the brain may be, as indeed it is, a collection of organs or parts that perform different functions. Anatomists and physiologists employ dozens of names to refer to the various regions of the brain. However, a casual inspection shows that it appears to have three main parts (Fig. 2-3). Directly on top of, and obviously an extension of, the spinal cord, is an agglomeration of protuberances and swellings that go generally under the name of the *brainstem*. Part way up the brainstem, protruding out toward the back of the erect human, is a bulbous mass called the *cerebellum*. Most conspicuous of all, in the human brain, is the *cerebral cortex*. This six-inch-thick sheet of gray-colored tissue is draped over and around the other parts of the brain in such a way as to fill tightly all the remaining space inside the skull. The wrinkles, folds, and convolutions of the cerebral cortex give the impression that nature has gone to considerable extremes to pack into the limited space available as much yardage of this sheet material as possible. As we shall see later, while other vertebrates also possess a cerebral cortex, there is a progression in nature in the size and degree of convolution of the cortex that appears to be directly related to the over-all intelligence of the creature involved.

When a human brain is dissected and subjected to the three-dimensional analysis that is so much a part of the business of the anatomist, it is found to consist of two types of material, *gray matter* and *white matter*. Reference has already been made to the fact that the cerebral cortex has a grayish color. Under the cortex and attached to it, however, is a mass of whitish tissue. This is also true of other parts of the brain. Their surfaces frequently consist of a mass of grayish-colored cells which are attached to, or perhaps supported by, a mass of whitish material differing in consistency and obviously in organic structure. Investigation shows that, as in the case of the spinal cord, an important constituent of the grayish material is a mass of cell bodies of neurons, while the whitish material consists solely of axons. The tracts of white tissue are the intercommunicating cables that connect the various parts of the brain. They are similar in construction and function to the white material of the spinal cord that carries the electric signals to and from the sensory and effector organs of the peripheral nervous system. Figure 2-4 shows how some of these major tracts of axons crisscross within the brain. They are arranged

Fig. 2-2. (See facing page.) The base of the brain. (*From Raymond H. Houser, Graphic Aids to Neurology, Series 1, Scientific Illustrators, Long Beach, California, 1957. By permission of the publishers.*)

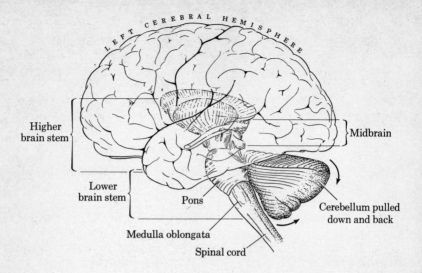

Higher brain stem

Midbrain

Lower brain stem

Pons

Cerebellum pulled down and back

Medulla oblongata

Spinal cord

LEFT CEREBRAL HEMISPHERE

Fig. 2-3. The three major parts of the brain (left side.) (*Reprinted from Wilder Penfield and Lamar Roberts, Speech and Brain Mechanisms, by permission of Princeton University Press. Copyright 1959 by Princeton University Press. London: Oxford University Press.*)

in bundles, a typical bundle involving literally millions of separate communicating nerve fibers—the equivalent of wires in electric circuits. The largest single aggregation of such interconnecting fibers is the cable, called the *corpus callosum,* that ties together the two symmetrical halves of the cortex (Fig. 4-1); it has been estimated that this communicating cable contains 300 million separate conductors! Other major bundles of nerve fibers connect various portions of the brainstem to separate regions of the cerebral cortex.

This organization of the interconnecting cables, together with other obvious aspects of the brain, strongly suggests that nature has found it desirable to divide its computing and data-processing apparatus into distinct subsystems, in much the same way that the computer designer has found it desirable to divide his equipment into an arithmetic unit, a control unit, a memory unit, and the like. Evidence that we shall examine later confirms the differentiation of the various portions of the brain, although the functional assignments are certainly not at all similar to those employed by the computer designer.

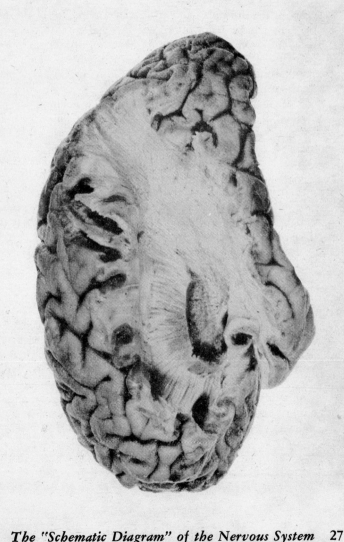

Fig. 2-4. The interconnections in the cortex. (*Reprinted from Wilder Penfield and Lamar Roberts, Speech and Brain Mechanisms, by permission of Princeton University Press. Copyright 1959 by Princeton University Press. London: Oxford University Press.*)

Composition of the Gray Matter of the Brain

Since the white fiber tracts constitute the cables that transfer information in electric form from one part of the brain to another, it is evidently in the various aggregations of gray matter between which these fiber tracts communicate that the actual business of the brain must be done. The gray matter contains the usual network of small blood vessels that permeate all organs of the body, bringing the required nourishing materials to the organ in question and carrying away the waste products generated by its functioning. Also in the gray matter are cells that perform one or another of the many housekeeping functions having to do with maintaining the proper chemical environment for the performance of the organ. However, the working elements of the gray matter, in whose behalf the special arrangement of blood vessels and supporting cells is provided, are neurons.

Although a neuron of the brain and a neuron of the peripheral nervous system are fundamentally the same kind of electrochemical component, they are not identical in structure. Except for those neurons whose long axons enter into the white fiber tracts that interconnect various portions of the brain, the axons of the brain neurons are generally much shorter than those in the peripheral nervous system. The dendrites, on the other hand, are typically more numerous, and these multiple input branches of the nerve cells are intertangled in the gray matter of the brain in a much more complex fashion than is characteristic of the nerve cells in the periphery or the spinal cord. There are neurons of many different sizes and shapes in the human brain, but on the average they are much smaller than those found in the other portions of the nervous system. Major regions of the brain contain neurons so small that more than one hundred million of them are packed into a single cubic inch of the gray matter.

But the operating components of the brain are still neurons, and a correct picture of the brain is that of a very large number of interconnected circuit elements, each of which sends its own pattern of electric impulses to the other circuit elements to which it acts as an input, in accordance with the pattern of impulses supplied to its own input terminals by the other circuit elements for which it is an output connection. This is also a valid description of an electronic digital computer. The computer scientist would suspect that such an arrangement might result in a capability for computational and logical performance.

Cerebral Terminations of the Peripheral Nerves

We have now confirmed that the general organization of the brain is orderly and computerlike—a set of interconnected subsystems, each subsystem consisting of an aggregation of multiply connected electric circuit elements of a type capable of receiving and generating the kinds of on/off signals that are characteristic of the nervous system. A natural next step in our exploration is to search for the places in the brain to which the afferent nerves send their impulses for processing and the places at which the efferent nerves receive the signals that they transmit to the peripheral motor mechanisms of the body. Fortunately, nature has been kind to the brain researcher by making it possible for explorations such as these to be performed on a fully conscious person or animal. There are no touch or pain receptors in the brain. Therefore, once the necessary portion of bone and membrane that protects the delicate material of the brain has been cut away under either general or local anesthesia, the patient can be restored to complete consciousness with his faculties operating normally while electric probes are pushed into various portions of the brain, voltages either measured or applied, and the results observed by the surgeon. The probe is typically a fine wire coated with insulating material, except at the very tip. When used as a tool to measure a voltage that may be naturally generated in the brain, the probe transmits to the recording instruments an indication of the electric potential at the spot in the brain immediately adjacent to its tiny tip. When used as a supplier of electric current from the outside apparatus, the probe sends that current into a similarly localized small volume of tissue.

Of course, experiments simply for the purpose of gaining information about how the brain works are not customarily made on human subjects. However, through the years many thousands of operations have had to be performed on human brains to relieve pathological conditions due to injury or disease. The brain surgeons have found that electrical measurements made with such probes as those just described can be an invaluable aid in determining the precise location of the injured tissue that must be removed or the incision that must be made to relieve the patient's condition. Since brain surgeons are frequently also research scientists, they usually make and publish precise records of their observations. The resulting literature constitutes a store of knowledge that is the source of much of the information we have about the working of the brain and nervous system.

In addition to the information obtained from the operating room, brain-research scientists, in common with their other medical contemporaries, have profited greatly from the fact that the processes involved in the evolutionary development of the various species have resulted in great similarities in the structure and function of the corresponding organs of related animals. Not only are the parts of the brain of a chimpanzee the same as those of the human brain, but they resemble the parts of the human brain in shape; and the extensive evidence now available indicates that they function almost exactly as the parts of the human brain do. And the brain of a dog is not much different, and the brain of a cat is not much different from that of a dog. While it does man's ego little good to hear this, it is even true that a great deal can be learned about the functioning of the human brain by studies on the brain of a rat or a squirrel.

For these reasons, much of the research on the human brain is done on animals. Ultimately, of course, any body of conclusions thus reached must be subjected to confirming tests made on humans to ensure that in each case extrapolation from animal to human brain function is valid. Usually, a suitable opportunity is sooner or later presented in the course of brain operations, and new confirmation is obtained of the validity of performing experiments on animals to learn how the human brain works.

Interestingly enough, cats seem to be the most popular subjects for brain research. They are high enough in the evolutionary scale to make extrapolation to the human brain generally safe; and they are more readily available, cheaper, and easier to care for than chimpanzees, which of course are closest of all animals to the human in terms of the anatomy and physiology of the brain. Cats have another interesting characteristic. Adult cats, even of different breeds, have skulls and brains of remarkably the same size and shape. This means that the research scientist, when working with cats, can place his electric probes accurately in the parts of the brain that he wishes to test by using a standardized set of three-dimensional anatomical maps. Nothing of the sort would be possible with most other animals, such as dogs, for example.

Returning now to our objective of locating terminating points in the brain for the peripheral nerves, let us conduct an imaginary experiment. Remembering that there is no sensation of touch or pain associated with the type of experiment we are about to describe, we can, if we wish, assume that we are dealing with a human subject. The experiment consists in insertion of an electric probe into a selected region of the brain, application of a stimulating voltage, and observation of the effect on the subject. Since the language of the central nervous system consists of on/off voltage pulses, the stimulating signal used by the surgeon is usually a train of short-duration pulses. Various pulse frequencies are used, although there appears to be a preference for 60 cycles per second, doubtless because this frequency is readily available and also is in the general range of frequencies naturally occurring in the nervous system. Each pulse is a few tenths of a volt in amplitude and a few milliseconds in duration.

Since, as we have seen earlier, the brain is composed of a number of functionally separate organs, we cannot know in advance just where in the brain we might expect to find the terminations of the peripheral nerves. However, it is certainly clear which part of the brain is easiest to work with. It is, of course, the cerebral cortex. This outer covering is readily accessible to the surgeon's probe and can be explored without risk of extensive damage to tissues of the brain that might be occasioned by forcing a probe too deeply into the underlying structures (although, as we shall see later, the brain appears to have a remarkable capacity for sustaining damage of this sort without noticeable effect upon its performance). Therefore the first experiments with probing techniques, and still today by far the most extensive experiments, have been made on the cerebral cortex. Fortunately for the purposes of our present objective, these experiments have proved fruitful. If the probe is inserted at the proper point of the cerebral covering and the voltage applied, a leg muscle will twitch; if inserted at a different point, a finger will move; if at a still different point, the mouth muscles will contract; and so on. These appear to be the points of departure of the electric signals sent by the brain to make these muscles perform. Nature employs a regular plan for these cortical terminations. The point on the cortex that controls the little finger of the right hand is adjacent to the point that controls the next finger of the same hand; this in turn is adjacent to the control point for the third finger; and so on. The cortical control points for the wrist and the muscles of the arm follow in sequence. It is therefore possible to map out on the surface of the cortex a picture of the body in terms of its cortical connections. Such a picture, called a *homunculus* (little man), is shown in Figure 2-5. The distorted and grotesque body parts are sketched around the surface of a vertical cross section of the brain cut through an area, called the *precentral gyrus,* that lies just ahead of the middle of the skull. This strip of gray matter, approximately one inch wide, runs out and down from the deep fore-and-aft cleft (the *longitudinal fissure*) that divides the brain into two hemispheres (Fig. 2-6). It is in this narrow strip that the cortical departure points for the motor commands to the muscles are found. Since the right-hand side of the brain controls the move-

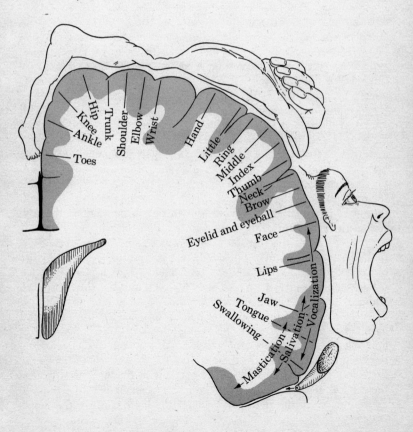

Fig. 2-5. Motor homunculus of man. (*After Penfield and Rasmussen, Cerebral Cortex of Man, The Macmillan Company. Reprinted from A. R. Buchanan, Functional Neuro-Anatomy, Lea & Febiger, Philadelphia, 1961. By permission of the publishers.*)

Hip
Knee
Ankle
Trunk
Shoulder
Elbow
Wrist
Toes
Hand
Little
Ring
Middle
Index
Thumb
Neck
Brow
Eyelid and eyeball
Face
Lips
Jaw
Tongue
Swallowing
Vocalization
Salivation
Mastication

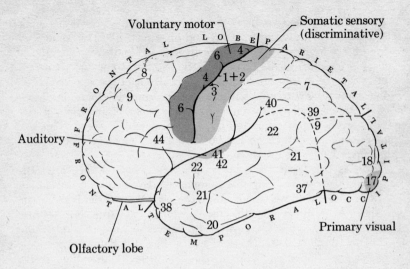

Fig. 2-6. The primary sensory and motor areas of the cortex, viewed from the left. (*Reprinted from Wilder Penfield and Lamar Roberts, Speech and Brain Mechanisms, by permission of Princeton University Press. Copyright 1959 by Princeton University Press. London: Oxford University Press.*)

ment of the left-hand side of the body, and vice versa, there are in fact two figures like 2-5; the omitted figure, which is simply the mirror image of the one shown, relates to the muscular control of the other half of the body.

The distortion of the little man of Figure 2-5 is a consequence of the fact that the area on the cortex devoted to the control of any particular part of the body depends, not on the size of the part, but on the extent of the detailed muscular control that is required. Thus, the brain devotes only a modest amount of cortical tissue to control the muscles in the foot and leg; it almost ignores the musculature of the body; but it is highly preoccupied with the mouth and the lips and seems to place top priority on the servicing of the hands and fingers. All this, of course, correlates nicely with the unusual dexterity exhibited by the parts that receive preferential treatment by the cortex. One might expect that animals less orally and manually developed than humans might have a different allocation of brain tissue to the various muscles of the body. And indeed, this is the case. The snout is unusually widely represented in the cortex of a pig, and for a horse as much cortex is devoted to mapping the skin around the nostrils as is assigned to all the rest of the body.

Apparently, the sensations of a human subject who is undergoing electric-probe measurements for plotting a map like that shown in Figure 2-5 are most curious. As mentioned earlier, there are no touch or pain receptors in the brain itself; the subject is not directly aware of the insertion into his cortex of the probe or of the application of the stimulating current. Therefore, the resulting movement of whichever one of his muscles is related to the point of insertion of the probe in the cortex comes to him as a considerable surprise. This is a movement over which he has no control and which, of course, was not preceded by the usual sensation of intent.

Just as there exists a *motor* strip on each half of the cortex, so there exists a *sensory* strip that contains the terminations in the cortex of the afferent nerves coming from the periphery of the body. Each sensory strip is parallel to the corresponding motor strip, but lies just behind it (Fig. 2-6). The cortical region in which the sensory strip is situated is called the *postcentral gyrus*. The stimulation of a touch receptor on a finger of the right hand results in the reception, at the appropriate point in the sensory strip of the left hemisphere, of a typical train of pulses generated by the receptor nerve endings in the right finger and passed along by the communicating spinal cord and brainstem to the cerebral cortex.

Since the brain is a collection of several organs, it would not be surprising if a body image composed of sensory- or motor-nerve terminations should appear in more than one place. Although no other region has been so extensively mapped as the cortex, such images have in fact been discovered in two or three other areas. For example, there is a homunculus in the cerebellum, the baseball-sized, bean-shaped lump of gray and white tissue that protrudes toward the rear from the top of the brainstem and is almost, but not quite, completely covered by the hind part of the cortex. The cerebellum, as we shall see later, plays an important role in the mediation and stabilization of complex body movements. For the proper performance of this dynamic stabilization function, the cerebellum appears to require a detailed pattern of sensory nerves to provide it with a continuous status report of the positions of the various portions of the body.

The optical mapping system of the human brain is of special interest and importance. Through the more than one million fibers of the optic nerve of each eye, the pattern of light and dark formed by the lens on the retina is transmitted to a specific set of neurons in the *occipital lobes* of the cortex (Fig. 2-6). Although the picture that is produced by the pattern of voltages reaching these positions at the extreme back of the head is a highly distorted one, topological continuity is preserved, in the sense that adjacent points in the retina are represented by adjacent positions on the cortex. The application of an electric stimulus to any of these cortical points causes the subject to see flashes of light at the corresponding point of his field of view. Similarly, the illumination of the retina by a single bright spot of light results in the arrival of the usual train of voltage pulses at the corresponding spot of the visual cortex.

It should be emphasized that the cortical connections described here are "permanently wired in." Except for the normal variation in size and shape of the brains of different individuals, all animals of a given species are "wired" in the same way. The nerve from the right little finger appears on the cortex at a standardized position characteristic of the species; the point on the occipital lobe that indicates the presence or absence of light in the lower right-hand corner of the field of view of the left eye is in the same position for one man as it is for another. No learning or adaptation is involved in the establishment of these nerve connections; the blueprint for their construction is contained in the genes, just as are the many other physical design details that specify that an embryo is going to become a human rather than a frog. We have seen evidence for the existence of potent control mechanisms that ensure the interconnection of the nervous system in the desired way, in the ability of the lower vertebrates with extensive powers of regeneration to reconnect cut or damaged nervous tissue in a strongly directed fashion.

And so we see that there is a considerable degree of orderliness in the way in which nature's input and output devices are connected to what appears to be the central data processor, the brain. Just as in what we imagine to be the analogous electronic computer systems, there are specific, regularly arranged terminal connecting points for the various peripheral mechanisms that provide to the central computer the information it needs for the performance of its computations. Similar regularity is exhibited by the array of output terminals in the brain from which the instructions produced by the data processor are sent out to the effector mechanisms.

A logical next step in our gradual approach to an understanding of the nervous system is to look for processes that can be clearly identified as either data-processing or computer/control functions. This will be the objective of the next two chapters.

BIBLIOGRAPHY

Brazier, M. A. B., *The Electrical Activity of the Nervous System* (ed. 2, The Macmillan Company, New York, 1960).

Buchanan, A. R., *Functional Neuro-Anatomy* (ed. 4, Lea & Febiger, Philadelphia, 1961), chap. 12, "The Sensory and Associative Mechanism of the Cerebral Cortex."

Penfield, W., and L. Roberts, *Speech and Brain Mechanisms* (Princeton University Press, Princeton, N.J., 1959), chap. II, "Functional Organization of the Human Brain, Discriminative Sensation, Voluntary Movement."

Snider, R. S., "The Cerebellum," *Scientific American,* August, 1958, pp. 84–90.

Sperry, R. W., "The Eye and the Brain," *Scientific American,* May, 1956, pp. 48–52.

Sperry, R. W., "The Growth of Nerve Circuits," *Scientific American,* November, 1959, pp. 68–75.

Peripheral Data Processing in the Nervous System

It is possible to define all the activity of the brain as one form or another of data processing. The receptor neurons provide information about the state of the outside world and of the internal organs; this is supplemented by the memory record of past experience; and the combined data are then processed by the neuronal circuits to yield some end result. Frequently with man, and almost always with the lower animals, the end result of the data-processing activities is a pattern of motor commands that stimulates the muscles or glands of the body into some kind of response that is appropriate to the incoming stimuli. Sometimes, in the case of man and probably some of the higher animals, the end result of the data-processing activities is mental in character: a thought or concept that may have to be combined with other thoughts or concepts before a directly observable physical activity results. The goal of this entire book may properly be defined as the achievement of understanding of how these "data-processing" activities of the brain are carried out, and it can be admitted at this point that we shall have moved only a short distance toward the goal by the end of the last page. The objective of the present chapter is much more restricted. Here we shall consider only the rearrangement of the raw data that is carried out by the peripheral nervous system before it passes the information provided by the sensory receptors along for the complex ministrations of the brain.

Our concern at this point really is with the economy of design of the nervous system. Certain kinds and amounts of information are needed to determine the proper response of the organism to the environmental and the internal conditions. But beyond a certain point, additional information is not only unnecessary but can be positively harmful, because it overloads neuronal circuits that could better be used for other purposes. Thus, while touch discrimination in our fingers is useful up to a certain point, we ordinarily have no need to localize tactile sensations closer than a few hundredths of an inch. This makes it possible for the Meissner corpuscles that serve the sense of touch in hairless skin to be multiplexed, in the sense that a number of such touch-sensitive endings can be connected to a single nerve fiber. The resulting averaging effect that determines the frequency of the action-potential pulses in the single conductor is a kind of data-processing operation that minimizes the number of nerve fibers required, diminishes the vulnerability of the sensory system to damage of the subsurface nerve endings, and prevents the wastage of the central neurons that would accompany an unnecessarily detailed barrage of tactile impulses.

Another simple equivalent of data processing, in the sense of providing input information in a form convenient for use in the control functions of the organism, is sometimes provided by special sensory receptors that directly measure physical quantities whose values would otherwise have to be determined by manipulation of the more usual types of sensory information. C. A. G. Wiersma, Professor of Biology at Caltech, has provided interesting evidence for the existence of such complex sensory receptors in the nervous system of the crayfish. In addition to stretch receptors that emit action-potential pulses of frequency determined by the relative displacements of the adjacent abdominal segments, Wiersma has discovered other receptors that send to the central nervous system indications of the relative velocities of the segments. This results in the transmission, over the bundle of nerve fibers involved, of a pattern of action-potential frequencies that, presumably, supplies the higher levels of the nervous system with the kind of rate information needed by the servo control circuit that governs the activities of the abdominal muscles.

But the peripheral nervous system does not confine itself to the employment of ingenious receptor neurons in its efforts to provide easily usable information to the brain. Networks of interneurons are also used to rearrange the primary sensory data into more acceptable form. Such peripheral data processing sometimes exhibits a respectable degree of computerlike sophistication. Since, for most animals, a large fraction of all the information that comes in from the outside world is visual, it is in the visual sensory systems that the most opportunity and necessity exist for processing and rearranging the input data before transmission to the brain. We shall consider three sets of experiments that have revealed interesting information on the processing of the primary visual data by the networks of interneurons.

The Beetles of Reichardt and Hassenstein

Bernhard Hassenstein, while still a student at the University of Freiburg, devised an ingenious technique of communicating with a beetle, which Werner Reichardt of the Max Planck Institute of Biology has employed to learn a great deal about how the insect's visual system works. The idea for the experiments started with the observation that many of the simpler animals tend to react to optical stimulation in a stereotyped, automatic fashion. If a distinctive pattern of light and dark is moved past such an animal, it will move its head or body to follow the motion. If the pattern has suitable contrast and speed of motion, its effect on the test animal seems to be quite compelling; a pattern having improper contrast, or moving too fast or too slow, elicits a less definite reaction. These qualitative observations led Reichardt to the idea that some automatic and precise relationship may exist between the nature of the visual stimulus and the animal's motor response. He set out to devise experiments for testing this hypothesis.

Since Reichardt's objectives were quantitative, his first problem was the establishment of methods of measuring the applied stimulus and the elicited response. It was not too difficult to regularize the input stimulus. The insect could be immobilized with its head centered on the axis of a surrounding cylinder, on the inner surface of which any desired sequence of light and dark patterns could be attached and rotated around the animal. Specification of the variation in brightness over the pattern, and of the rate of rotation of the supporting cylinder, would then fix the important variables of the stimulus in adequate and measurable fashion.

A measurement of the motor response of the subject animal was harder to come by. Here was where Hassenstein's ingenious technique of man/beetle communication came in, for it amounted to a means whereby the insect could "tell" the experimenter when the optical stimulus caused it to feel an urge to turn, and in what direction, and how strong an urge it was!

Figure 3-1 shows the experimental arrangement. The beetle's back is glued to a piece of cardboard by means of which the insect can be suspended in the air, with its head positioned on the vertical axis of the rotating cylinder described above. The device used by the beetle to "talk" to the experimenter is called a *Y-maze globe*. It consists of six pieces of curved straw that join at four points to form Y-like junctions. The beetle automatically clings to the structure when it is presented and, in this situation, ordinarily feels the urge to walk. Of course, the insect cannot move; consequently, as its legs perform the walking motions, the Y-maze globe turns in a direction opposite to that in which the beetle would move if it were walking freely. But, after a few steps, a Y junction always reaches the beetle, and a right or left choice has to be made. After the choice is made and the junction has passed by, the animal is in the same situation as before; after a few more steps it has to choose again, and so on. If, owing to the optical stimulus provided by the pattern of light and dark on the surrounding rotating cylinder, the insect feels more of an urge to turn in one direction than the other, this will be indicated by the choices it makes at the successive Y junctions encountered as it "walks" along. If the turning bias produced by the optical stimulus is a weak one compared with the other random physiological factors that on the average would cause the insect to choose right and left turns with equal frequency, the number of turns to one direction will only slightly exceed the number to the other direction. A stronger optically induced turning urge will result in a higher proportion of directed turns. Thus the insect is immobilized, but nevertheless "tells" the experimenter the direction and magnitude of its urge to turn.

An important incidental discovery made by Hassenstein when he was originally working out the Y-maze-globe technique was that the weight of the globe was critical. A 30 per cent increase or decrease from the optimum value would prevent the beetle from performing the walking motions on which the experiment depended. The optimum value turned out to be the weight of the insect itself. This appeared to be related to the habit of this type of beetle (*Chlorophanus*) of hanging from the under side of a twig or leaf and "walking" along in inverted fashion. When erect, in the experimental situation, normal behavior seemed to depend on the existence of the usual tension in the leg muscles, produced by a suspended weight roughly equal to that of the insect. On such seemingly unimportant details the success of biological experiments frequently depends.

To understand Reichardt's results, we must know something about the construction of the beetle's eye. Like other insects, this beetle has a compound eye, composed of many small fixed optical units, or *ommatidia*. Each ommatidium has its own lens that focuses light from a preferred direction on its own small retina and thereby produces action-potential pulses in the outgoing fiber of the associated retinal nerve cells. Early work had established that the turning reaction in the beetle was produced by the arrival on successive ommatidia of distinctive light/dark transitions in the moving field of view. The evidence was that the neural signal controlling the motor response involved the action of interneurons, each of which combined

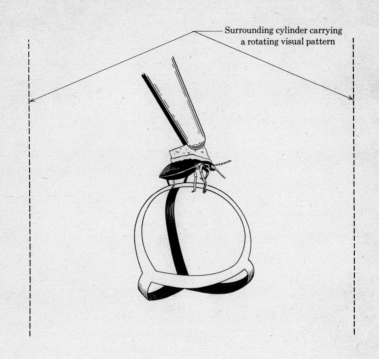

Fig. 3-1. The beetle with the Y-maze globe. (*After Sensory Communication*, ed. by Walter A. Rosenblith, The MIT Press and John Wiley & Sons, Inc., 1961. By permission of the publishers.)

Surrounding cylinder carrying a rotating visual pattern

and processed the light-intensity data supplied by several neighboring ommatidia. Reichardt set out to determine whether he could devise a quantitative physical model for the interneuronal data processor that would fit the observed facts.

To obtain the data needed for the design of the model, Reichardt carefully recorded the strength of the beetle's turning response, as indicated by the statistics of the Y-maze rotation, as a function of various parameters of the stimulating optical pattern. In one sequence of experiments, the rate of rotation of the cylinder was kept constant, and the turning response was measured for each of a series of light/ dark patterns. The quantitative relationship between pattern con-

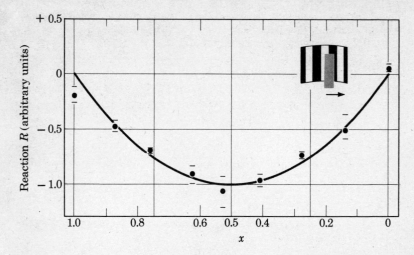

Fig. 3-2. Optomotor reaction plotted as a function of fractional difference in reflectivities of dark and light stripes, for a given cylinder speed. (*From Sensory Communication, ed. by Walter A. Rosenblith, The MIT Press and John Wiley & Sons, Inc., 1961. By permission of the publishers.*)

trast and turning response permitted certain conclusions to be drawn about the nature of the interneuronal coupling between ommatidia. Another sequence of experiments involved determinations of how the turning reaction of the beetle varied with the rate of rotation of the cylinder as it carried a given striped pattern around the insect.

Using only linear circuit elements, Reichardt was able to devise an electric network model with properties that would almost exactly duplicate the stimulus/response measurements on *Chlorophanus*. The core of this model was, in biological terms, a layer of interneurons, each receiving inputs from only two ommatidia, but with one input delayed with respect to the other by means of a low-pass filter. The interneuron was then assumed to produce an output proportional to the product of its two inputs. (It is not clear that neurons can perform in this way, but it would not be surprising if they could, by means of a suitable combination of their threshold, nonlinear, and time-decay properties.) Such multiplication, with one signal delayed relative to the other, will be recognized by the circuit engineer as an arrangement that correlates the signals from the two ommatidia. The final output signal of the network, corresponding to the driving force for the beetle's turning-response motor mechanism, was obtained by taking the difference between the smoothed outputs of adjacent interneurons. Such a circuit arrangement produces effects like those observed in the beetle experiments: its turning output changes sign with direction of rotation of the optical pattern, changes properly with the contrast of the light and dark stripes in a test pattern, and has maximum magnitude at an optimum cylinder speed. Figures 3-2 and 3-3 show how well the mathematical theory could be made to fit the observed performance of the beetle, by proper choice of circuit constants. The agreement is quite respectable even when compared with the results of many purely physical experiments; for a situation in which the experimental observations consist of quantitative measurements on the behavior of a living animal, the agreement between theory and experiment is remarkable indeed.

Once the model was worked out, it provided other predictions about how the insect's reaction should vary with detailed changes in the optical stimulus pattern employed. Figure 3-4 shows some of the patterns that were used on the inner surface of the rotating cylinder, while Figure 3-5 displays the theoretically predicted curves and the experimentally observed points. Some of these observations

Fig. 3-3. Optomotor reaction as a function of cylinder speed, for a given cylinder pattern. (*From Sensory Communication, ed. by Walter A. Rosenblith, The MIT Press and John Wiley & Sons, Inc., 1961. By permission of the publishers.*)

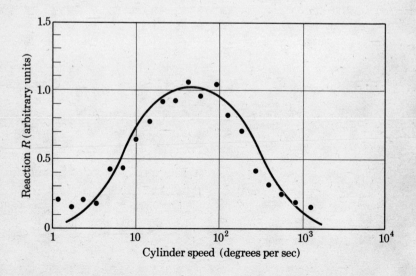

confirmed that changes in the sequence of contrast values in the moving pattern could result in major and predictable changes in the behavior of the beetle. Other of the tests showed that equally striking pattern changes could be made without influencing the turning response, if these changes were of the type to which correlation circuits would be expected to be insensitive. Both kinds of results seemed to show that the insect solves the differential equations involved in almost exactly the same way that Reichardt does.

It is not necessary to suppose that Reichardt's model is a precise electrical analog of what exists in the eye of the beetle. It is most unlikely that any of the neuronal components have exactly the properties of the linear filters and correlating circuits of the electrical engineer. Nevertheless, the agreement between theory and experiment is too striking to ignore. Reichardt would appear to have established that a kind of data processing goes on behind the retina of *Chlorophanus* featured by something very close to the multiplication of one receptor output (after some time-averaging) by the delayed output

Fig. 3-4. Periodic cylinder patterns. (*From Sensory Communication, ed. by Walter A. Rosenblith, The MIT Press and John Wiley & Sons, Inc., 1961. By permission of the publishers.*)

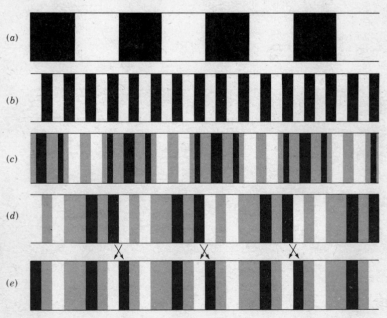

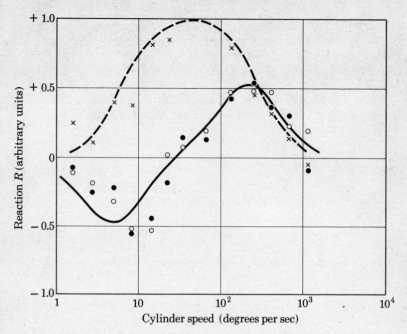

Fig. 3-5. Optomotor response as a function of cylinder speed, for various patterns. Curves for theory; points from experiment. (*From Sensory Communication, ed. by Walter A. Rosenblith, The MIT Press and John Wiley & Sons, Inc., 1961. By permission of the publishers.*)

of an adjoining receptor. The remarkable reproducibility and consistency of the observed responses of the insect also appear to imply a direct utilization by the animal of the output of the retinal processing network for the direction of its locomotion processes. Presumably the output of the special data-processing circuit that Reichardt investigated is employed by the brain as a bias on the synchronized pattern of muscle signals it sends to the legs of the insect to cause it to walk. In this way the physiological need of the animal to "track" a nearby moving object is automatically satisfied, without the employment of a computing mechanism in the brain itself.

Reichardt is currently extending his observations to flying, as well as crawling, insects. For such subjects he employs an electromagnetically actuated torque servo to measure the turning effect of the insect's beating wings, as it tries to respond to the stimulus of the surrounding moving pattern. Similar work on flies is under way at Caltech, while at the University of California at Los Angeles a snail turns a ping-pong ball in response to the stimulus of a surrounding rotating visual pattern. Detailed circuit models have not yet been worked out, but the optomotor response of flies and snails has been found to be automatic and reproducible, like that of the beetle. Apparently a capability for rearranging primary visual data by a process equivalent to the solution of a set of simultaneous differential equations is a rather general property of the retinal interneurons of lower forms of animal life.

The MIT Frogs

J. Y. Lettvin, H. R. Maturana, W. S. McCulloch, and W. H. Pitts, of the Research Laboratory of Electronics of the Massachusetts Institute of Technology, have reported a fascinating series of observations on the data processing occurring in the eye of the frog. Like Reichardt and Hassenstein, they employed an experimental arrangement by means of which controlled optical stimulus patterns could be displayed in the field of view of one of the eyes of an immobilized test animal. Their arrangement, however, was three-dimensional rather than two-dimensional: the frog was positioned with its eye at the center of a hemisphere of 7-inch radius, on the inner dull surface of which small light- or dark-colored objects could be placed in various positions or moved around by the manipulation of a permanent magnet on the outer surface of the hemisphere.

The MIT group departed also from the technique of Hassenstein and Reichardt in that they did not use behavioral observations for measuring the response of the frog. Instead, microelectrodes were inserted into the optic nerve and measurements made directly on the electric signals sent toward the brain over individual nerve fibers. These probe measurements were made at various points along the frog's visual tract, including the actual terminations of the axons of the optic nerve in the brain.

The frog, being a vertebrate, has an eye fundamentally similar to our own. The image of the outside world is focused on the rods and cones of the retina. These primary photoreceptors produce some kind of replica, in electric form, of the incoming pattern of light and dark. Anatomical studies show that, just as in the eyes of the beetle and of the human, the axons of the primary photoreceptors do not connect directly with the optic nerve that goes to the brain, but instead terminate in several layers of extensively cross-connected interneurons that lie behind the rods and cones in the retina. Some of these interneurons are in turn connected to the fibers of the optic nerve. We have seen evidence that the roughly analogous interneurons in the eye of the beetle perform extensive processing and re-arranging of the visual information before passing it on to the brain. The MIT group hoped that their microelectrode technique similarly would reveal what kind of "picture" was transmitted over the optic nerve and how it compared with the generating visual pattern.

The results bordered on the spectacular. It was found possible to distinguish four complete "pictures" of the surrounding external field of view that were transmitted concurrently over four distinct sets of fibers in the optic nerve. The analogy that comes most readily to mind is that of color television, wherein separate pictures, in the several color modalities, are simultaneously transmitted over the intercommunicating channel and then recombined in the receiver to produce the desired effect. Supporting this analogy was the further discovery, arising from the probe measurements made at the brain terminations of the optic nerve, that the "pictures" at this receiving point were in registration: the optic fibers carrying the four different types of information about the visual conditions at a particular spot on the retina terminated accurately one below the other in four successive layers of brain tissue.

But the color-television analogy must not be pursued too far, for the four pictures transmitted by the optic nerve of the frog are nothing like the simple proportional representation of the original light intensity that characterizes television. There is evidence that the retinal interneurons do a thorough job of modifying the incoming information before sending it along to the brain. For example, a strange property possessed by all four optical representations is in-sensitivity to the general level of illumination, over intensity changes of several hundred to one. This would make it appear that the frog knows it is day rather than night, but cannot tell whether the day is bright or dull.

In most respects, however, the properties of the four different visual images were found to be quite different from one another. The MIT group characterized the four types of image in terms of the kinds of visual information found to be most effective in produc-ing a picture. Their descriptive terms for the four sets of fibers are *sustained contrast detectors, moving-edge detectors, net dimming de-tectors,* and *net convexity detectors.*

The picture composed of the signals from the sustained contrast detectors contains only edges of high brightness gradient. That produced by the moving-edge detectors is like the sustained contrast picture in that only boundaries of abrupt brightness change appear, but differs in that it is visible only if the boundary is moving. One could imagine that the first picture would provide the animal with a sort of outline drawing of its surroundings, much like a simple pencil sketch with no shading or fill-in between the boundaries of sharply delineated features. This would probably be an adequate view of the surroundings for general orientational purposes. The motion sensitivity of the second picture, that produced by the moving-edge detectors, might provide survival value by increasing the animal's responsiveness to the presence of enemy or prey. However, the remaining types of picture, those provided by the net dimming detectors and the net convexity detectors, appear to be much more directly related to such survival needs.

The fibers termed net dimming detectors respond only to a sudden reduction of illumination. These fibers have a large "receptive field" in that each receives processed data from the rods and cones covering a large portion of the retina (as much as 15 degrees). As a result, the response of any fiber becomes stronger as the dark object that suddenly blots out light from a part of the field of view becomes larger. It is easy to imagine that the impulses arriving at the brain-tissue layer where the net-dimming-detector picture is portrayed are used by the frog for the avoidance of attack by larger animals.

But the most interesting of all is the picture supplied to the brain of the frog by the net convexity detectors. These fibers do not respond to changes in general illumination or to straight edges of contrast, fixed or moving. Instead, they respond only when a small dark object enters the field of view. For the 7-inch distance at which the stimulus objects were displayed to the test animal, it was found that the object had to be an inch or less in diameter in order to produce an appreciable response. The response increased with decreasing diameter down to a dimension of approximately half an inch. It maintained its maximum value for diameters between half an inch and about an eighth of an inch. For still smaller diameters, a decrease in the strength of the nerve impulse set in. These responses occurred for stationary small dark objects, but they were stronger when the objects were moving, especially if the motion was jerky rather than smooth.

Little imagination is required to connect the kind of picture produced by the net convexity detectors with the bug-catching proclivities of the frog. The angular dimensions of the dark objects that produce maximum response of the neural detectors cover a range that corresponds nicely with the angular dimensions of flies when viewed from the distance to which a frog can extend its tongue. Moreover, the enhanced strength of the nerve impulse produced by irregular motion of the small dark object across the background is compatible with the well-known fact that a frog ignores a food object until it moves, at which time it responds promptly and effectively. Referring again to a television analogy, it is as though the screen were dark except for any spot in the field of view occupied by a dark bug-sized object, with this slightly illuminated point bursting into prominence upon the motion of the object. To test this interpretation, the MIT group prepared a color photograph of the natural habitat of a frog, from a frog's-eye view—flowers and grass. They found that waving this picture around at a 7-inch distance from the frog's eye produced no response in the net-convexity-detector fibers. If, on the other hand, they held this background picture steady and moved a fly-sized object around on it, they obtained an excellent response from the neurons. There seems little doubt that the visual system under investigation constituted the frog's "bug-perceiver."

The MIT work is not complete. Investigations are under way to attempt to learn what kinds of addition, subtraction, filtering, and correlation interconnections are employed by the retinal interneurons, whereby the primary visual data supplied by the rods and cones are processed to yield a final "picture." It is to be anticipated that detailed neuronal circuit arrangements, possibly similar to those worked out by Reichardt for *Chlorophanus*, will ultimately be identified as the mechanism underlying the transformations of the received visual information in the eye of the frog before it is passed along to the brain.

As with the work of Reichardt and Hassenstein, the success of the MIT experiments on frogs is inspiring searches for similar phenomena in other animals. For example, Wiersma has already identified fibers in the optic nerve of a crab that transmit information about large objects moving in the visual field. And it is easy to imagine that there are mechanisms in the visual systems of the higher vertebrates, including man, that perform data processing generally similar to that observed in the frog. Of course, there must also be differences; for instance, the human species does not need a special "bug-perceiver" type of network. But our visual system possesses other properties that seem not entirely unrelated to those observed in the frog. There is a property of invariance in our perception of objects that has long puzzled the psychologist. We recognize triangles, circles, cubes, spheres, disks, and faces for what they are. Yet we know that their distances from the eye, orientations, and conditions of illumination greatly affect their images on the retina. Somewhere in our nervous system, transformations of the raw visual data must take place that extract topological information independent of these distortions and afford us our relatively high degree of perception invariance. The work on beetles and frogs would suggest that some of the data processing involved may be carried out in the peripheral nervous system before the visual information is passed on to the brain.

Measurements on the human species have not yet been made, but significant work has recently been done on cats, by D. H. Hubel and T. N. Wiesel of the Harvard Medical School. Their observations are as interesting for the differences they indicate between frogs and higher animals such as cats (and presumably man) as for the similarities. In particular, they have found evidence that some processing of the primary visual data may be carried out by means of the detailed pattern of interconnection between the fibers of the optic nerve and the neurons of the visual cortex.

The Harvard Cats

The experimental arrangement employed by Hubel and Wiesel was similar to that of the MIT group in that the test animal—in this case, a cat—was arranged with its open eye at a fixed position in front of a screen on which visual images could be displayed. The animal was kept physically stabilized and inert throughout the experiment by means of paralyzing drugs. As in the MIT work, the effects of various visual patterns were observed by inserting microelectrodes directly into nerve tissue of the optical system and measuring the local electrical effects. However, there was one important difference in emphasis. The MIT investigators were primarily interested in the data processing occurring in the eye itself and therefore made most of their measurements on the fibers of the optic nerve. Hubel and Wiesel, on the other hand, concentrated most of their attention on the electric signals in the cortex. In the cat, as in man, the so-called "primary visual cortex" lies at the extreme rear of the covering of the brain (Fig. 2-6).

Hubel and Wiesel's preoccupation with the state of affairs in the cortex rather than in the optic nerve was largely dictated by earlier indications that the data processing done directly in the eye of the cat may be considerably less extensive than that performed in the eye of the frog. Some peripheral rearrangement of the data was known to occur, but it seemed to be of a relatively simple kind. In the cat, circular symmetry always seemed to be preserved; an optic fiber arriving at the cortex was always found to be stimulated maximally by a circular pattern of light or dark accurately centered on a small group of retinal receptors. To be sure, some fibers responded best to a small bright spot in a dark field and others to a small dark spot in a bright field, but there did not appear to exist, in the optic nerve of the cat, a richness or variety of forms of processed visual data comparable with those in the optic nerve of the frog.

At first glance, it may seem odd that the cat, whose behavior obviously indicates a much greater and more varied employment of visual data than the frog, should nevertheless send less highly organized information from eye to brain. However, in later chapters we shall have a number of occasions to observe a tendency for nature to transfer to the cortex of the higher animals responsibility for functions performed in other portions of the nervous system of less well endowed creatures. The cat is a much more intelligent animal than the frog; it would be consistent with this tendency for its visual data processing to be performed more centrally.

Indeed, this turned out to be the situation. When Hubel and Wiesel inserted a microelectrode into a cortical neuron and laboriously determined which spots on the retina had to be illuminated to produce a change in the frequency of the action-potential pulses, they found an entirely different state of affairs than that observed when the microelectrode measured the activity in a fiber proceeding to the visual cortex. The *receptive field* of the cortical neuron (the area on the retina within which illumination changes produce effects) was never circular, as it always was for the input fibers. Straight lines, not circles, were found to dominate the response geometry of the cortical neurons! For a given neuron, the most effective illuminating shape was frequently a slit, with long dimension many times greater than its width. Sometimes it was an edge of sharp contrast, but always a straight edge, never a round one. And the orientation on the retina of the axis of the slit or straight edge was usually critical, a change of only 5 or 10 degrees in angle having a major effect on the responsiveness of the cortical neuron under test. When the microelectrode was pushed into the visual cortex accurately at right angles to its surface, evidence was found for a high degree of registration of the "images" made up of the electric activity of neurons in the successive layers of the cortex. To be sure, the neurons sequentially penetrated by the microelectrode in such a column of tissue usually had different types of receptive fields—some responded best to slits, some to straight-edge contrast changes, some fired when the light went on, some when it went off, and so on—but the axes of the receptive fields were found to be accurately the same. In addition, the receptive fields of the neurons in a single cortical column were found to overlap on the retina, although they were not identical. If the microelectrode was removed and reinserted at a nearby point on the surface of the cortex, the neurons in the new column were again all found to have a common axis of receptive field, which, however, might have an orientation quite different from the orientations of the axes characteristic of other nearby parallel columns of cortical tissue. From measurements on several hundred individual neurons in the visual cortex, Hubel and Wiesel concluded that there was no evidence for preferred retinal orientation of the receptive-field axes—approximately equal numbers of cortical columns were observed to respond best to horizontal lines of light, vertical lines, or to lines at angles in between.

The fact that all the cortical neurons measured, and not just those in layers remote from the points of connection of the incoming optic fibers, were maximally responsive to straight slits and edges of illumination suggests that the transformation of the visual data from circularly to linearly symmetrical form is accomplished at the point where the visual data enter the cortex, rather than in subsequent layers of processing neurons. Such a transformation would presumably involve a scheme of neuronal connectivity whereby the various fibers coming from the receptors located in a long narrow region of the retina would all provide inputs to the same cortical neuron. Admittedly, in the complexity of the responses of a few cortical neurons to the properties of "on-ness," "off-ness," and movement of the stimulating patterns of illumination, Hubel and Wiesel found reason to believe that cortical data processing was also sometimes involved. Nevertheless, their observations were all consistent with the conclusion that much of the rearrangement of the raw optical data that occurs in the visual system of the cat is carried out before the signals become immersed in the deeper layers of the cortex.

It seems almost certain that the phenomena studied by Hubel and Wiesel are directly pertinent to some of the peculiar subjective attributes of visual perception that were briefly touched upon at the end of the preceding section. Our unusual sensitivity to the presence of straight lines of light and shade in whatever we are looking at has always puzzled the psychologists. If, as seems likely, man's visual system is organized much like the cat's, we would now appear to have a solid physiological explanation for this fact of perception: we are unusually sensitive to straight lines because each neuron in our visual cortex receives inputs from linear arrays of retinal receptors. Explanations for other aspects of the subjective phenomena of perception were suggested by the properties of some of the neurons whose responses to the conditions of retinal illumination were so complex as to imply the intermediation of cortical data processing. There were instances, for example, when a single cortical neuron would respond to a slit or straight edge of contrast almost independently of the position of the illuminating pattern on the retina. Nevertheless, angular orientation of the slit or line of contrast had to be preserved accurately; a slight rotation around the preferred direction would completely extinguish the response of the cortical cell. Such neuronal elements, that do not much care where in the field of view a straight line of illumination is located but are very much concerned with its angular orientation, may well underlie the neural mechanisms that permit man and other higher vertebrates to identify triangles, squares, and other straight-edged geometrical figures, regardless of their distance or position in the field of view.

Certainly a great deal more information than what has so far been hinted at by the results of this work will be required to provide a complete understanding of the puzzling differences that are known to exist between the image of the outside world focused on the retina of the eye and the resulting subjective sensations in the brain. Nevertheless, it seems no exaggeration to conclude that Hubel and Wiesel have made a good start in understanding some of the processes underlying the phenomena of perception invariance.

Despite our digression into interesting perceptual matters that are dependent upon cortical data processing, the principal point of the discussion of this chapter has been that not all the "intelligence" of the nervous system resides in the brain. And despite the particular examples presented here, it should not be concluded that rearrangement of sensory data prior to transmission to the brain is a property unique to the visual part of the nervous system. Another extensive body of evidence is now developing that indicates the operation of similar principles in the channels of communication connecting the ear and the brain. Moreover, the shape of the "little man" on the sensory cortex (Chap. 2) does not represent the points of arrival of afferent fibers carrying impulses in an unbroken path directly from touch receptors in the skin. Instead, the individual sensory stimuli are extensively interconnected and rearranged in the interneurons of the spinal cord and brainstem before finally being handed on to the cortex.

In view of the fact that the basic components are the same throughout the nervous system, it is not too strange to find that some of the necessary data processing is done in the periphery. This might be expected to result in presenting the incoming sensory information to the brain in a form or "language" that it can more readily deal with, and also in minimizing the number of communicating channels required. The computer designer does things this way. Apparently, so does nature.

BIBLIOGRAPHY

Hubel, D. H., and T. N. Wiesel, "Receptive Fields, Binocular Interaction and Functional Architecture in the Cat's Visual Cortex," *Journal of Physiology*, vol. 160 (1962), pp. 106–154.

Lettvin, J. Y., H. R. Maturana, W. S. McCulloch, and W. H. Pitts, "What the Frog's Eye Tells the Frog's Brain," *Proceedings of the Institute of Radio Engineers*, vol. 47 (1959), pp. 1940–1951.

Reichardt, W., "Autocorrelation and the Central Nervous System," in *Sensory Communication*, ed. by W. A. Rosenblith (The MIT Press and John Wiley & Sons, Inc., New York, 1961), pp. 303–317.

Wiersma, C. A. G., "Coding and Decoding in the Nervous System," *Engineering and Science*, October, 1959, pp. 21–24.

Wiersma, C. A. G., T. H. Waterman, and B. M. H. Bush, "The Impulse Traffic in the Optic Nerve of Decapod Crustacea," *Science*, vol. 134 (1961), p. 1435.

Automatic Control Circuits in the Nervous System

Control Loops Not Involving the Brain

We have seen that data processing occurring at lower levels of the nervous system frequently rearranges the incoming sensory stimuli into forms more directly meaningful to the organism and thereby simplifies the brain's task of interpretation. The brain also receives assistance from other nervous centers in the determination and control of muscular and glandular responses to sensory inputs. Some of the simpler of the stimulus/response loops are, in fact, located entirely outside the brain. Not only does such an arrangement leave the central computer mechanism free to concentrate on the management of sophisticated processes requiring a higher order of complex control, but the short communication channel involved also frequently affords a more rapid response to a stimulus than would otherwise be possible. Withdrawal of the hand from a fire is an example of the kind of action that we might imagine would constitute a reasonable candidate for local implementation. And indeed, nature does it this way.

The hand-out-of-the-fire kind of response is termed a *reflex action,* or simply a *reflex,* to connote its automatic, unthinking character. There are many examples of reflex actions. For some of them the nervous circuits involved have been thoroughly explored and are well understood. This is true, for example, of the familiar knee-jerk reflex, the involuntary upward kick occurring when a rubber mallet is applied briskly to the soft spot just under the kneecap of a crossed leg. A chain, or "reflex arc," of only two interconnected neurons is required to control this process.* The mechanical shock of the mallet generates an electric signal in the femoral nerve, and this signal is

---

* This is an example of the kind of "schematic" statement referred to in Chap. 1. Actually there are many parallel fibers in each segment of the chain of neurons.

transmitted by the long fiber of the receptor to a point in the gray matter of the spinal cord. Here the electric signal is passed to an effector nerve cell whose long axon proceeds to the quadricipital muscle of the leg, where the resulting release of chemical mediating substance contracts the muscle and produces the observed upward kick.

Another example: when a cold object is applied locally to the skin, a reflex arc through the gray matter of the spinal cord, this time involving a chain of several neurons, activates the muscles of the hair follicles to produce the familiar phenomenon of "goose flesh." A similar neuronal circuit constricts the capillary blood vessels just under the skin at the point of application of the cold object, thus reducing the amount of cooling of the blood stream.

Probably there are several thousand reflex arcs in the human body. Some are simple, such as those described; others control multiple interrelated reactions to the input stimuli. Nature employs these local interconnections of short chains of neurons to produce automatic reactions whenever the character of the situation is such that the health of the organism can be protected by a simple response. Such reflexes do not involve precise muscular control. This is why they can be accomplished by interconnections of local groups of neurons, without the mediation of the sophisticated computing and control capabilities of the brain.

Oscillators in the Nervous System

The nervous systems of the lower animals supply many examples of configurations of neurons that produce periodic output signals for the control of rhythmic bodily functions. Sometimes the oscillatory circuit is located near the muscles it drives, sometimes in the brain. This appears to be more a matter of convenience of equipment arrangement than anything else.

One interesting example of a neuronal oscillatory circuit is found in the lobster. It consists of a ring of nine* interconnected neurons for the generation of the periodic electric impulses that control the heartbeat. In this instance, nature has simplified its cabling problem by locating the ring of neurons in the heart itself, underneath a flap of muscle. This neuronal heartbeat oscillatory circuit can be removed intact from a freshly killed lobster and connected to electronic measuring instruments, whereby the faithful neurons will be observed to continue to emit their activating pulses 60 times per minute, for

* In this case there are, in fact, only nine nerve cells involved!

many hours after the lobster for whom they were performing this vital function has been killed and perhaps eaten by the scientist who is conducting the experiment.

The fish that navigate by electric-field-strength measurements (Chap. 1) employ a single oscillatory circuit to synchronize the discharge of the specialized neurons that send the field-producing currents into the water. The electric organs of *eigenmannia,* for example, discharge at a constant frequency of about 350 cycles per second, day and night. The frequency is not influenced by excitement or the proximity of food or other fish, but does vary somewhat with temperature. The *Torpedo* fish behaves similarly, but operates at only about 100 cycles per second.

The song of a cicada is originated by an oscillator in the insect's brain. Here an interesting new circuit refinement has been added—a subharmonic generator. The centrally originating frequency is 200 cycles per second, while the neuronal arrangement in the sound muscles drives them at only 100 times per second.

In many lower animals neuronal oscillators are responsible for the rhythms involved in walking, swimming, or flying. The swimmerets of a crayfish, wings of a locust, and crawling muscles of an earthworm are centrally directed. The locomotor muscles themselves may be deactivated by cutting their neuronal connections, but the oscillatory circuit in the brain will continue to send its synchronizing impulses out to the ends of the cut nerves.

Such local, special-purpose neuronal circuits appear to embody the same kinds of principles that the computer engineer utilizes in the design of his machines. In the spinal reflex mechanisms, the employment of a switching circuit to operate a motor mechanism in accordance with a sensory impulse seems very similar to simple control techniques long used by the physical scientist. Even the interconnection of a group of neurons to produce a timed sequence of pulses to control the heartbeat of a lobster or the wingbeat of a locust has a satisfying (though possibly deceptive) appearance of simplicity about it—every electronics engineer knows how to build a circuit that will generate a timed series of pulses by connecting the output of an on/off flip-flop element to the activating input through a transmission medium involving a time delay, such as a chain of slowly charging cell bodies.

Not all the automatic control activities of the nervous system are so simple, however. As the level of complexity increases, we find ourselves dealing less with peripheral mechanisms and more with the machinery of the brain itself.

Simple Feedback Control Loops in the Brain

When the light dims, the pupils of our eyes dilate so as to increase the stimulus supplied to the rods and cones. When the light is strong, the pupils constrict to prevent damage to the sensitive nerve endings of the retina. This is one of many simple regulative functions carried out in the brain. The standard trains of voltage pulses initiated by the retinal neurons first of all undergo a blending or integrating process, resulting in an electric signal representative of the average light intensity over the entire field of view. This sensory input is conducted by suitable nerve fibers to a point near the top of the brainstem. There a connection is established with outgoing nerve fibers which provide the electric instructions to the constrictor pupillae muscle that in turn adjusts the degree of dilation or contraction of the pupil of the eye.

This light-reflex arc is one of many examples of feedback control mechanisms in the brain. Such feedback mechanisms are well known to the computer scientist. They are characterized by the use of the measurement of some physical quantity to control a motor mechanism that in turn adjusts the magnitude of the measured quantity to bring it to a predetermined desired value. In the instance of the light-reflex arc, the electric signal produced by the summation of the responses of the rods and cones provides a constricting impulse to the pupillary muscles if it exceeds the standard value which represents the level of illumination at which the retina performs most effectively. As the pupillary dimension is decreased, a point is finally reached where the magnitude of the signal produced by the integration of the stimuli from the rods and cones becomes equal to the reference value that is built into this portion of the computing mechanism of the brain, at which point a balance is reached and no further tendency persists for additional contraction of the pupils.

The way in which the body protects itself from overheating is another interesting example of feedback control exercised by the brain. The body employs two principal mechanisms for dissipating the excess heat generated by high outside temperatures or unusual physical exertion. One of these compensating mechanisms consists in evaporative cooling by perspiration; the other consists in enhanced thermal radiation from the blood, the circulation of which is increased by dilation of the network of subsurface blood vessels. The control center for these cooling mechanisms is in the hypothalamus, a part of the brainstem very close to the top forward end of the structure (Fig. 4-1). The circuit for the temperature-control system is somewhat unusual, in that its sensing device is located within the

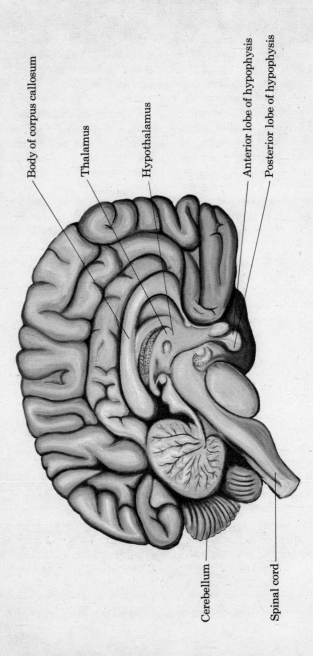

Body of corpus callosum

Thalamus

Hypothalamus

Anterior lobe of hypophysis

Posterior lobe of hypophysis

Cerebellum

Spinal cord

Fig. 4-1. Vertical section through fore-and-aft plane of symmetry of the brainstem and associated structures. (*After Raymond H. Houser, Graphic Aids to Neurology, Series 1, Scientific Illustrators, Long Beach, California, 1957. By permission of the publishers.*)

control system itself rather than in a peripheral position connected to the control system by the usual cable. There is a good reason for this arrangement. The function of the temperature-control system is to maintain constancy of the temperature of the vital internal organs, rather than, for example, the surface skin. But the hypothalamus itself, located in the front top of the brainstem and completely surrounded by the cortex and other major organs of the brain, is in as well-protected and vital a spot as could be devised for the measurement of the most significant temperature of the body, that of the brain itself. Therefore, in this instance, nature has chosen to locate the controlling sensing device within the portion of the brain that also supplies the computer/control functions. Temperature-sensitive neurons produce an electric voltage that varies with deviations of the temperature of the blood circulating through the hypothalamus from the desired normal value of 98.6°F. This electric signal passes into the multiple nerve fibers that traverse the muscular walls of the blood vessels directly under the skin, as well as to the nerves that control the sweat glands. Thus, when the hypothalamic temperature measurement indicates that the blood in the brain is getting warmer than it should be, the surface blood vessels dilate and the sweat glands perform their assigned functions. A temperature change of only a few hundredths of a degree in the blood coursing through the hypothalamus produces an observable response in the cooling mechanisms.

Complex Computer/Control Operations of the Brain

Many of the automatic responses controlled by the brain involve the concurrent regulation of a large number of different muscles or other organs of the body. The neural mechanism involved may be continuously acting, with the mission of determining the reaction of the muscles and glands to some persistent aspects of the external or internal environment. On the other hand, many of the brain-directed reflexes produce a complex "single-shot" motor response that is synchronized in time and space and triggered by some special sensory stimulus.

The operation of the cerebellum provides an interesting example of a continuously acting automatic control function that is at the same time complex and precise. The cerebellum has been characterized as a sort of private secretary to the consciously motivated cerebral hemispheres of the brain. It seems to accept general directions as to the nature of a movement that we want our body to execute and work out the detailed pattern of instructions that must be sent to the large number of muscles involved to ensure smooth and stable performance. Without a suitable automatic compensating mechanism, the shift in center of gravity caused by raising the right arm would probably be enough to cause us to fall over. The cerebellum watches out for problems of this nature. It receives signals from all the muscles of the body indicating their elongation or contraction, and supplements this information with data obtained continuously from the otoliths and semicircular canals that provide neuronal information as to the position of the head and, if we are turning, its rate of movement. Although the complex computing technique by means of which the cerebellum achieves dynamic stabilization of the body during movement is not well understood, it appears to be characterized by a distinctive pattern of electric waves of frequencies from 200 to 400 cycles per second. These electric waves pass along to the other parts of the brain, where they appear superimposed upon the lower-frequency signals characteristic of the noncerebellar sensory and motor impulses.

Computer technology seems to provide good analogies to the action of the cerebellum. An electronic computer that controls the flight of an airplane or a guided missile, for example, typically employs an equipment organization in which the detailed step-by-step stabilization of the flight pattern is separated from the function of over-all navigational control. Stable platforms, accelerometers, gyroscopes, and other equivalents of the otoliths, semicircular canals, and muscular-contraction sensors of the body, are the basic input devices for computing equipment that solves the set of equations yielding the control signals to aerodynamic fins, rocket nozzle deflectors, or other "muscular" devices required to keep the vehicle on a stable course. This dynamic stabilizing subsystem appears, at the present state of knowledge, to be an electronic analog of the cerebellum in the brain. In aircraft or missile control, an over-all navigational instruction calling for a turn, an increase or decrease in speed, or the like, is generated from sensory data entirely separate from the stabilizing inputs just described. This navigational instruction then serves as an overriding or biasing signal that, when superimposed upon the stabilizing or "cerebellar" inputs, results in the achievement by the vehicle of the desired new course under the smooth, step-by-step control of the dynamic stabilizing subsystem.

The stabilizing mechanisms designed by the engineer incorporate computing circuits of considerable sophistication and accuracy. Similarly, there is every reason to believe that the accomplishment of smooth, integrated motion of the dozens of muscles involved in the acts of walking or sitting down requires the equivalent of a solution within the computing mechanism of the brain of mathematical equations containing many terms, each of which must be measured and manipulated with a considerable degree of precision.

Other examples of complex coordinated patterns of muscular activity involving automatic, continuous control by the brain are not hard to find. Breathing employs more than ninety muscles, which perform their contractions and expansions in suitable rhythm as a consequence of the electric impulses sent out from the brain to over a thousand individual nerve fibers. Swallowing food is an amazingly complex process. Muscles in the diaphragm and the tongue must perform a synchronized operation. At the critical moment, the soft palate must move back to protect the nose cavity, the cartilages of the larynx must displace themselves to close the windpipe, and the epiglottis must duck out of the way before the mouthful of food passes by. And just the performance by the uninterested reader of the simple act of raising his hand to his mouth and stifling a yawn requires the transmission from the brain of precisely related electric control signals to synchronize the contraction of 58 different muscles working on 32 separate bones in the hand and arm, not to mention the considerable fraction of the 31 muscles of the face that move the features and produce its various expressions.

The other type of brain-controlled reflex, in which a complex sequence of spatially and temporally interrelated motor actions is triggered by a single sensory stimulus, is also of considerable interest. Such reflexes are of great importance in the preservation of our health and welfare. In addition, they constitute the first evidence we shall have examined for the existence in the brain of *stored programs,* or subroutines of muscular and glandular action that, like the stored programs of electronic digital computers, are called forth automatically upon the arrival at the input terminals of predetermined patterns of sensory stimuli.

The "startle" reflex is one we have all experienced. It can be produced by a sudden, unexpected, loud noise. We close our eyes and duck our head, bend our knees, and bring our elbows in close to our sides. Slower in tempo, but equally automatic, is the vomiting reflex of, for instance, the cat. Vomiting can be induced either by tickling the throat, introducing foul food into the stomach, or injecting apomorphine into the veins. Any of these separate stimuli results, immediately and automatically, in precisely the same chain of events: the animal assumes a typical body posture and opens its mouth, expiration stops and is replaced by deep inspiration, the blood pressure drops and the heart slows; then salivation occurs, certain muscles relax while others contract, and vomiting begins.

Thus, in these complex brain-controlled "stored-program" reflexes, the mere influx of a sensory stimulus jars a large collection of the cells of the body out of their separate organized activity and galvanizes them into action as a single unit discharging a common task. This highly organized set of reactions is accomplished with a pattern that is precisely synchronized in space and time, without the conscious volition or control of the animal involved. In Chapter 5 we shall examine evidence that such stored programs of response are not only important to the health and welfare of cats and humans, but play a surprisingly large role in the behavior patterns of the lower animals.

Response Selection: The Reticular Activating System

In the more complex applications of electronic computers, a requirement sometimes arises for the computer to choose between two or more different modes of response to the input information that affects it. Consider, for example, the guidance system of a long-range target-seeking missile. During the major portion of the flight from the launching point to the target, a "mid-course" guidance mode is likely to be employed, wherein the information used by the computer for steering the missile comes over a radio link with the launching base or, perhaps, is generated internally in the missile through inertial components. For the final portion of the trajectory, however, it may be the plan to shift from this mid-course guidance mode to a terminal "homing" mode in which information obtained from a radar in the nose of the missile is employed by the computer to home directly into the target. Such an automatic shift from mid-course to terminal guidance modes may be achieved by programming a portion of the computer to monitor the signal coming from the radar and to switch the entire computer to its terminal mode of operation when a target echo of sufficient strength is detected.

Something of the sort must surely go on inside the brain. Most of the muscles and other organs of the body can be involved in many different reflex actions, and they are likely to be called upon to respond in different ways, depending upon which behavior "program" is being implemented. The facial muscles cannot shape themselves for a yawn and at the same time participate in a sneeze; sometimes one input stimulus must be responded to, sometimes another. In a machine with the extreme variety of possible behavior patterns possessed by the body, some kind of priority setting or program-selecting mechanism would appear to be of considerable importance.

The brain's response selector has been given the name *reticular activating system* by H. W. Magoun and his coworkers at the University of California at Los Angeles. The reticular activating system consists of a mass of undifferentiated neurons that extend from the top of the spinal cord through the brainstem on up into the thalamus and hypothalamus. These two structures are at the extreme top and forward part of the brainstem and are well inside, but not a part of, the surrounding cerebral cortex (Fig. 4-1). The hypothalamus, part of which is included in the reticular activating system, appeared in our earlier discussion as the seat of temperature control of the body. The recticular formation gets its name from the fact that it looks like a more or less homogeneous network of cells; it shows little evidence of organization into anatomically distinct "nuclei," although it passes through and around a number of nuclei in traversing the length of the brainstem. Close examination of the reticular formation shows that it consists of a mixture of large and small neurons, many, but not all, having short axons.

Nature appears to have gone to great pains to cause essentially all the incoming and outgoing communication channels of the brain to pass through the reticular system. This is done by means of "collaterals." For example, a main nerve coming from the spinal cord and carrying sensory information to the cortex does not go directly through the reticular formation, but as it passes by, its main fibers send off smaller branches to terminate on reticular neurons. A collateral arrangement is also found in the motor nerves as they pass by the reticular formation on their way from the higher centers of the brain to the main cable of the spinal cord. Similar branches are displayed by the nerves running to and from the cerebellum. But the reticular activating system does not content itself with wire taps on the communication lines that pass by it; it also has direct lines of command to the stations of interest to it. These receiving stations include half a dozen major areas of the cortex and probably all the nuclei of the brainstem. The reticular activating system also sends its fibers down the spinal cord, where it exercises its influences on the peripheral sensory and motor systems.

Electrical measurements made by means of fine probes placed within the reticular activating system reveal an interesting property: the response of its neurons is "unspecific." A single neuron in this region may respond to stimulation of a touch receptor in the foot, a sound receptor in the ear, a light receptor in the eye, or a chemical receptor in the stomach. The reticular neurons appear to perform some kind of summation of the over-all nervous activity of the organism. Such integration would be of limited usefulness if all reticular nerve cells were to perform it in the same way. Fortunately, this does not appear to be the case. Although many neurons in the reticular activating system may respond to the same set of nervous stimuli, their responses are not quantitatively alike. One neuron may be more sensitive to optical stimuli than to pain; another neuron may show the reverse emphasis. The resulting weighted averages would appear to be just what is needed to monitor the incoming stimuli for patterned relationships that might indicate the necessity for one or another type of response by the muscles and glands of the body.

There is also direct evidence that the reticular activating system is able to produce the kinds of effects on the operation of the muscles and glands that would accompany the role of a response-selecting mechanism. It seems to be able to sensitize or "awaken" selected nervous circuits and desensitize others. This is sometimes accomplished by selective muscular activation: electric signals sent over reticular nerve fibers down the spinal cord to terminate on the relay nerve cells whose axons pass out to the muscles achieve a sort of "volume-control" action that increases or decreases the magnitude of the muscular response. Sometimes the reticular activating system works on the input side of the response mechanism; it turns down the volume control of certain input stimuli and lets others come through. Figure 4-2 shows how electric stimulation of certain neurons in the reticular formation diminishes the magnitude of the signal transmitted from a peripheral touch receptor to the brain.

Concurrent with the selection by an organism of one of several alternate behavior patterns, there is often need for adjustment of some of the operating parameters. In our missile example, the shift from mid-course to terminal guidance usually must be accompanied by changes in the dynamic response characteristics of the steering mechanism. During the final approach to the target, a tighter kind of "muscular" control of the missile is required. If, for example, it is deflected by a gust of wind, a compensating correction must be made more quickly and more energetically than would be necessary earlier in the flight. For this reason, the servomechanism that controls the steering fins must be automatically modified, upon shifting to terminal guidance, so that a smaller deviation from the desired path results in a larger restoring "muscular" response, that is, a larger surge of power to the motor that controls the deflecting fins.

The recticular activating system includes among its capabilities this kind of adjustment of the dynamic response characteristic of the body mechanism. In fact, an almost exact analog of our "servo-tightness" guided-missile example is provided by one of the prevalent theories of the so-called *gamma-efferent mechanism* of motor control.

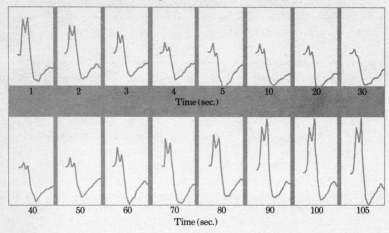

Before, during and after reticular stimulation

Time (sec.)

Time (sec.)

Fig. 4-2. Reduction of action potential produced by stimulated touch receptor, owing to the "volume-control" action of the reticular activating system. (*From R. Hernandez-Peon et al., Acta Neurologia Latinoamericana, vol. 2 (1956), pp. 8–22. By permission of the publishers.*)

In this process, the muscular command emitted by the brain does not act directly on the muscle effector nerves, but instead appears to adjust the "zero point" of a stretch-sensitive receptor attached to the muscle so that its firing rate will be at a minimum when the muscle subsequently achieves the degree of stretch desired. The actual change in the stretch of the muscle is then believed to be accomplished through a spinal reflex circuit that connects the output of the stretch-receptor nerve back around to the muscle-effector nerve. This reflex circuit automatically causes the muscle to seek out just the degree of contraction that will minimize the firing frequency of the stretch receptor. In the language of the computer engineer, this is an effective *position-control* servomechanism, useful when the controlled organ needs to hold its position despite external deviating forces of a varying or unpredictable nature. Our brain seems to employ this control mechanism to maintain suitable postural interrelationships among the parts of the body in the presence of complex and disturbing effects such as those caused by walking or running. This gamma-efferent mechanism appears to be neatly analogous to the part of a missile guidance system that brings the missile heading back into alignment with the direction of a gyroscopic element if deviations are produced by gusts of wind or other extraneous influences. The "tightness" of this kind of control system—the magnitude of the force that is brought to bear to counter a deviation from the desired position—will be increased or decreased if the amount of the "error signal" produced by a given deviation is increased or decreased. In this context Figure 4-3 is most interesting, for it seems to display exactly this kind of tightness-control effect: the frequency of the signal sent out by a stretch receptor to indicate a given degree of extension of the attached muscle can be either increased or decreased by electric stimulation in different parts of the reticular activating system!

Reticular influences on the muscles are numerous and varied. Apart from such special modifications of muscular function as those just described, the general muscle tone of the body—the degree of contraction that characterizes the normal resting muscles—is controlled by the recticular activating system. Interference with certain of the communication channels from the reticular system to the muscles (by cutting of some of the nerves or by suitably placed lesions) results in extreme muscular contraction; interference with

Fig. **4-3.** Increase and decrease in stretch-receptor output frequency caused by stimulation of excitatory and inhibitory reticular-formation neurons. The amount of stretch of muscle spindle is shown to the left of the records. (*After E. Eldred, R. Granit, and P. A. Merton, Journal of Physiology, vol. 122* (1953), *pp. 498–523. By permission of the publishers.*)

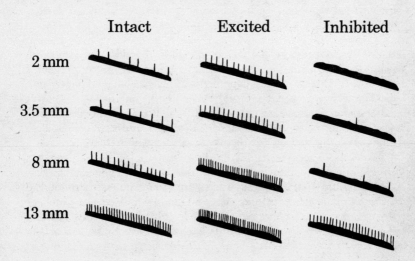

other of the efferent fibers of the reticular formation causes the muscles to relax completely. Electric stimulation or lesions in another part of the reticular activating system interfere with the normal dynamic balance of the body's servomechanisms in such a way as to cause rhythmic muscular quivering similar to the shaking palsy of Parkinson's disease.

Thus there is abundant evidence that the effector neurons of the reticular activating system exercise a considerable degree of control over the signals transmitted by the afferent and efferent nerves and thereby affect many if not all of the nerve-controlled operations of the body. This seems to fit nicely with the evidence that some of the reticular neurons perform a sort of integration of the sensory nervous activity of the body to derive outputs of the general type needed for controlling the selection of a suitable "stored-program" response pattern from among those available to the organism. An obvious question is whether direct evidence exists that our inference is correct—that the reticular activating system does indeed combine its capabilities to select and implement behavioral response patterns. An affirmative answer is strongly indicated by research on certain of the glandular-control functions of the reticular activating system.

Everyone knows something about the workings of the endocrine glands. They secret substances called hormones directly into the blood, and these hormones have a great deal to do with the functioning of our internal organs. The thyroid hormone controls basal metabolism, the rate at which our "engine" idles; a hormone from the adrenal glands increases the blood pressure; the pancreas secretes insulin that regulates the use of sugar by the body; and so on. It is not so commonly known, however, that the endocrine glands affect one another: for example, feeding dogs on adrenal cortex causes their thyroids to store more thyroxine. By all odds, the endocrine gland that exerts the greatest effect upon the other endocrine glands is the pituitary gland, or hypophysis. This half-inch-diameter, reddish gray, egg-shaped body projects from the middle of the lower surface of the brain into a little cup in the base of the skull (Fig. 4-1). The pituitary, like the other endocrine glands, secretes its own direct-acting hormones. (Its best-known hormone is the one that has to do with general body growth.) However, the pituitary gland has an additional important role: it controls the other endocrine glands. If the thyroid gland is to be ordered into more intense activity, the pituitary gland manufactures and sends into the blood a quantity of thyroid-stimulating hormone (TSH). If the adrenal cortex is lying down on its job, it is urged into greater efforts by means of the adrenocorticotropic hormone (ACTH) sent to it from the pituitary through the blood stream.

While the pituitary controls the other glands, it, in turn, is controlled by the ultimate authority, the brain. Specifically, it is again the hypothalamus that exercises the necessary supervision. This is a physically convenient arrangement, for the pituitary gland is very close to the hypothalamus, being separated from it by only a ½-inch length of glandular tissue. The "process-control computer" that sends commands to the pituitary gland for the release of one or another of its endocrine activating agents appears to be located in the front part of the hypothalamus. This is the control center where the sensory nerves report their findings as to the physical and chemical state of the body; on the basis of these findings the necessary calculations are made to determine whether increases or decreases should be ordered in the hormonal activity of the endocrine glands. Presumably, several computer control programs are stored in the neuronal memory system of the hypothalamus—one for each of the patterns of interrelated glandular activity appropriate to various overall situations. One program might be suitable for a sexual situation, another for a fear situation, and so on. If our concept of the role of the reticular activating system is correct, we might expect to find that it acts as a set of switches in series with the hypothalamic computing circuits, arranged so that the hypothalamus cannot activate any of its glandular-control programs unless the corresponding "switch" of the reticular activating system is closed.

Now let us consider some laboratory experiments that have been performed on female cats and rabbits. Under handling and manipulation of the parts of such an animal in connection with the experiments performed on it, the glandular-control program activated by the reticular-formation/hypothalamus/pituitary combination is likely to be the "stress-reaction" program. In the stress reaction, the pituitary secretes ACTH into the blood. This stimulates hormonal activity by the adrenal glands that, in turn, adjusts the activity of the various organs of the body to deal better with the special problems posed by the stressful conditions. If a female animal is in its anestrous state—that is, not in heat—stimulation of the sex organs, like any other form of laboratory manipulation, will lead only to the stress reaction. However, if the animal is in its estrous condition, either as a result of the natural sexual cycle or following injection of suitable hormones, this kind of stimulation produces quite a different result. Under these circumstances, and only under these circumstances, an electrode in the midbrain reticular activating system will indicate a distinctive electrical pattern when the vaginal-nerve receptors are stimulated. This electric activity in the recticular activating system is accompanied by electrical effects in the anterior hypothalamus, which can also be experimentally observed. The chemical result is the secretion by the pituitary gland of a substance called gonadotrophin, which upon reaching the ovaries triggers ovulation and thereby completes nature's pattern for the accomplishment of the important reproductive function.

The analogy to the automatic transfer from mid-course to terminal guidance in the control mechanism of a missile is a close one. In the missile, shift from one pattern of behavior to the other is triggered by the appearance of a radar target echo in the input data. In the animal, change in mode of behavior is triggered by the sensory input from chemical receptors indicating the presence of the estrous-producing hormone in the blood stream. The response-selection nature of the reticular activating system is confirmed, in this case, by the observation that suitably placed lesions in the reticular formation prevent ovulation in the circumstances just described, although the anterior-hypothalamic/pituitary mechanism remains operative and can be directly stimulated so that ovulation results. Damage to the reticular formation puts out of commission the "program-selection" mechanism that ordinarily determines what kind of response is to be made to a given physiological situation.

In earlier years, when the brain was less well understood than it is now, it was frequently likened to the central switching office of a telephone system. The function of the brain was described as being that of handling many different "calls" coming in from the various sense organs, sorting them out, and "plugging in" each one to an outgoing line that would connect it to the muscle or gland that its sensory information needed to activate. Today we know enough about the brain that we no longer feel it necessary for analogies to be quite so superficial. However, there might be some point in preserving this old analogy for application to the reticular activating system, instead of to the brain as a whole. If we include in the function of the central switching station the task of assigning priorities— of deciding which incoming nervous messages are to be amplified and listened to, and which are to be minimized, ignored, or caused to wait their turn—we have a pretty good description of how the reticular activating system seems to work. The examples chosen have illustrated the point that the reticular activating system is involved in the control of a wide range of the muscular and glandular responses of the body. It appears to provide the mechanism for selecting responses from among the many different "behavior programs" stored in the brain and preventing what might otherwise be chaotic un-controlled competition among various antagonistic modes of response.

Computerlike Nature of the Automatic Brain Mechanisms

In a treatment such as this one, in which some of the properties of the brain are explored from the point of view of the computer scientist, it is proper for us to place considerable emphasis on these automatic control circuits of the brain. We are consciously attempting to consider first those properties of the human brain that appear most closely related to familiar subject matter. These circuits are of such a nature. The computer scientist may well be impressed by the fact that there are several thousand such systems continually operating in the body, but he is not likely to be overawed by the nature of the operations involved. Feedback control systems that employ electric indications of physical parameters of a process to provide motor signals serving to adjust these parameters to desired standard values are an old story to him. So are stored-program arrangements for triggering previously planned patterns of activity of the output devices. The computer scientist knows how to design combinations of circuit elements to accomplish these results. And, when provided with the required sensory-input and motor-output devices, he can design the circuits so that, like the central nervous system, they consist solely of large numbers of suitably interconnected simple circuit elements. At the present state of his art, the computer designer would employ electrically operated on/off switches to perform the necessary computing and control functions. The neurons of the central nervous system clearly possess the attributes that he would need for his simulation of the reflex control systems of nature, and probably some other properties that would be very useful to him if his science were sophisticated enough today to permit him to employ their additional capabilities.

Therefore, nature's automatic control systems should have a sense of familiarity about them to the computer scientist. He should see here a large number of parallel, "permanently wired" control circuits, with the blueprint of the interconnections apparently supplied in the genes that determine the physical construction of the embryonic organism. Even the extent and complexity of these permanent, parallel computing subsystems need not really be worrisome, for the human brain contains some ten billion neurons, whereas the most complex computers contain only tens of thousands of electronic on/off switches. With ten billion circuit elements to work with, the computer engineer also could devise a machine of impressive capabilities.

There is another reason for emphasizing the automatic control functions of the central nervous system. These are the really important functions of the brain. They keep the organism alive and healthy. It is only from a narrow human point of view that conscious thought and the so-called higher mental processes are of much significance. Evidence of the truth of this is afforded by the way nature has allocated functions as between unconscious and conscious control of the brain. Nature clearly does not yet trust the recently developed and not very well proved "higher" intellectual capabilities of man for the performance of any really vital functions, such as breathing, regulation of the heartbeat, control of the parts of the throat to prevent strangulation during eating, or regulation of the chemical balance of the digestive organs. To be sure, since this book has the disadvantage of being written from the highly distorted, narrowly human point of view, a disproportionate amount of attention is going to be devoted, in later chapters, to what we humans have arrogantly come to call the "higher intellectual processes." Nevertheless, when science has developed to the point of providing us with a clear understanding of the detailed anatomy of logical processes, we shall probably find that most of the capacity of the human brain is devoted to the unconscious automatic regulation of the bodily processes without which life would fail. We have just recently discovered that digital computers that can perform mathematical operations and exercise control of complex processes are, by their very nature, also capable of the performance of logical processes. It is probably only because of this fundamental, and perhaps almost accidental, identity in the mechanisms required for computer/control and for logic that nature has, in the last million years or so, been able to afford Homo sapiens the luxury of employing the small portion of his nervous equipment that can be spared from really essential duties for pursuing the hobby that we have named the "higher intellectual activities."

BIBLIOGRAPHY

Benzinger, T. H., "The Human Thermostat," *Scientific American,* January, 1961, pp. 134–147.

Bullock, T. H., "Neuronal Integrative Mechanisms," *Recent Advances in Invertebrate Physiology* (University of Oregon Publications, Eugene, Ore., 1957), pp. 1–20.

Bullock, T. H., "The Origins of Patterned Nervous Discharge," *Behaviour,* vol. XVII (1961), pp. 48–59.

French, J. D., "The Reticular Formation," *Journal of Neurosurgery,* vol. XV (1958), pp. 97–115.

Hagiwara, S., and T. H. Bullock, "Intracellular Potentials in Pacemaker and Integrative Neurons of the Lobster Cardiac Ganglion," *Journal of Cellular and Comparative Physiology,* vol. 50 (1957), pp. 25–47.

Magoun, H. W., *The Waking Brain* (Charles C Thomas, Publisher, Springfield, Ill., 1958).

Snider, R. S., "The Cerebellum," *Scientific American,* August, 1958, pp. 84–90.

Permanently Wired-in Behavior
Patterns of Lower Animals

This is a book about the human brain. Nevertheless we have already devoted considerable attention to the nervous systems of other animals, and we shall continue to do so. The basis for the expectation that animal studies will prove pertinent to understanding of the human nervous system is the time-honored principle, so often verified by the biologist, that similarity in structure and similarity in function usually go hand in hand. And the fact is that the nervous tissue of the lower animals is remarkably similar to our own. We find the same neuronal building blocks with similar arrangements of dendrites and axons, and similar operating characteristics. We find the same tendency for groupings of richly interconnected neurons to occur at crossroads between the incoming streams of sensory data provided by the afferent nerves and the outgoing systems of orders sent over the efferent nerves to the muscles and other effector mechanisms. In some instances, the aggregations of neurons that appear to perform the data-processing tasks in lower animals have the semblance of a full-blown brain, although usually of modest size and complexity by comparison with the human organ. In other instances, a small animal might employ one or more groupings of neurons, or "ganglia," appearing, from their construction and from the general understanding of these matters that we have been developing, to be the sites of special-purpose neuronal reflex or control centers.

Because of these anatomical similarities the neurologist rather confidently expects to be able to transfer much of the knowledge acquired from experiments with the simpler species to man and the other higher animals. Soundness of the extrapolation is usually confirmed when an opportunity arises to observe directly the corresponding human neural phenomenon.

But if such reasoning by analogy is sound, it ought to work both ways. What is learned about the properties of neuronal aggregates through studies on the higher animals should also sometimes be capable of application to the lower ones. We have seen that the neural equipment of humans and other higher vertebrates includes a large number of reflex circuits whereby stereotyped patterns of muscular response are automatically triggered into existence by the occurrence of specific sensory stimuli. This suggests an interesting possibility: Could we have here the basis for an explanation of an aspect of animal life that has always been a mystery to scientist and philosopher alike—the ability of some of nature's lowliest and simplest creatures to engage in highly organized and seemingly purposeful behavior that frequently appears to involve an improbably high content of intelligence? Could their apparently reasoned acts instead be only the results of the triggering of patterns of automatic reflexes, built into the animal at birth, not involving conscious intelligence at all? To be sure, such a question does not bear directly upon the operation of the human brain, but it is believed to be a justifiable digression in view of its general interest. Therefore this chapter will be devoted to an explicit attempt to test how far we can go in explaining the puzzling behavior of the lower forms of animal life by invoking the operating properties of the same kinds of permanently wired-in reflex circuits that we have found to be so important in the central nervous system of man.

Reflexes and Tropisms

Upon the approach of a possible enemy, a barnacle abruptly closes its shell, a tube worm snaps its exposed feeding tentacles back into its protective tunnel of sand, a sea squirt contracts into a gelatinous blob, burrowing bivalves withdraw their soft protruding siphons into the sand. A sea urchin turns its pointed needles in the direction of approaching danger, and the pincerlike jaws that inhabit the spiny jungle at the base of the needles stand up, ready to seize any enemy that comes too close.

These have indeed been found to be simple reflex actions. The barnacle, tube worm, sea squirt, and bivalve possess tiny photocells among their sensory neurons. The shadow cast by an approaching enemy causes these photoreceptors to generate their standardized trains of voltage impulses that stimulate the muscles employed in the resulting avoidance reaction. Even the more complex reaction of the sea urchin is of the same nature, although the receptor neurons in this case appear to be, not photoelectric, but chemical; they "taste" the surrounding salt water for signs of the characteristic flavor of an enemy. The completely automatic and local nature of the response is demonstrated by the fact that a tiny chip broken away from a living sea urchin's shell, with only a single spine or a single stalked beak attached to it, will show the same alarm and preparation.

In addition to reflexes, nature makes extensive use of tropisms in regulating the behavior of its simpler creatures. A *tropism* is an automatic response differing from other reflexes only in that it affects the movement of the complete organism. When an earthworm digs down and finds the moist decaying vegetation on which it thrives and at the same time avoids the surface where it might furnish a meal for a passing sparrow, it is not the intelligent, planned procedure that it appears to be. The muscles that turn the front end of the worm and thereby determine its direction of locomotion are constructed so as to receive their electric control signals from photosensitive receptors on either side of the head. As a result, the earthworm automatically heads away from the light in such a direction as to equalize the amount of illumination received by the left- and right-hand photoreceptors. This causes the worm to travel toward the darker regions, where it finds food and safety. The completely machinelike, unreasoning nature of this performance has been nicely demonstrated by exposing a worm simultaneously to two separate sources of light of controllable intensity and observing that the path followed is always one that orients the worm, in accordance with the positions and relative intensities of the lights, to equalize the amount of illumination of its two photoreceptors; and this occurs even though it may impel the worm along a course opposite to the one in which the proper conditions for food and safety are to be found.

The machinelike nature of the reflexes and tropisms that so extensively regulate the behavior of the lower animals was not appreciated as soon as it might have been by workers in the field. This was probably because these animal responses do not have the precision and detailed reproducibility that is usually observed in the commoner reflexes of higher animals. The spines of the sea urchin are likely to display a certain restless motion, even when no stimulus is present, and the orientation toward a potential enemy may involve a certain hesitation or lack of precision, together with a persistence of some of the original restless motion, even after the enemy has been sensed. In similar fashion, an earthworm, when exposed to light, does not instantly snap into an opposite heading and pursue a precisely straight course steadily away from the source of illumination. Instead, the trajectory pursued is modulated by wormlike twistings and turnings; these deviations may become particularly severe if, for example, it is necessary for the worm to avoid an obstacle that lies in its path. The reason for such unprecise response is that most tropisms do not provide such an overriding source of control voltage to the organism's effector mechanisms as to overshadow completely the effects of other sources of command signals. While the earthworm possesses neuronal connections that provide a steady bias to its muscles so that they tend to turn it away from a source of illumination, it also possesses a behavior pattern that provides for detouring around obstacles. Its actual muscular response at any given instant is a combination of these and several other reinforcing or competing built-in reflex or tropism mechanisms.

The restlessness of the spines of the sea urchin also results from a competing control signal, but one of a different kind. The nerve cells of these lower animals, like many of those in the human body, do not always wait to receive a specific stimulus before "closing the switch" and sending a voltage pulse out over the axon. Instead, there is a certain amount of random firing of the neurons. In the large and complex nervous systems of the larger animals, so many neurons must act cooperatively to produce significant movement of principal organs that the occasional random firing of a few neurons cannot produce a conspicuous result (although an occasional flicker of an eyelid or twitch of a muscle may be due to this cause). In some of the small and primitive animals that we are now dealing with, however, there may be only a few interconnected neurons in the circuit that controls a major element of the body. Under such circumstances, the random firing of one or two neurons can easily produce observable restless movement of the affected part.

Complex Tropisms

Tropisms that are themselves turned on or off by the presence or absence of other stimulating factors, or combinations of tropisms, can increase immeasurably the apparent "purposefulness" of the behavior of a simple organism. For example, the larvae of barnacles appear to decide whether they want to swim toward the surface or away from the surface of the sea. This apparent exercise of free will has been traced to a prosaic temperature-reversible tropism that causes the barnacle larvae to seek light in the cold and avoid it in warmth; similarly, many aquatic crustaceans, such as the water flea *Daphnia*, tend to swim downward in a bright light and upward in darkness.

An interesting tropistic mechanism causes the caterpillars of the goldtail moth (*Porthesia chrysorrhoea*) to leave their hibernating nests in early spring and crawl to the only portions of the shrubs where their leafy food is to be found at that time of the year. The tropism involved is one whereby an adequate amount of warmth automatically causes the caterpillar to leave its nest and start crawling toward the light; it can be induced at any time by an experimenter simply by applying heat. This tropism results in the caterpillar climbing as high as it can go, which is to the top of the shrub where the new growth of green leaves first emerges early in the spring. However, if other effects than this simple tropism were not operating, the caterpillar would be in difficulty as soon as it had eaten the green leaves at the top of the shrub, for its food from then on would have to be found at lower levels; reaching such levels would be in conflict with a tropism that continuously impels it upward. This problem has been handled by nature by causing the upward-climbing tropism to operate only when the caterpillar is hungry. Therefore, having eaten, the caterpillar is free to creep in any direction and will eventually make its way down and find the new leaves as they commence to open.

As with all tropisms, the behavior of the goldtail moth is completely unreasoning. For example, if caterpillars are taken as they are leaving the nest and put into a glass tube lying near a window, they will all collect in the end of the tube nearest the light and stay there. If a few young leaves from their food shrub are put at the other end of the tube, farthest from the light, the hungry, unfed caterpillars will remain held captive near the lighted end of the tube, and there they will stay until they starve.

Tropisms, like the reflexes of higher animals, appear to be a direct consequence of the way the nerves and muscles have been put together. Usually they contribute to the health and well-being of the organism. The latter result, of course, would be an inevitable consequence of evolutionary selection; creatures with tropisms that lessen their chances of survival would presumably not have won out in the struggle for species existence. It is only when the creature is placed in historically abnormal or unusual circumstances that tropisms can work against survival, as in the instance of the caterpillars and the lighted tube. Similarly, the prawns that accumulate around the positive pole of a pair of electrodes placed in their tank do so because of a normally unimportant feature of their construction that weakens the effectiveness of their muscles when electricity passes through them in one direction and strengthens their effectiveness when the current is in the other direction. Moths and other phototropic insects that are irresistibly impelled to seek their own destruction in a flame are accidentally constructed so that superimposed upon the random motions characteristic of their flight is a steady "downhill" pull toward the light. If electric currents in the ocean or open flames in the forests had been important features of nature in the past, it is likely that prawns and moths would not have survived the evolutionary processes.

Although combinations of tropisms and simple reflexes seem to account for a surprising portion of the behavioral responses that the lower animals need to survive, such simple "wired-in" nerve circuits do not by any means constitute the extent of nature's provision for unthinking, unlearned, but constructive and complex behavior. Let us now pass to the evidence for the existence of stored programs not dissimilar to those we found in the human brain, whereby elaborate sequences of interrelated actions may be called forth by the receipt of suitable stimuli.

"Stored Programs" of Behavior

As these words are being dictated from a shady spot just off Waikiki Beach, several birds are moving about in the grass a few feet away, occasionally stopping to peck at whatever it is that birds peck at in such grassy areas. Two species of birds are represented; they differ greatly in size and coloring, but they also differ in another way. One species progresses across the grass by hopping on both feet; the other's gait is a walk, one step at a time. While the two species of birds are physically quite different, this difference in their method of locomotion is not a consequence of muscular requirements or any other special aspects of their construction that we ordinarily consider to be physical. The birds that hop could just as well have been designed to walk, and the birds that walk could just as practicably have been designed to hop. What is involved is a difference in behavior. Birds of the one species inevitably become hoppers, and birds of the other species inevitably become walkers. They have no capability of changing their behavior patterns; the hoppers could no more walk than they could change their size and coloring, and the walkers will go through life taking their steps one at a time.

Birds provide many instances of species-connected peculiarities of behavior. Thus, while there is a similarity among the cries of alarm of all gulls, the number, pitch, and frequency of the staccato cries that constitute such a call vary between species. Then there are the four groups of birds that constitute the conventionally recognized family of titmice (Paridae). There are no physical features to differentiate these four groups, but their nest-building habits are quite different. One group always nests in hollow trees or other cavities; a second group builds an oval nest with lateral entrance in bushes and trees; a third group builds a peculiar retort-shaped nest of plant down worked into feltlike consistency; the fourth group builds a stick nest with a lateral entrance. While these birds are apparently physically identical, their innate, unlearned, nest-building habits serve to identify them as different species as clearly as though the four groups were marked with red, yellow, blue, and green feathers. In fact, it is not unusual for behavioral characteristics to provide important clues to the proper classification of animal species. For a long time, the group of desert birds called sand grouse (Pteroclididae), which has downy young greatly resembling young grouse (Tetraonidae), was considered to be a member of a closely related family. Later, more careful analysis of physical characteristics led to the suspicion that sand grouse were more closely allied with pigeons. This suspicion was finally confirmed and the classification corrected by employment of a behavior characteristic. While nearly all birds scoop water up with their bills and then let it run down into their stomachs by lifting head and neck, pigeons have a very different drinking behavior; they stick their bills into the water and simply pump it up through the esophagus. The fact that sand grouse are the only other birds with this behavior strongly reinforced the anatomical findings which placed them next to pigeons.

Inherited behavior patterns are by no means confined to birds. Separate family classification has been assigned to different groups of grasshoppers largely because of differences in their habits of cleaning their antennae. Thus, the Acrididae place a leg on one antenna and clean the antenna by pulling it through between the leg and the ground. Physically similar, the Tetrigidae family differ in that they clean their antennae by stroking them with the legs, which in turn are cleaned by being pulled through the mouth. And in the sea there are hermit crabs with the instinct to find castoff shells as houses for their unprotected abdomens, and other crabs that protect themselves by holding stinging sea anemones in their claws. There is the elaborate flight instinct of the squid, with its ejection of ink and a right-angle turn at the crucial moment. There are the octopuses, which have the instinct to build little walls of stones behind which they can lurk unseen.

Since the ability to learn is a characteristic that is possessed, to some extent at least, by a surprisingly large proportion of animals, including some that we consider to be quite inferior, it is necessary always to be alert to the possibility that behavior patterns such as those described may be the consequence of indoctrination of the young by their parents. For many years it was in fact assumed that learning processes were responsible for most of the adaptive behavior exhibited by animals. Only with the advent of experiments in which the animals were carefully reared, from birth or from the egg, without access to others of their kind, was it determined that much of what had been assumed to have been learned existed in the organism at the time of birth as a finished and complete pattern of behavior. Certain newly hatched birds, for example, will automatically crouch down in the nest when a hawk passes overhead. This is not simply a response to a dark object in the sky. The shape must be hawklike; a robin can pass overhead without evoking the slightest reaction. Then there is the so-called thermometer bird, or bush turkey, of the Solomon Islands. It lays its eggs in a heap of mixed plant material and sand, with all the eggs arranged to lie with the blunt end upward. Each chick, on breaking out of the blunt top of its egg, wriggles and struggles in such a way that its stiff feathers, which point backward, gradually cause it to work its way up to the top of the heap. On reaching the surface, the chick dashes cross country into the shade of the nearest undergrowth. Certainly, no learning is involved in this response pattern of the newly hatched chick. Similarly, a female canary that has been isolated from birth builds a nest competently the first time suitable material is presented and the occasion arises. And a caterpillar, when it is about to pupate, spins a cocoon. It has never seen its parents or a cocoon and yet automatically sets about to construct an edifice that, when analyzed, is a masterpiece of engineering.

Although observations such as those just described show conclusively that learning from experience is not occurring, the inheritance at birth of such detailed and purposeful behavior patterns is so different from anything we humans experience that it is necessary for us to fight against the tendency to imagine that reasoning intelligence is involved. We must therefore not ignore the evidence on this point. Consider again the thermometer bird, which on emerging from the egg executes exactly the kind of wriggling motion needed to bring it to the surface of the heap and then changes to a new mode of motion to bring it to the protection of shade. If the chick, after having emerged, is once more dug into the heap, it is quite incapable of coming out again but stays there struggling ineffectively until it dies. Its movements are now of the type adapted to running to shade, and not of the type that will bring it to the surface. And the caterpillar that builds such a wonderful cocoon displays the completely automatic nature of its performance if it is interrupted in the middle of its task and the half-finished cocoon removed; it does not start again from the beginning, but spins only what remained for it to do, in spite of the fact that the resulting half cocoon is completely useless for protection. The octopus that so "intelligently" builds a stone wall behind which it can hide unseen will with equal vigor construct the wall out of transparent pieces of glass, if this is the material that happens to be handy.

In the light of present knowledge, we can only conclude that these specific and detailed behavior patterns are built into the organisms at birth. The same kind of kinetic embryonic forces that determine the configuration of the animal, its coloring of skin or feathers, and all the millions of details that constitute the blueprint for its physical construction also act to determine the detailed pattern of interconnection of the neurons in its brain; and the patterns of behavior thus produced are as unique to the species as such obviously physical characteristics as size, shape, and coloration.

"Intelligence" of Insects: Triggering of Successive Stored Subroutines

A special challenge to our hypotheses is provided by the unusually elaborate patterns of conduct exhibited by some insects, such as ants, termites, bees, and wasps. For years, man has been fascinated by the complex behavior patterns of these insects. He has read into their organized behavior strong elements of similarity to the reasoning processes of humankind. Let us see if this interpretation survives close analysis, or if our concept of permanently wired-in neuronal circuits again appears to fit the facts.

Consider, for example, the solitary wasps. When the time comes for egg laying, the wasp *Sphex* builds a burrow for the purpose and seeks out a cricket which she stings in such a way as to paralyze but not kill it. She drags the cricket into the burrow, lays her eggs alongside, closes the burrow, then flies away, never to return. In due course, the eggs hatch and the wasp grubs feed off the paralyzed cricket, which has not decayed, having been kept in the wasp equivalent of deep freeze. To the human mind, such an elaborately organized and seemingly purposeful routine conveys a convincing flavor of logic and thoughtfulness—until more details are examined. For example, the wasp's routine is to bring the paralyzed cricket to the burrow, leave it on the threshold, go inside to see that all is well, emerge, and then drag the cricket in. If, while the wasp is inside making her preliminary inspection, the cricket is moved a few inches away, the wasp, on emerging from the burrow, will bring the cricket back to the threshold, but not inside, and will then repeat the preparatory procedure of entering the burrow to see that everything is all right. If again the cricket is removed a few inches while the wasp is inside, once again the wasp will move the cricket up to the threshold and reenter the burrow for a final check. The wasp never thinks of pulling the cricket straight in. On one occasion, this procedure was repeated forty times, always with the same result.

To the computer scientist, there must be a sense of familiarity to this type of behavior. It has the earmarks of a set of subroutines recorded in the permanent memory system of a computer and called into play by the appearance of certain conditions of the input data. In the instance of the solitary wasp, some triggering mechanism, perhaps the physiological state of the female, sets into motion the series of subroutines associated with the preparing of a nest and the laying of eggs. The first subroutine called forth is the preparation of a burrow. The completion of this subroutine is the trigger for the next, which consists in the searching down of a particular species of cricket and paralyzing it. This in turn is the trigger for the next act in the drama, bringing the cricket to the threshold of the burrow. The presence of the cricket at the threshold of the burrow is the signal for the wasp to go inside for a last check around. Emergence from the burrow and finding the paralyzed cricket at the threshold is the signal for pulling the cricket into the burrow, and so on. Just as in the design of complex programs for electronic digital computers, subroutines appear to be stored and triggered into operation by the particular combinations of stimuli called for by the stored control program of the mechanism.

This concept of stored subroutines that are triggered by specific stimuli goes a long way toward accounting for the surprising variety of detailed inherited behavior patterns exhibited by insects. A bee that has found food will, on its return to its hive, execute a characteristic wagging dance by means of which the direction, distance, amount, and quality of the food source are communicated to the other bees. But a worker that has found food will perform her dance as artistically in the absence of other bees as in the presence of an audience. All that is necessary to trigger the performance is stimulation of her antennae.

The social insects—ants, termites, and bees—all appear to be patriotic, in the sense that they will drive out and frequently sting to death individuals from other hives. But the trigger is odor. All is changed if the interloper is protected long enough to acquire the scent of the new hive. In fact, suitably odor-conditioned insects of entirely different species will frequently be allowed to live indefinitely in a colony of ants or termites.

The senses of odor and taste are used as triggers in many ways by the insects. The great devotion to their queen of termite workers, hundreds of whom are generally seen to be in attendance upon her, appears to be a simple consequence of the fact that she exudes an especially rich and fatty secretion; their apparent attentions consist in licking her to get something for themselves, sometimes so violently that they rasp holes in the royal side. Superficially similar, but for an entirely different purpose, is the phenomenon displayed by certain species of spiders, whereby the male is stimulated to suitable attentions toward the female by a doubtless agreeable substance that she exudes over her body.

Because of the specificity of the trigger mechanisms, these innate response patterns are, by human standards, ridiculously rigid and inflexible. Thus, a male nocturnal moth may fly unerringly to his mate for a distance of more than a mile; yet, if the feathery antennae that serve the male as sense organs are cut off, not only is he incapable of finding the female but, if placed alongside her, is incapable of mating. The trigger for this act apparently is the smell stimulus normally supplied by his sensory antennae. The odor that so stimulates the male moth is generated by two little scent organs located near the tip of the female's abdomen. These organs can be cut out without particularly inconveniencing the female. If they and the operated female are then put in a cage with a normal male not deprived of his antennae, his built-in pattern of mating actions will be triggered, but will be entirely directed toward the source of the stimulus; he will make vain attempts to mate with the two little scent glands but will entirely ignore the female.

An invertebrate animal may starve to death in the midst of plenty if the particular plant or animal material that serves as food for its species happens to be missing. Or an insect may doom its race (or at least its local colony) to extinction because of the absence of the particular stimulus that is required to set off its pattern of nest building or egg laying. While a *Sphex* wasp provides its grubs with crickets, the *Ammophila* must find and paralyze a caterpillar before it can continue with its nest-building and egg-depositing routine; the *Sceliphron* wasp recognizes only spiders as suitable larva food, and the *Podium* uses roaches. The *Pronuba* moth can lay its eggs only in a yucca plant, and a species of Trinidad mosquito can be triggered to deposit its eggs only by the presence of the leaves of a bromeliad plant floating in a pool of stagnant water.

So there is, indeed, abundant evidence of the employment by nature in the insects and lower animals of "permanently wired-in" inherited patterns of behavior. Ranging from simple reflexes and tropisms up through complex patterns of multistage behavior triggered into performance by the occurrence of specific stimuli, these automatic, machinelike responses have many of the earmarks of the library of subroutines that can be stored in the memory of an electronic computer and triggered into operation by the occurrence of a prescribed set of relationships among the data supplied to the computer by its input devices.

When a single organism possesses a number of reflexes, tropisms, and stored subroutines, each triggered by its own prescribed input stimuli, all of which can occur concurrently and sometimes in competing fashion, the complexity of the behavior of the animal is much increased and the machinelike nature of its responses is thus obscured. The superposition on these responses of a certain degree of randomness, arising from the spontaneous firing of the neurons, also enhances the "lifelike" character of the behavior. Furthermore, it must be admitted that the kinds of automatic mechanisms discussed in this chapter do not constitute the complete story of the behavior of insects and lower animals. Like electronic computers that modify their behavior in accordance with experience, these simple natural computers have a limited ability to learn. Although this does not have nearly so large an influence upon over-all behavior as in the case of higher animals, it is nevertheless a real and complicating factor that contributes materially to the appearance of detailed unpredictability in the behavior of even some surprisingly low forms of living creatures. But this need not detract from the sense of familiarity that the computer scientist should feel for the behavior of the lower animals. The detailed performance of some of his machines can also be unpredictable.

Nature's Computer Fabrication Techniques

It is the existence in the nervous systems of the lower animals of permanently wired-in patterns of response to specific situations that constitutes the subject matter of this chaper; techniques employed by nature for accomplishing the construction of these computer/control circuits are essentially outside our scope. Nevertheless, in spite of the convincing nature of the evidence that we have examined, it would be disturbing if what were known about nature's methods of constructing living creatures were to be found in conflict with the requirements of a hypothesis that ascribes a major role to inherited automatic patterns of behavior. Therefore, we must conclude our present considerations by a glance at the pertinent features of the existing state of knowledge concerning the transmission of inherited characteristics in living organisms.

To be sure the immediate problem is clearly defined, let us recall that our present position, as computer scientists, is that we believe we have a sort of understanding of the automatic behavior we have been studying. By using electronic circuit elements and techniques presently available to us, we feel that we know how to build computer/control systems with permanently wired-in reflexes, tropisms, and behavior subroutines triggered by specific input stimuli; and such systems would in general exhibit the kinds of performances we have been studying. To be sure, we are a little worried about synthesis of animal responses to specific visual patterns, for our theory and laboratory experimentation has carried us only a small way toward a complete understanding of these matters, but we have made a start and have confidence that we shall one day be much less awkward in our handling of such problems than we are now. It is also true that the 250 neurons in the brain of an ant and the 900 neurons in the brain of a bee appear to us to be impressively small numbers of computer building blocks for the storage and control of the complex behavior patterns of these social insects; we are sure that we would have to use many times this number of electronic switches to accomplish the same task. A somewhat unsatisfactory rationalization for this difficulty is to say that, when we understand better than we do now the tricks that nature has worked out to control the behavior of these social insects, we shall discover the existence of a large number of short cuts like examples that have already been given—the employment of odor or taste in specific circumstances as an attraction device that directly results in the performance of acts that otherwise might require complex control machinery. A more satisfactory basis for an explanation is provided by our knowledge that a neuron is a much more complex component than a simple on/off switch—that in some circumstances, at least, a single neuron may possess a number of modes of operation which cause it all by itself to constitute a simple computer. Of course, this further emphasizes the disparity in size between the circuit elements the computer scientist has learned to build and those that nature employs. But this disparity, impressive though it is, offers no logical difficulty to the computer scientist; he too will be able to accomplish great miniaturization of his components once he has developed a technique for fabrication of devices on a molecular level.

It is, in fact, nature's techniques of miniaturized construction that we now wish to inquire about.

The Molecular Mechanisms of Genetics. One of the most important and fascinating fields of modern science is genetics. In the last several decades, geneticists have learned a great deal about how nature prepares the blueprint and detailed plans for construction of each of its creatures. This blueprint exists in the nucleus of every cell in the body of each animal. The design information is organized into tiny specks called chromosomes, visible under a high-power optical microscope. Every human cell contains 23 pairs of chromosomes. Each cell of the fruit fly contains 4 pairs, of the mouse 20 pairs, of garden peas 7 pairs. Under the much greater magnifying power of the electron microscope, a structure is observed in each chromosome that is consistent with its division into a large number of still smaller parts. These smaller subdivisions of the chromosomes are called genes. The gene is the basic unit of heredity. It has been established that the principal working part of the gene is a gigantic molecule of *deoxyribonucleic acid*—DNA, for short. Each DNA molecule carries a coded message, written in a four-letter alphabet. Each of the four letters is represented by one of four different types of standard molecular fragments, or "nucleotides." These letters are arranged in a linear array along the "backbone" of the DNA molecule. The resulting message, conveyed by the several thousand genes that comprise the chromosomes of each cell, has a length of about ten billion letters—a few more for a man, a few less for a mosquito! This is the equivalent of one thousand large volumes of ordinary printed material. The original copy of the set of manufacturing instructions with which each animal starts its life comes to it in the fertilized egg—half from its mother, half from its father. As this original cell divides, and the resulting cells divide again and again to form the final adult organism, the one-thousand-volume library of manufacturing instructions is faithfully duplicated at each cell division until, in a human, about one hundred million million copies have been made. And it is this library of instructions, and this alone, that determines whether the resulting animal is to be a flea, an earthworm, or a man.

Of course, a set of specifications is of little value unless arrangements are provided for actual fabrication of the desired structure in accordance with these specifications. Some of nature's fabrication arrangements are now known. For example, the DNA molecules, which are exclusively confined to the nucleus of the cell, act as templates for the formation of molecules of *ribonucleic acid,* or RNA. Each RNA molecule is very similar to the DNA molecule that supervises its synthesis out of the raw materials floating around in the nucleus. In fact, the RNA molecule is believed to carry an exact duplicate of the coded message arranged along the backbone of the parent DNA. RNA differs slightly from DNA in the atomic composition of the nucleotides that make up the four-letter alphabet of its message, and in the chemical composition of its long backbone, but the accuracy of the resulting set of specifications is not diminished by these differences. The chemical differences between RNA and DNA do have an important result, however. They permit RNA to leave the nucleus and travel to the surrounding cytoplasm of the cell, where the real business of fabrication of the materials for constructing the organism is carried on.

Once in the cytoplasm, the RNA molecules guide the formation of specific kinds of protein material, the enzymes. Apparently the particular arrangement of "alphabet" nucleotides along the backbone of the RNA molecule operates in some sort of lock-and-key fashion, through the employment of chemical forces, to assemble out of the material of the surrounding cell the right kinds of ingredients and arrange them in the proper order for the fabrication of the types of enzyme molecules required by the embryonic growth processes. The enzymes accomplish their effects, in turn, by highly specific catalytic properties whereby they govern just what chemical reactions take place in the cell fluids to build the kinds of organic material that, finally, constitute the tissue, bones, and blood of the completed organism.

This brief description of how the genetic material controls the embryonic growth processes is, of course, far from complete. One obvious deficiency of the discussion, for example, is that it provides no explanation for the vital phenomenon of cell differentiation. If every nucleus of every cell contains the same, complete genetic specification for the entire organism, why do not the processes described always cause all enzymes specified in the DNA/RNA code to be indiscriminately produced, thereby resulting in a mass of homogeneous, undifferentiated cells? Obviously, mechanisms must exist that selectively activate parts of the gene-directed enzyme formation. A start has been made toward an understanding of these mechanisms by James Bonner and his associates at the California Institute of Technology.

The Caltech group has established that histone, a protein constituent of the chromosomes, inhibits the DNA-directed synthesis of RNA in the nucleus. In laboratory experiments, it was found possible to control the rate of RNA generation at will by adding or withholding this ingredient. It is also known that changes in the histone content of cells are sometimes associated with important metabolic phenomena. In some instances, at least, tumor cells have been found to possess an abnormally low concentration of the growth-inhibiting histone (Cruft et al., 1954). And there is also evidence that the transition of a plant from the vegetative to the flowering state is preceded by a massive loss of histone from the cells that participate in flower formation (Gifford, 1963). These observations, together with the determination that histone produces its effects through inhibition of the DNA-controlled synthesis of RNA in the cell nuclei, have led Bonner to put forth some very interesting speculation. He suggests that histone may possess a variety of different structures, each form of which is a specific inhibitor of the RNA-generation effectiveness of a particular DNA molecule. If so, some kind of programming mechanism, yet to be identified, could control the abundance of the different types of histone and thereby selectively turn on and off the effects of different portions of the DNA material in the genes. This, in turn, would regulate the generation of the different kinds of RNA molecules and, through them, the various types of enzyme proteins manufactured in the cytoplasm. In this way, cells could be caused to develop differently in accordance with their positions in the organism and the timing of their growth processes.

It is still too early to be sure that we have, in the results obtained in the Caltech laboratories, the basis for a complete explanation of the most important phenomenon of cell differentiation. However, new discoveries, such as those of Bonner and associates, are flowing out of research laboratories at a rapid rate. Their cumulative effect is not to upset the DNA/RNA theory of genetics, but rather to extend it and to fill in its gaps. There seems little doubt of the essential validity of these modern molecular concepts of the genetic processes.

General Features of Modern Genetic Theory. An extensive treatment of the theory of genetics is beyond the scope of this book and certainly well beyond the competence of the author. For our present purposes, we need concern ourselves with only two or three of the features of the theory. To begin with, the blueprint, or better, the library of specifications, contained in coded form in the genes, extensive though it is, is still not complete enough to describe in detail how every cell is to be fabricated and connected with the other cells of the body. Fortunately, this degree of detail is not necessary. We have already seen an example of the kinds of short cuts nature has learned to use in its technique for ensuring proper interconnection of peripheral neurons with their corresponding components in the brain. The genetic message need not include such detail as "the neuron in the retina of the eye that is 1,048 from the left and 579 up from the bottom must make connection with the neuron in the left occipital lobe of the brain that is exactly 104,954 cells left of the center line and 3,045 cells up from the mid-line of the calcarine fissure." If this were required, the one thousand volumes of specifications to which the genetic content of the human being is equivalent would not begin to stretch far enough to permit the desired machinery to be defined. But instead we saw in Chapter 2 that the instruction coded into the genes for this part of the job order is simply that each retinal neuron must establish contact with a cortical neuron of the same relative content of two specified chemicals and that, further, such simplified instructions are coupled with a method of design of the nerves and associated structures that permits the searching axons to wander about more or less at random during the course of the embryonic development, thus providing opportunity for close approach to any given target neuron. Hence the required end result is achieved with a great reduction in the length of the genetic message that otherwise would be needed. It is likely that nature employs many such ingenious simplifying devices to minimize the communication problem and make it possible for the necessary specifications of the individual to be transmitted by the no more than approximately ten billion nucleotides in each cell that appear to be devoted to that purpose.

Although it is these genetic specifications coming to the new individual from its parents by means of the sperm and egg cells that determine whether it will be an amoeba or a chimpanzee, the inherited specifications are not identical for all amoebae or for all chimpanzees. The inherited characteristics that differentiate individuals, as well as those that differentiate members of different species, are a consequence of the fact that the genetic library of specifications differs in some details from one individual to another. These various libraries of specifications corresponding to individuals of different characteristics within a species seem to possess remarkable stability and permanence. Not only are the genetic specifications replicated without error thousands of billions of times as a single multicelled individual grows from the original sperm and egg cell, but also apparently they can be propagated successively through many generations without substantial modification. It is likely that those of us in the twentieth century who have light eyes or hemophilia come by this characteristic through an unbroken chain of successive reproduction and transmission of the same complex coded pattern of thousands of precisely arranged genetic molecules, through generation after generation, extending back into prehistoric times.

Although genetic libraries of specifications are remarkably stable, they are not completely changeless. A breed of cattle characterized by long legs will sometimes produce a short-legged offspring. Cats and dogs are occasionally born without tails. These spontaneous changes in content of the genetic instructions propagated from parent to offspring are known as *mutations* and appear to be a form of cosmic accident. Many, perhaps most, such mutations are produced by radiation. A high-energy charged particle arising from the cosmic radiation that continually permeates space or from natural radioactive minerals of the earth occasionally passes through the sexual equipment of a prospective parent in such a way as to disarrange the pattern of molecules in the genes of one of its cells—to produce a "typographical error" in its library of specifications. This error or change is then reproduced in the sperm cell or ovum that ultimately participates in the formation of a new individual, and a modified library of specifications is then propagated by that new individual to its offspring. Mutations, however caused, result in new genetic specifications that are as stable and reproducible as the original genetic instructions and can therefore be passed along for generation after generation. When, by X-ray-induced mutation, fruit flies are produced with white eyes, it is found that after seventy-five generations flies with the mutant gene possess eyes as white as those first produced! And the breeders of race horses, beef cattle, and new varieties of dogs all make use of the permanence and continuity of the genetic design information handed along from parent to offspring. They know that, if once developed and then kept uncontaminated, a new genetic strain producing the characteristics they desire in their animals will thenceforth breed true.

Of course, mutations provide the raw material for evolution. If the new characteristics resulting from the mutation have survival value, the individual is apt to live longer and have more offspring than its nonmutated contemporaries. Many of these offspring, in turn, will be more successful than their contemporaries in surviving until they reproduce offspring; thus the next generation will have a still higher proportion of individuals whose cells contain the new genetic specifications. Individuals with the new characteristic with higher survival value may ultimately displace completely the unfortunate inheritors of the old-fashioned set of genes.

Genetic Control of Behavioral Characteristics; Evolutionary Hypothesis. Interesting and important though all this may be, what is its pertinence to our present subject of the "permanently wired-in" computer/control functions of the brain? Simply this: these behavioral characteristics are also a consequence of the physical construction of the organism—in this case, of the specific way in which the neurons are interconnected. The specifications for these interconnections, like those for the more obviously physical characteristics of the organism, are carried by the genes. The same built-in mechanism by means of which the genetic blueprints, in their interaction with the surrounding chemical materials, compel precise adherence to their design specifications in the embryonic growth of the muscles or visceral organs, automatically and accurately "wires" the neurons into the precise computing/control circuits required by heredity. And the same processes must control the evolutionary development of inherited behavior characteristics. <u>Presumably, changes in the inherited behavior patterns of individuals are produced by mutations in the genes that specify the wiring of the neurons.</u> If the change in behavior results in increased survivability for the individual affected, the descendants of the individual will grow more numerous from generation to generation, and the new behavioral characteristic will ultimately become typical of the species.

At least in the case of simple reflexes and tropisms, it is as easy to visualize the workings of evolutionary principles upon behavior as upon the more obviously physical characteristics of the species. A mutation in the neuronal scheme of the nocturnal moth resulting in a more effective interconnection between the sensory neurons responsive to the scent of the female and the effector neurons controlling the flight muscles could easily result in a new strain of moths of enhanced mating effectiveness. If individuals of this new strain produced on the average 20 per cent more progeny than the non-mutated individuals, only four generations would be needed for a colony of moths of the new strain to attain twice the population of a colony of old-style moths of initially the same size. Of course, in an actual situation in which the new strain starts out as a tiny minority element in an unmodified population, with no artificial forces at work to speed the process by controlled interbreeding of the individuals having the desired characteristics, much longer periods of time are required by the evolutionary processes to produce noticeable changes. On the other hand, we must remember that the population in any one generation of insects and some of the other lower animals may run into many billions and also that the life span of an individual in these lower forms is so short that a complete generation may be compressed into a few weeks or months. Therefore it is easy to imagine that nature, in the millions of years it has had for working its evolutionary wonders, should have found its random statistical methods adequate for refinement to today's state of the reflexes and tropisms that form so much of the basis of behavior of some of the simpler forms of life.

But simple reflexes and tropisms are one thing—the inherited behavior pattern of a solitary wasp or of a social insect appears to be quite another. Consider the complex, precise pattern of interneuronal wiring needed in the memory and control system of a wasp to provide the set of subroutines and triggering arrangements involved in its nest-building activities. <u>Is it really logical to assume that this pattern could have been arrived at by evolutionary selection from among the literally millions of different ways in which the dendrites and axons of only a few hundred neurons can conceivably be interconnected?</u> This question, of course, was raised more generally a few decades back about all evolutionary processes, including those responsible for properties that appeared to be simpler than those that concern us here. The question lost much of its cogency as improved methods for determining the age of the earth revealed that nature's evolutionary processes have been going on much longer than had originally been thought. However, in the nineteenth century, prior to these geophysical developments, the Lamarckian evolutionists had a way of reconciling the apparent shortness of the time that had been available for evolution with the extensiveness of the resulting accomplishments. They believed that acquired characteristics could be inherited. If, with the passage of time, the individuals of successive generations of a species made more and more use of their legs in running down their prey, the increased musculature in the legs thus acquired by an individual would somehow be passed on to his offspring who would, as a result, start out in life with stronger legs than the parent and evolve from there. It is easy to see that such a hypothesis would be particularly effective for explaining the evolutionary development of inherited behavior. With such an approach, we could reason as follows. If, for whatever cause, a female wasp while under the influence of the biological urge to make a nest and lay eggs comes across a certain species of caterpillar, stings it, and brings it to its burrow just before the urge to lay eggs becomes controlling, the no doubt pleasurable associations in the brain of the wasp between the egg laying and the caterpillar episode could in some way produce changes in the genetic material passed on to the next generation of wasps and result in some probability that they, too, would associate the two kinds of behavior. By such a hypothesis, given many generations to work with, we could probably develop a fairly comfortable feeling about the adequacy of evolutionary processes to account for the remarkably detailed inherited behavior patterns of some of the lower animals.

Unfortunately for the Lamarckian hypothesis, all the modern science of genetics conspires against it. No one has ever succeeded in showing the slightest effects on subsequent generations of any kind of physical or behavioristic experience of previous individuals (with the exception of the special experiment of exposing the parents to radiation and thereby inducing mutations to occur at a rate higher than normal). Numerous investigators have tried every device they could think of to modify by special conditioning of the parent the genetic information transmitted to an offspring. In the course of this work, "animals and plants were drugged, poisoned, intoxicated, illuminated, kept in darkness, half smothered, painted inside and out, whirled around and around, shaken violently, vaccinated, mutilated, educated, and treated with everything except affection from generation to generation." *

One investigator even cut off the tails of generation after generation of mice, only to find the tails of the final progeny as long as those of the first. Not only such experimental evidence, but also the increasingly well-established basic theory of genetics, leads to the conclusion that there is nothing in the experience of the parents that can have any effect whatever on the "library of specifications" contributed by them to their offspring. The genetic instructions that will one day be passed along to subsequent generations are precisely determined at the instant the sperm and egg cells meet and initiate the processes of embryonic cell division that finally result in the adult parent. Only unpredictable, random mutations, probably for the most part produced by radiation, but never the result of intervening activity or experience of the parent, can make changes in the "literary content" of the genetic package.

The fruitlessness of any attempt to find an accelerating factor in the evolution of inherited behavior leaves us in the position of having to rest our confidence in the validity of the existing hypothesis on the statistical effectiveness of the large numbers of individuals and generations involved. Perhaps we can be adequately comfortable in contemplation of this situation if we again recall the propensity of natural processes toward ingenious simplifying techniques. It is likely that throughout the ages the evolutionary processes of nature have automatically developed certain packaging concepts for the specification of neuronal wiring diagrams. A mutation in a gene that is involved in the specification of the nervous system probably results, not simply in the reconnection of individual neurons, but instead in a change of the method of deployment or in the weight factor associated with an aggregation of interconnected neurons, without thereby upsetting the operational integrity of this more or less self-sufficient package. If this hypothesis is correct, the number of random mutations required to carry the inherited behavior

---

* A quotation from H. J. Muller, the American geneticist who received the Nobel prize in 1946 for his discovery of the production of mutations by means of X-ray irradiation.

of a developing species through a wide range of variations could easily become mere hundreds instead of millions. When the science of genetics has developed to the point where the library of specifications passed on from parent to offspring can be decoded, we shall probably discover a large number of simplifying factors such as this. These simplifying factors, coupled with the tremendous capacity for change inherent in the basic principle of evolution when applied to billions of individuals over millions of generations, will presumably be found adequate to explain what appears today to be the remarkable specificity and sophistication of the inherited patterns of behavior of some of the insects and lower animals.

Genetic Control of Behavioral Characteristics; Direct Evidence. Evolutionary hypotheses are by their very nature difficult to confirm by factual observations. However, no such uncertainty need extend to the interpretation of the experimental evidence for the genetic specification of behavioral characteristics. In experiments with rats, for example, strains have been isolated that exhibit marked differences in their behavior toward strangers. In one genetic strain, extreme aggressiveness and hostility is displayed; in another strain of rats that in other respects appear identical, the behavior is docile. These behavioral characteristics breed true, just as do the physical characteristics determined by the genes. In another animal experiment, a particular gene of a fruit fly has been identified that controls one of the details of behavior during the act of mating. Specifically, a modification in this gene decreases the strength and duration of the vibrations of the wings and antennae with which the male fly caresses the female at a certain stage in the courtship procedure!

Evidence for the hereditary control of the properties of the neurological circuits is also supplied by human victims of genetic defects. *Phenylketonuria,* a defect that often causes mental retardation, has been determined to be hereditary in nature. So is *juvenile amaurotic idiocy.* The obscure *Kuru disease,* which regularly kills nearly half of the members of a particular remote tribe in New Guinea, is another case in point. This disease, which causes progressive degeneration of the nervous system, has been traced to a single defective gene. And several other mysterious diseases of the nervous system are suspected to be genetic in nature. These include, for example, two different types of muscular tremor, each highly specific to local population groups in New Guinea, a progressive dementia found in certain islands of the Western Pacific, and so on.

With the growing understanding by physicians of the possible genetic significance of the symptoms of their patients, clues to the existence of hitherto unrecognized hereditary defects are being discovered at a rapid rate. Because so many more humans than animals come under medical scrutiny, it is from such sources, rather than from animal experiments, that most new evidence is coming for neurological genetic defects.

In summary, the inextricably intertwined modern concepts of evolution and genetics appear to provide an explanation of the development and propagation of permanently wired-in computer/control networks of the type required to account for the inherited patterns of behavior of many of the lower animals. The same evolutionary/genetic mechanisms, of course, would also appear to be responsible for the development of the many reflex mechanisms in the higher animals, which we have seen are so similar to the inherited behavior patterns of lower forms and which contribute so much to survival capability. None of this is to say that there exists today anything like a complete understanding of these complex matters. But in view of the evidence that has been secured so far, it would be difficult to question the validity of the basic concept of a library of specifications transmitted by the genes in coded form from one generation to the next. In the ensuing years, it is to be expected that great progress will be made in deciphering the genetic code. When more is known about the physical and chemical laws by means of which the structural pattern of a gene controls the molecule-building processes in the surrounding protoplasm, we may be able to work out a detailed translation of the messages conveyed by the genes of a specific individual. It is not inconceivable that eventually the designers of computer/control devices will learn to synthesize the types of genes that control the formation of the nervous system in animals. If so, they may be able to fabricate computer components from organic materials on a molecular scale, as nature does, to substitute for the current electronic devices that in future terms of reference may appear fantastically naïve, large, and inefficient.

BIBLIOGRAPHY

Asimov, I., *The Intelligent Man's Guide to Science* (Basic Books, Inc., Publishers, New York, 1960), "The Cell," pp. 497–551.
Bastock, M., "A Gene Mutation Which Changes a Behavior Pattern," *Evolution*, vol. 10 (1956), pp. 421–439.
Bonner, J., R. C. Huang, and N. Maheshwari, "The Control of Chromosomal RNA Synthesis," in press.

Cruft, H., C. Mauritzen, and E. Stedman, "Abnormal Properties of Histones from Malignant Cells," *Nature,* vol. 174 (1954), pp. 580–585.

Dobzhansky, T., "Eugenics in New Guinea," *Science,* vol. 132 (1960), p. 77.

Eibel-Eibesfeldt, I., "The Interactions of Unlearned Behaviour Patterns and Learning in Mammals," in *Brain Mechanisms and Learning,* ed. by Fessard, Gerard, Konorski, and Delafresnaye (Charles C Thomas, Publisher, Springfield, Ill., 1961), pp. 53–74.

Emerson, A. E., "The Evolution of Behavior among Social Insects," in *Behavior and Evolution,* ed. by Roe and Simpson (Yale University Press, New Haven, Conn., 1958), pp. 311–335.

Gajdusek, D. C., "Kuru: An Appraisal of Five Years of Investigation," *Eugenics Quarterly,* vol. 9 (1962), pp. 69–74.

Gifford, E. M., Jr., "Variations in Histone, DNA and RNA Content During Flower Induction," in press.

Horowitz, N. H., "The Gene," *Scientific American,* October, 1956, pp. 79–90.

Huang, R. C., and J. Bonner, "Histone, A Suppressor of Chromosomal RNA Synthesis," *Proceedings of the National Academy of Sciences,* vol. 48 (1962), pp. 1216–1222.

Mayr, E., "Behavior and Systematics," in *Behavior and Evolution,* ed. by Roe and Simpson (Yale University Press, New Haven, Conn., 1958), pp. 341–362.

Muller, H. J., "The Darwinian and Modern Conceptions of Natural Selection," *Proceedings of the American Philosophical Society,* vol. XCIII (1949), pp. 459–470.

Pittendrigh, C. S., "Adaptation, Natural Selection, and Behavior," in *Behavior and Evolution,* ed. by Roe and Simpson (Yale University Press, New Haven, Conn., 1958), pp. 390–416.

Taylor, J. H., "The Duplication of Chromosomes," *Scientific American,* June, 1958, pp. 37–42.

Thompson, W. R., "Social Behavior," in *Behavior and Evolution,* ed. by Roe and Simpson (Yale University Press, New Haven, Conn., 1958), pp. 291–310.

Thorpe, W. H., "Some Characteristics of the Early Learning Period in Birds," in *Brain Mechanisms and Learning,* ed. by Fessard, Gerard, Konorski, and Delafresnaye (Charles C Thomas, Publisher, Springfield, Ill., 1961), pp. 75–94.

Wells, H. G., J. S. Huxley, and G. P. Wells, *The Science of Life* (Doubleday & Company, Inc., Garden City, N.Y., 1938), book eight, chap. I, "Rudiments of Behavior"; chap. II, "How Insects and Other Invertebrates Behave"; chap. III, "The Evolution of Behavior in Vertebrates."

chapter 6

Electrical Nature of Conscious Mental Processes: Brain Waves and Epilepsy

Having disposed of the lower animals and their inherited patterns of behavior, let us now return to our proper subject, the human brain. Before our digression we had learned something about the electrical nature of nerve action; we had observed the orderliness of the equipment arrangement and point-to-point wiring schematic of the nervous system; we had examined evidence for complex data-rearranging activity in peripheral interneurons; and we had studied some of the automatic computer/control circuits of the spinal cord and the brain. In this chapter we shall for the first time encounter evidence that our conscious or "mental" activities also possess electrical attributes. The evidence we shall consider comes out of the related fields of brain waves and epilepsy.

Brain Waves: Electroencephalography

Human brain waves were discovered in 1924 by Hans Berger of the University of Jena, Austria. By pasting small metal strips to the scalps of his subjects and running wires from these strips to a sensitive galvanometer, he was able to measure tiny electric potentials of a few hundred-thousandths of a volt that would wax and wane in irregular fashion, apparently as a consequence of some aspect of the operation of the brain. By photographically recording the successive positions of the moving element of the galvanometer on a continuous roll of paper pulled steadily past the instrument, he was able to study the manner in which these minute potentials varied with time. The resulting wavy pattern inspired the name "brain wave" for the product of his investigations.

Berger discovered that the wiggles on his recording paper were not entirely random, but instead displayed certain periodicities and regularities. Most interesting of all, he found that the pattern of the tracings changed in a consistent and identifiable fashion when the general "state of mind" of the subject changed, as from relaxation to alertness.

Berger's original paper did not excite much attention. The brain voltages he was measuring were so weak as to lie just at the threshold of detectability with the nonelectronic techniques then available. It also appears that Berger himself was not a particularly effective advocate of his own ideas and did little to call attention to their importance. As a result, it was not until 1934 that the reality of human brain waves began to be accepted, when British investigators confirmed Berger's findings. Meanwhile, the development of high-gain vacuum-tube amplifiers by the radio engineer rapidly simplified the task of obtaining reliable measurements of the tiny electric potentials involved.

The lack of interest that greeted Berger's original paper of 1929 (he waited five years before he published!) was surpassed only by the overenthusiasm for brain waves of the late 1930s. It was easy for popular writers with unrestrained imagination to speculate about the use of radio receivers (which were themselves somewhat mysterious in those days) to provide telepathic communication by picking up brain waves at a distance and deciphering them in terms of their thought content. Although serious workers in the field did not subscribe to these flights of fancy, nevertheless there was hope that the many wiggles in the tracing of a brain wave could one day be interpreted to yield detailed information about mental processes. This expectation has not been realized. We know today that the voltage indications provided by electrodes on the outside of the scalp can reflect only the average electrical state of so many millions of neurons over such a large portion of the brain that there is no possibility by this means of obtaining the specific kind of data that would be necessary to unravel a thought process. Nevertheless, the records of brain waves, or *electroencephalographs* (EEG), as they have been named, have proved to be very useful. They are now used routinely in clinics and operating rooms for the diagnosis of certain types of nervous-system disorders. Electroencephalographic equipment has also become a valuable tool of the research laboratory; in conjunction with other measuring instruments, it has helped provide a great deal of the information we now have about how the brain works. And for the purposes of this treatment, the EEG is of particular interest because it is the first example that we shall consider of an electric indication related to the "state of mind" of an individual.

The brain-wave pattern of a human or other vertebrate displays the individual's state of alertness. The typical patterns shown in Figure 6-1 illustrate this clearly. These patterns were measured on a human

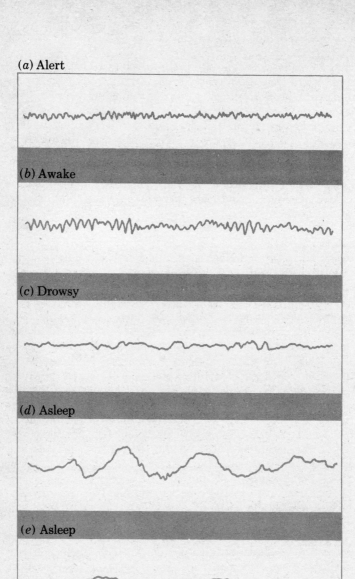

(a) Alert

(b) Awake

(c) Drowsy

(d) Asleep

(e) Asleep

$\bigg| = 100\,\mu\text{V}$ $\longmapsto\!\!\!\longmapsto$ 1 second

subject, with the electrodes placed toward the back of the head, where experience shows the principal rhythms to be strongest. Part (a) is the EEG for a subject who has his eyes open and is alert to his environment; it consists of a low-amplitude, rapidly changing pattern. Part (b) is the trace for the same subject when he is resting with eyes closed, relaxed, his mind free from absorbing or worrisome subjects; the voltage swings to higher values than in (a) and the record is characterized by a low-frequency periodicity, which can clearly be seen in the figure. This regular waxing and waning of the brain-wave potential occurs approximately ten times per second in a normal relaxed adult human and has been named the *alpha* rhythm. Although the alpha pattern is characteristic of relaxation, it gives way, in turn, to other patterns when the subject becomes drowsy (c), and when he falls asleep (d); here the range of voltage variation is greatest of all, but it occurs in a long, slow, rolling wave. After a few hours of sleep, the EEG looks more like (e). If, instead of falling asleep, the subject loses consciousness because of excessive acceleration, such as that which produces blackout of pilots in a tightly maneuvered high-speed aircraft, the EEG pattern becomes even flatter than the curve of (e), the brain-wave voltages sometimes disappearing completely.

Before we consider the explanation of these electric waves in the brain, we may take note of an interesting space-age application of brain-wave techniques. At the Brain Research Institute of the University of California at Los Angeles, methods are being developed for measuring the general performance capability of subjects when exposed to the unusual environmental conditions that might be encountered in space flight, such as extreme acceleration and vibration. Brain waves have been found to provide a more direct and accurate indication of mental alertness than can be obtained by visual observation or other physical measurements made on the subject. The conversion of the normal EEG pattern of alertness into one of sluggish inattentiveness during increasing acceleration is easy to follow, and high-G blackout is indicated by a dramatic flattening of the wiggles of the brain waves. There is even evidence of synchronous forced driving of the brain waves by extreme vibration; this might well incapacitate the subject for the performance of skilled or mental chores, although it is unlikely to produce observable effects on the

Fig. 6-1. (See facing page.) Changes in the EEG of a normal human during alertness, drowsiness, and sleep. (*From M. A. B. Brazier, The Electrical Activity of the Nervous System, ed. 2, The Macmillan Company, New York, 1960. By permission of the author and copyright holder.*)

instruments customarily used to monitor the state of physical well-being of the astronaut.

In the interest of more rapid development of useful techniques, the work of the Brain Research Institute has been largely done on cats and monkeys rather than on men. However, the applicability of such techniques to humans has been subjected to an interesting verification in a study supported jointly by the Royal Norwegian Air Force, the United States Air Force, and the Ford Foundation. In this study EEG recordings were made on pilots as they performed combat maneuvers in jet fighter aircraft. Wide individual variations were found in the degree to which the brain waves were affected by such relatively severe maneuvers. By a subsequent review of the personnel files, a close correlation was also discovered between the extent to which a pilot's brain waves were affected by the maneuvers of the flight test and the number of accidents or near accidents in his past record!

The Nature of Brain-wave Phenomena

At first glance, the existence of brain waves does not seem surprising. We know that the operation of the brain is electrical in nature and that at any instant millions or billions of its neurons may be opening or closing their electrically activated switches and sending currents hither and yon. Since all electric currents produce effects that can be detected at a distance, why should we be surprised to measure minute electric potentials between metal strips pressed tightly against different portions of the scalp? The answer is that it is not the mere existence of electric potentials that is surprising, but rather the shape of the voltage wave that is sometimes observed. To be sure, the typical "alert" pattern (Fig. 6-1a) could well be the combined effect of the millions of tiny currents flowing in different directions and at different instances of time in those neurons that are close to the external measuring electrode; this is exactly the kind of voltage trace known as "noise" by physicists and communication engineers, and it is known to be produced by the summation of a large number of random, unrelated tiny electrical effects. But the pattern of Figure 6-1b is something else again. It is the regularity in the waxing and waning of its voltage—the alpha rhythm—that has from the beginning produced the interest in brain waves. Such regularity can be explained only on the basis of a considerable degree of synchronism of the neuronal currents. The matter is made even more impressive when measurements are made simultaneously from pairs of electrodes pressed against the back of both sides of the head and these measurements compared with one another by modern electronic "cross-correlation" techniques. By such methods, it is found that it is not just in small local regions that the neuronal currents are synchronized with one another. Instead, such coordinated synchronized currents extend throughout a substantial portion of the entire brain!

Because the operation of the nervous system largely consists in conduction of on/off pulses, it was originally thought that the alpha waves represent a concurrent, synchronized firing of large numbers of neurons. The bulk of recent work, however, supports the view that firing of the neurons probably is not directly involved. Instead, it seems that these brain-wave potentials are produced by a more generalized flow of electricity through and among the tangled mass of dendrites that constitutes such a prominent feature of the gray matter of the brain. The resulting dendritic potentials are believed ordinarily not great enough to cause the neurons to go into their characteristic voltage-pulsing mode. However, the waxing and waning of the dendritic potentials probably does cause a corresponding waxing and waning in the ease with which the neurons fire on receiving from other neurons the kinds of specific impulses that underlie the computing, control, and thought processes. In other words, the alpha rhythm seems to denote the propagation throughout the neurons of a periodic wave of sensitization. Presumably it it would be during the intervals of high sensitivity that the brain would be most apt to take note of and start acting upon sensory information coming in over its peripheral neurons if the sensory signal should become strong enough to require attention by the organism.

This interpretation of the alpha rhythm is reminiscent of the timing pulses used to synchronize an electronic digital computer. The net result in each case is to cause the various elements of the system to be sensitized and ready to operate only at discrete periodic intervals of time. On this hypothesis, there is an interesting test of reasonableness that we can apply to the alpha-rhythm frequency. In the design of an electronic computer, the interval between successive synchronizing pulses is usually made as short as possible in order to maximize the speed of computation. "As short as possible" works out to be the time required for all the components that must participate in a computing step to perform their various operations. For the fast-acting switches of modern electronics, this interval is usually measured in millionths of a second or less. Since nature has shown so many evidences of her efficiency, we would expect that the alpha-rhythm interval of about 0.1 second might be related to the time required for the neuronal pulses to traverse whatever length of chain of neurons is typical in the performance of their complex processes.

There is indeed some evidence for the validity of such conjecture. For one thing, the time required for a neuron to fire a single pulse in response to an incoming stimulus, then recover and get ready to fire again, is a few thousandths of a second; a computing chain of dozens to a hundred neurons in series, a number that at least seems reasonable, would be consistent with the alpha frequency. This line of speculation is strengthened by experiments showing that the time required by the brain after the receipt of a sensory impulse to formulate a simple muscular-response command is approximately 0.1 second. Perhaps more to the point, however, are some other interesting experiments performed at MIT by J. S. Barlow. In these experiments, the brain waves of a human subject were measured while he was exposed to occasional sharp, bright flashes of light. It was found that each flash of light stimulated an entire train of brain waves, having almost the frequency of the alpha rhythm. Apparently, the sudden discharge of large numbers of neurons in the visual cortex produced by the bright flash of light was able to put the entire system into oscillation. This is, of course, a familiar phenomenon to the electrical engineer. The sudden discharge of electricity into an oscillatory circuit will always put the circuit into oscillation at its resonance frequency; the oscillations will then decrease in amplitude at a rate determined by the internal resistance, or "damping coefficient," of the circuit. In the MIT experiments, the resonance frequency determined in this way was very close to the frequency of the normal alpha rhythm of the subjects tested. We shall also find it of interest later that the damping coefficient was fairly high: each flash of light was followed by only ten or fifteen measurable brain-wave oscillations.

But all of this is highly speculative. To be sure, it seems unlikely that the final explanation of the alpha rhythm will not include the ingredient of a natural resonance of some of the circuitry of the brain with period related to the time required for currents to circle the typical chain of interconnected neurons. Also, the evidence seems fairly convincing that the alpha rhythm does indicate a periodic synchronized sensitization and desensitization of the neurons. However, it has certainly not yet been established that this is in fact a "timing-pulse" situation analogous to that occurring in electronic computers. In any event, the analogy cannot be too close, because of the disappearance of the alpha rhythm during alertness or concentration. This disappearance seems to suggest that, when the brain actively goes to work on conscious thought, its various portions no longer operate in synchronism, but split up and separately perform their assigned chores. In computer terminology, the conscious thought processes appear to employ nonsynchronous techniques. The synchronous arrangement seems to be employed only during relaxation, possibly for the purpose of continually scanning or monitoring the incoming sensory data for "out-of-tolerance" conditions; these, when found, may then trigger an automatic alert system that reorganizes the internal connections of the brain into an arrangement more suitable for consciously dealing with the problem at hand.

Let us now return from the field of speculation to the more solid ground of actual observation. Electroencephalography has had dramatic success in the diagnosis and explanation of epilepsy. The results of this work are particularly interesting to us because of the clues they provide to the electrical nature of emotional and intellectual processes.

Epilepsy

A severe epileptic fit (*grand mal*) is a horribly spectacular performance. A vivid description is given in the Funk and Wagnalls *New Standard Encyclopedia* (1937):

. . . the patient, it may be without warning, utters a strange inarticulate cry, and falls suddenly to the ground insensible, as if struck by lightning. He becomes deadly pale, his body rigid, with the back arched and the features set, and he ceases to breathe. Soon the color changes, the face becomes livid purple, the veins of the neck swell up and pulsate, the eyeballs protrude, a gurgling sound is heard in the throat, and death seems imminent. But almost immediately breathing begins again, and the whole body is thrown into a series of successive convulsive twitchings or jerkings. The trunk and limbs are thrown about in various ways, the face is hideously contorted, the tongue jerked out between the teeth, the jaws convulsed so that the teeth may be broken.

It is not surprising that superstitious awe should have attached itself to this disease and that, in an earlier day when secret potions and incantations were used instead of antibiotics for the treatment of common ailments, epilepsy should have been considered peculiarly suitable for treatment by religious and mystical techniques. One of Hippocrates' best-known essays constituted an appeal to his fifth century B.C. contemporaries to recognize that "the sacred disease" (the title of his essay and the name then given to epilepsy) was no more a manifestation of the direct intervention of the gods in human affairs than any other disease—that it had natural causes and would someday yield to ordinary cures.

It now seems that Hippocrates was right, but it has required nearly twenty-five centuries to develop enough understanding of the workings of the brain and techniques for measuring its behavior (including electroencephalography) to permit us to provide any very solid backing for Hippocrates' claims.

It is now known that the kind of epileptic fit described above is but an extreme form of a brain disease that may have many varied manifestations. In its mildest form, an epileptic attack may consist of no more than a momentary tingling or sense of numbness in some part of the body, or in the appearance to the subject of flashes of light or blind spots in his field of view. In one form of epilepsy, the victim may simply experience short mental blackouts, lasting only a second or so, that may occur several times a day, not noticeable to his associates, and scarcely to the victim himself. Sometimes a tingling sensation or numbness that starts at one part of the body will spread rapidly to adjacent areas; and the affected parts may then go into uncontrolled convulsions which, in turn, may spread until most or all of the body is involved and the patient loses consciousness. There is even a severe form of the disease wherein the patient remains completely aware of all that is going on while his muscles stop working, causing him to fall to the ground in a state of complete helplessness until the attack passes.

Of particular interest are certain psychical manifestations of the disease. Although for many patients warning of an impending attack is provided by a physical sensation in a particular part of the body, for others the forerunner of the attack is a strong emotional sensation. This may be a feeling of ecstasy or exaltation. Frequently there is an overpowering sensation of *déjà vu*, a feeling of having been there before; it seems to the patient that he has in the past lived through exactly the same experiences in precisely the same circumstances as those that currently confront him, and that he should be able to predict what will happen next. It is easy to see how epileptics with a mystical turn of mind could easily read religious significance into the ecstatic aura preceding an attack and confuse the intense *déjà vu* sensation with divine revelation. This is made easier if their form of the disease also includes the hallucinations or visions of imaginary events that are not uncommon prior to an epileptic fit. It was probably the honest conviction of many epileptics that they were divinely inspired that gave rise to the term "the sacred disease."

One final nontechnical word about epilepsy before we investigate how it is related to brain waves: epilepsy, at least in moderate degree, seems to be entirely compatible with unusual intellectual achievement. Examples of famous epileptics are Julius Caesar, Peter the Great, Mohammed, and Napoleon Bonaparte, not to mention

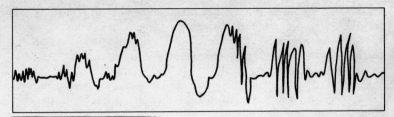

Fig. 6-2. Shape of EEG at the onset of an epileptic seizure. (*After B. W. Konigsmark, A. F. Abdullah, and J. D. French, Electroencephalography and Clinical Neurophysiology, vol. 10 (1958), pp. 687–696. By permission of the publishers.*)

more modern victims such as Dostoevski, who wrote vividly of the dramatic inspirations that sometimes come to an epileptic just before an attack.

What causes epilepsy? Brain waves have provided a partial answer. The EEG of an epileptic is usually not a normal one. The alpha rhythm is typically disturbed by irregular fluctuations. If EEG measurements happen to be under way when an attack comes on, the brain wave puts on a spectacular performance. The small, 10-per-second voltage variations are replaced by huge, slow, rolling waves of potential that at the actual onset of the attack break over into a train of equally large amplitude several-per-second spikes. Figure 6-2 shows how the brain wave might look at the onset of an epileptic seizure.

The modern interpretation of the spectacular brain wave accompanying an epileptic seizure ascribes the initial long, rolling waves to correspondingly large and slow swings in the dendritic potential in the brain—voltage variations similar to but larger and slower than those responsible for the alpha rhythm. Like the alpha waves, these initial epileptic potentials periodically increase and decrease the activation threshold of the neurons, but do not cause them to fire. As the waves build up, however, they ultimately produce such sensitization during the facilitating half of their swing that the neurons break down and discharge spontaneously. At this point the brain wave, as illustrated by Figure 6-2, changes over into a large spike pattern.

Although not all details of the interpretation of epileptic brain waves have been established with certainty, many supporting experiments on the brains of humans and animals have developed general agreement that the mammoth spikes so characteristic of epileptic seizures accurately reflect the spontaneous, uncontrolled firing of most or all of the neurons within an appreciable region of the brain. If the affected region is in the sensory cortex, the victim may have a sensation of numbness, tingling, or other combined and confused feelings referred to the part of the body whose afferent nerves terminate in the misbehaving portion of the brain. If the discharge occurs in the motor-control areas, spontaneous and uncontrollable motions of the affected parts may be the result. In the true *grand mal* attack, it seems possible that the uncontrolled neuronal discharge spreads so widely as to include essentially all the neurons of the brain, thereby causing all the sensory and motor processes of the body to be swung wildly and indiscriminately back and forth throughout the entire range of variation permitted by the physical design of the body parts. It is indeed fortunate for the victim that such an attack always produces unconsciousness.

Much light has been thrown upon the phenomena of epilepsy by the study of "focal fits"—epileptic seizures resulting from small brain injuries. The aftermath of wars has kept our brain-research scientists well supplied with material for these investigations; the high-velocity projectiles of modern warfare provide a great variety of focal brain lesions for the advancement of science. Approximately 50 per cent of such brain wounds result in some form of epileptic symptoms, although fortunately the effects in these cases are often slight. In fact, the mildness of the epileptic tendency contributes to the specificity of the information that the research worker can obtain; if every epileptic attack resulted in a *grand mal* seizure, it would be impossible to establish any correlation between the location of the brain wound and the part of the body most directly stimulated into abnormal sensations or activities.

The evidence from these studies shows that, whenever an area of cortex is damaged, this area is inclined to develop an abnormal rhythm of spontaneous activity. In fact, brain damage that has not been produced by bullets and is not externally evident is frequently located by means of the abnormally spiked brain waves picked up by electrodes when pressed against the skull over the defective tissue. Such a localized improperly discharging neuronal area, however, does not necessarily affect the sensations or behavior of the patient. As we shall see later, a great deal of redundancy is built into the brain, and much of its tissue can be destroyed or cut out entirely without producing any observable effect on mental or physical capabilities. Undoubtedly many people go through life carrying in their heads regions of brain tissue which, owing to birth injury or childhood accident, is functioning improperly or not at all. These people may never experience any mental or physical symptom to suggest that all is not well; nevertheless, it is probable that an EEG would reveal the presence of a spontaneously discharging, abnormal region.

An epileptic attack occurs only when the spontaneous, uncontrolled discharge of the damaged region, for some reason, spreads into the surrounding healthy tissue. Trouble ensues as soon as the undamaged neurons that are participating in preserving the mental and physical health of the individual are pulled off their normal useful jobs by the invading electric currents and organized into a kind of wild cerebral demonstration wherein they join their defective neighbors in projecting their currents back and forth in a meaningless fashion. If this recruiting of healthy neurons by unhealthy ones extends only a small distance away from the region of brain damage, the attack is mild, with symptoms restricted to the functions controlled by this adjacent neuronal tissue. If the currents projected into the healthy area by the misbehaving neurons are large enough, however, and if the particular construction of the victim's brain is such as to give it less than normal resistance to such recruiting activities, the effect may spread over the entire brain, with the resultant catastrophic *grand mal* seizure.

One of the most significant results of the research on focal fits was this discovery that in an epileptic attack it is normal, as well as damaged, tissue that misbehaves. The possibility of throwing healthy material into a runaway condition by the injection of excess electric current suggests that even the normal brain may not enjoy a wide margin of operating stability. This, in fact, has been established to be true. For example, there are certain drugs that temporarily increase the sensitivity of the neurons. In large enough doses, such drugs produce epileptic convulsions in anyone. There is also an interesting electronic technique for producing epileptic effects. We have seen earlier how the sudden appearance in the visual cortex of a large pulse of current resulting from a bright flash of light into the eyes puts some of the brain into a damped electric oscillation with frequency approximately the same as that of the alpha rhythm. If, instead of a single pulse of light, a periodically flashing light is used with frequency near that of the alpha rhythm, a person with epileptic tendencies will begin to display uncontrollable jerking of the arms and legs, and may be driven into a full-scale convulsion if the experiment is unduly prolonged. In computer terms, this suggests that the epileptically inclined person is one who, for some reason, has either a tighter coupling among the various portions of brain tissue whose electric resonance gives rise to the alpha rhythm, or a lower resistance to or damping of that rhythm once it is initiated.

A technique involving a combination of sensitizing drugs and the synchronous-flicker test has been used to measure the epileptic susceptibilities of normal persons. When this measuring technique was applied to a group of crack airplane pilots who had scored high on a series of elaborate psychiatric tests, had very fast reflexes, and had performed expertly in situations calling for swift decisions and maneuvers, they were found to be surprisingly close to the epileptic in their nervous sensitivity! They were twice as sensitive as the average person—another interesting indication that unusual nervous sensitivity, which is so tragic in its extreme form, may, in moderate doses, contribute to the effectiveness and productivity of the individual.

The study of epilepsy and its causes has produced, as an interesting by-product, a method for treating entirely unrelated forms of mental illness. Some years ago, in studying the literature, a Swiss investigator noted that schizophrenia, the most common form of mental illness, seemed rarely to occur among epileptics. It had also been observed that schizophrenics would sometimes recover after having a spontaneous convulsion. The obvious inference was that there is something in the convulsive process, so commonly experienced by epileptics, that tends to prevent or correct whatever mental abnormality is responsible for schizophrenia. Although more recent analysis of the statistical anticorrelation of schizophrenia and epilepsy has cast doubt on the adequacy of the data from which the original inference was made, the inference itself has proved to be sound. Today, many of the successes achieved in the treatment of mental illness are obtained by the use of convulsive therapy. While there are chemical methods of inducing convulsions, such as the one mentioned above, it is more usual to employ an electrical method. Electrodes are placed on the head of the anesthetized, unconscious patient, and a pulse of electricity lasting a few tenths of a second enters the skull through one electrode, passes through the brain, and leaves through the other electrode. This produces the equivalent of an epileptic convulsion. (The patient is premedicated with a muscle relaxant to prevent damage due to the uncontrolled thrashing of arms and legs, and the attack is shorter in duration than a typical *grand mal,* but the principle is the same.) A series of such treatments a few days apart over a period of several weeks frequently restores to normality a patient who previously seemed hopelessly insane.

It would be an overstatement to assert that the means by which electroconvulsive therapy achieves its results are well understood. A way of looking at it, which may have some validity, is as follows: Mental illness is caused by the formation of new habits of thought that are different from, and considerably less sound than, the individual's normal thought patterns. These new habits must involve new patterns of interconnection among the neuron chains in the brain.

Presumably these new neuronal interconnections, if they have been used only a short time, are tenuous and not too firmly established. The old interconnections are still there and ready for use, but somehow are being bypassed by the disturbed brain in favor of the new circuits. When strong electric currents are sent through the brain, momentarily all neural activity is disrupted and disorganized. When the excess currents stop at the end of the convulsion, there is a tendency for the old and normal neuronal interconnections to be reestablished because of their greater stability and lower susceptibility to the weakening effects of saturating currents.

Whether or not this is the correct explanation of the action of electroconvulsive therapy, the computer scientist will immediately think of an amusing analogy. In some complex electronic computers the momentary occurrence of suitable abnormal conditions can induce a kind of runaway situation wherein currents are propagated continuously around closed loops of components in a manner entirely contrary to the normal mode of operation. This might be called a form of schizophrenia of the computer. It can be cured, as in the human case, by sending a large pulse of current all through the system. When the pulse dies out, the wild components are usually found to have joined the team once again.

Summary

Before leaving the subject of brain waves and epilepsy, let us be sure that we understand the principal significance of what we have learned. From measurements on normal subjects electroencephalography provides additional hints that the brain possesses at least some properties which are largely determined by the workings of the established laws of electric circuits. Of particular significance, for our purposes, is the unambiguous correlation between brain waves and degrees of mental alertness.

By the application of brain-wave techniques to the study of epilepsy, not only has light finally been thrown on this mysterious malady, but still more clues have been unearthed as to the electrical nature of mental phenomena. It is now clear why epilepsy comes in so many forms with such diverse symptoms. All depends on the part of the brain that is affected. Since all sensations and physical actions of all parts of the body are controlled by various portions of the brain, the range of symptoms that can be displayed by epileptics is almost as wide as the variety encompassed by the diverse details of human behavior.

Of particular interest are the psychic manifestations of the disease.

The overpowering feelings of awe, inspiration, excitement, ecstasy, and clairvoyance that sometimes precede an attack, as well as the elaborate visual and mental hallucinations that are occasionally experienced, provide the first evidence presented in this treatment that the higher intellectual and emotional processes are controlled by the same kind of neuronal electric currents as those that regulate our muscles and glands and provide us with our sensations and reflexes. It is even possible that some of our great art, literature, and religion owes its inspiration to the uncontrolled electric discharge of small regions of damaged tissue in the brains of creative people!

BIBLIOGRAPHY

Adey, W. R., et al., "EEG Records from Cortical and Deep Brain Structures during Centrifugal and Vibrational Accelerations in Cats and Monkeys," *Institute of Radio Engineers Transactions on Bio-Medical Electronics,* vol. BME-8 (1961), pp. 182–188.

Barlow, J. S., "Rhythmic Activity Induced by Photic Stimulation in Relation to Intrinsic Alpha Activity of the Brain in Man," *Electroencephalography and Clinical Neurophysiology,* vol. 12 (1960), pp. 317–326.

Brazier, M. A. B., and J. S. Barlow, "Autocorrelation and Crosscorrelation Studies of the EEG in Man," *Electroencephalography and Clinical Neurophysiology,* vol. 8 (1956), p. 325.

Brazier, M. A. B., *The Electrical Activity of the Nervous System* (ed. 2, The Macmillan Company, New York, 1960).

Pfeiffer, J., *The Human Brain* (Harper & Row, Publishers, Incorporated, New York, 1955), chap. 11, "The Sacred Disease."

Russell, W. R., *Brain, Memory, Learning* (Oxford University Press, Fair Lawn, N.J., 1958), chap. IX, "Epilepsy."

Sem-Jacobsen, C. W., "Electroencephalographic Study of Pilot Stresses in Flight," *Aerospace Medicine,* November, 1959, pp. 797–801.

Walter, W. G., *The Living Brain* (W. W. Norton & Company, Inc., New York, 1953), chap. 4, "Revelation by Flicker."

Control Centers of Emotion and Consciousness

The phenomena of brain waves and epilepsy have provided us with indications that the conscious activities of the brain may involve electrical processes similar to those we have found to underlie the automatic control functions. But so far we have only indications. We need more information before we can intelligently speculate as to whether computerlike processes may be capable of explaining these mental activities. In this chapter, we shall learn more about the relations between electrical and mental phenomena, and shall in particular examine what is known about the specific regions of the brain that control our emotional and conscious processes.

Clues from Comparative Anatomy

We have already had occasion to observe how the biological scientist is aided in his difficult investigations by the essential interspecies continuity of nature. We have seen that the brain of the chimpanzee is not notably different, either in structure or function, from that of man; the dog and cat are remarkably similar to the chimpanzee; and most of what is learned in experiments with rats finds its close analog in the anatomy and physiology of the higher animals. Of course it is never possible to predict with certainty that the results of experiments on one species will be applicable to another species. However, such extrapolations have a strong inferential validity, resting upon many independent confirmations that similar-appearing and similarly situated organs of different animals do in fact perform similar functions. Confidence is further strengthened by the fact that detailed differences in the anatomical configurations of similar organs frequently appear to be logically related to observable differences in the activities or capabilities of the animals. The amount of tissue allocated by the cerebral cortex to the control of the human hand, the porcine snout, and the equine mouth is only one of many examples of this anatomical-physiological interrelationship.

The methods of comparative anatomy can be used to seek clues as to which portions of the brain are most likely to participate in the control of emotional processes. We know that emotion is exhibited by all higher animals; it is not unique to man, nor is it even particularly a specialty of his. From outward indications at least, alligators, rats, and birds are as proficient in emotional matters as we are. Exactly the opposite we believe to be true with respect to higher intellectual or thought processes. Observation has convinced us that, in this category, animals can be arranged in a logical sequence. We believe that men are more intelligent than chimpanzees, and they in turn are brighter than dogs or cats. We know that

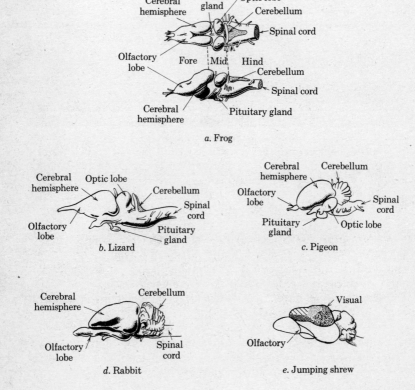

a. Frog

b. Lizard

c. Pigeon

d. Rabbit

e. Jumping shrew

chickens are not very smart, and those with experience in such matters are convinced of the stupidity of lizards and alligators. The inference that is pertinent to our present line of inquiry is obvious: the portions of the brain responsible for higher intellectual achievement are most likely to be those which show the greatest progressive elaboration from the least intelligent animals up to man; the portions of the brain involved in emotional behavior are most likely to be those that do not show progressive elaboration from species to species. Let us now see what can be deduced by application of this simple assumption.

Figure 7-1 shows the progression in the anatomy of the brain from

Fig. 7-1. (See also page 114.) Progression in the anatomy of the brain from lower to higher vertebrates. (*After H. G. Wells, J. S. Huxley, and G. P. Wells, The Science of Life, Doubleday & Company, Inc., Garden City, N.Y., 1938. By permission of the copyright holders.*)

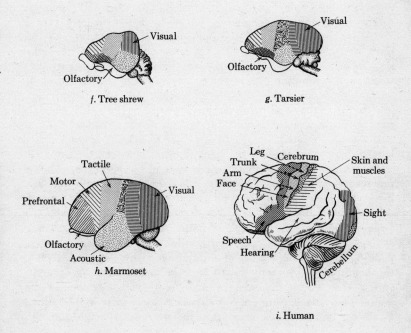

f. Tree shrew

g. Tarsier

h. Marmoset

i. Human

frog to human. (In viewing these side projections, it should be remembered that the brain is always symmetrical about the fore-and-aft mid-plane; there are two identical cerebral hemispheres, two olfactory lobes, two optic lobes, and so on.) Although the differences from animal to animal are extensive, the similarities leave little doubt that all these brains are built on the same basic plan. In each case, the spinal cord enlarges into a bulbular brainstem; this displays on its top side (back side, for an erect human) first a cerebellum, the organ that, as we saw in Chapter 4, is involved in the stabilization of intricate movements of the body, and then the optic lobes, the terminal points of the hundreds of thousands or millions of fibers originating in the retinas of the eyes. At the forward end of each brain are always found the two olfactory lobes, to which are attached the nerves from the nostrils. And there are always cerebral hemispheres that originate in the fore part of the brain and extend back and sometimes over some of the structures of the brainstem.

Some correlations can easily be established between the sizes of the structures and the characteristics of the animals. For example, compare the cerebellums of the pigeon and the lizard. Their relative sizes are consistent with the interpretation that the complex and highly coordinated bodily maneuvers of flight require a correspondingly complex cerebellum, whereas the limited nature of locomotion of the lizard can be adequately served by a rudimentary organ. Similarly, the large size of the optic lobes of the pigeon and the small size of its olfactory lobes seem reasonably related to the relative importance to the bird of sight and smell. The large olfactory lobes of the jumping shrew are consistent with the fact that its behavior is dominated by the sense of smell; indeed, some jumping shrews have such long and mobile noses that they are known as elephant shrews.

If we ignore structural variations that appear to be directly related to corresponding variations in physical characteristics, we are left with only one major anatomical feature of the brain that exhibits progressive variation from one species to another—the cerebral hemispheres. A swelling scarcely larger than other brainstem protuberances in the frog, the cerebral hemispheres become steadily larger as we move up the scale of animal intelligence. As the hemispheres grow from one species to the next, they push backward, expanding around the brainstem until, in monkeys, apes, and men, the hemispheres by their growth have become a covering (that is, cortex) that surrounds and hides most of the other regions of the brain. The obvious inference is that it is the functions performed by the cerebral cortex that contribute to man his intellectual superiority over the other animals. Conversely, we would expect to find in the relatively unchanging brainstem the centers of control for the processes that keep us alive and for the kinds of behavior that we share with the animals, such as emotion.

Before examining further the consequences of this line of thought, let us see if what is being said is consistent with what we already think we know about the localization of functions in the brain. On this new inference from comparative anatomy, we would not expect that the cortex would be essential to the operation of the senses, the muscles, the glands, or the reflexes that keep an animal alive and healthy. Rather, to be completely logical, we would not expect the cortex to be required in any of these activities except possibly that of smell. Apparently the cerebral hemispheres got their start in association with the olfactory input to the brain; therefore it might not be surprising to find the cerebral cortex essential to this function. However, another interpretation is also possible: even in the primitive animals, the cerebral hemispheres may constitute only an elaboration and refinement mechanism, associated primarily with the sense of smell in the brains of those animals whose survival and well-being depend primarily upon their effective use of this kind of sensory input.

The concept of the cortex as an organ of elaboration and refinement rather than as a necessary participant in the sensory and motor actions of the nervous system is strengthened by another kind of anatomical evidence. As the hemispheres evolved from the simple forebrain of the frog to the gigantic cerebral cortex of man, they also developed new connections to the brainstem. Bundles of nerve fibers traveled out from the hypothalamus, the thalamus, the reticular formation, and other brainstem centers to adjacent sections of the surrounding cerebral cortex. It is as if each important portion of the brainstem was finally provided with its own piece of cortex to assist it in performing its functions, whatever they might be. This indeed implies that the development of the cerebral cortex would not bring into play the existence of any qualitatively new capability, but instead would only make it possible for the individual to perform his normal functions in a more elaborate, precise, and effective manner. This is, of course, one way of defining intelligence.

But is the physiological evidence all consistent with this anatomical interpretation? Part of it is, of course. What we learned in Chapter 4 about the automatic processes fits the pattern. The examples we studied did not just happen to be of functions controlled by the hypothalamus or other portions of the brainstem; so far as is known, no bodily processes vital to the maintenance of life are controlled by the cortex. An animal can live for weeks after its cerebral cortex has been completely removed. After such an operation, a cat will pull its paw away from a thorn that pricks it; it will swallow milk and reject acid that is placed in its mouth; it will stand and walk around, go "miaow," and even purr occasionally. But, in these responses, it appears to be essentially unconscious. It does not appear to have thoughts; it seems to be an automaton.

All this is nicely consistent with our inference from comparative anatomy. However, we have learned some other things that do not obviously fit the concept of the cerebral cortex as solely an organ of elaboration and refinement. What about the precise cortical mapping of visual and other sensory stimuli that we found in Chapter 2 to constitute such a comfortable analogy with the wiring methods employed in electronic computers? And the similar orderly arrangement on the cortex of points of departure of the electric command signals to the muscles? Are these cortical involvements simply for the purpose of elaboration and refinement? Could we see, feel pain, and control our muscles if our cortex were to be removed?

For humans, the answers to such questions must be assembled from clinical observations on many patients with one form or another of brain damage. These observations appear to pose no challenge to our inference from comparative anatomy as far as motor control and sensory response are concerned. Removal of the precentral gyrus (the motor strip of the cortex illustrated by the homunculus of Fig. 2-5) results in permanent paralysis of the opposite side of the body, but only in so far as skilled or delicate movements are concerned. Gross movements are not interfered with, and even the relatively delicate but unskilled movements of the face and mouth are only slightly impaired after removal of cortical face area. A generally similar situation obtains with respect to removal of the postcentral gyrus (the sensory strip of Fig. 2-6). Tactile discrimination is greatly impaired, but not all sensation is lost.

With respect to vision, however, the situation is quite different. Removal of the visual cortex in man causes total blindness. Here we appear to have a real incompatibility with the thesis that the cortex is only an instrument of refinement and elaboration. A qualitative difference appears to have arisen somewhere along the line of progression from the lower animals to man. A frog with cerebral hemispheres removed, for all its automatism of behavior, appears to see as well as before. Do we have here evidence of discontinuity in the species-to-species development of the brain that must shake our confidence in the inferential arguments of comparative anatomy? Fortunately, apparently not. At least, there is another possible explanation. There is nothing in the principles of comparative anatomy inconsistent with the transfer of function from one organ to another, provided that this occurs in a continuous and orderly fashion from one to another of the related species of animals. Although in all vertebrates the optic nerves proceed from the eyes to the same general location on top of the brainstem, in man and the higher mammals nerve fibers continue on to the visual cortex. During the course of progressive refinement and elaboration culminating in the brain of man, it is conceivable that more and more of the business of vision was gradually transferred from the brainstem to the visual cortex of the cerebral hemispheres. If carried far enough, this could ultimately make the cortex essential, not only for the interpretation and elaboration of visual images, but even for the recognition of light and darkness. There is, in fact, good evidence that this is what has taken place: if the visual cortex of a rat is destroyed, discrimination between complex patterns is no longer possible, but it can still recognize food and avoid obstacles when it runs; a dog with destroyed visual cortex is more seriously handicapped but can still discriminate between light and darkness; in the monkey, a very crude type of light discrimination remains; total blindness occurs in man. It would appear that we do not after all have to give up the inference we have reached from a study of comparative anatomy.

To recapitulate, in approaching the problem of where in the brain are likely to be found the control centers for different types of behavior, we have found a clue from a structural comparison of the brains of animals of related species. We have subjected this clue to certain tests of reasonableness that have not seriously challenged its apparent validity. Therefore, we shall now follow the clue and see if it helps us find the answers we seek. Specifically, we shall search for the centers that control emotional behavior in the old brain that the human species shares in relatively unchanged form with many lower animals—the brainstem and its appendages. If this search is successful, we shall have increased confidence that the cerebral cortex, the organ that has changed most in the progressive development of the species, will be found to be the key to man's superior intellectual accomplishments.

Technique of Deep Electrical Measurements in the Brain

The principal methods of searching for localization in the brain of the control of functions such as emotional responses are electrical in nature. Wires that are completely insulated except for their very tips are pushed into the various structures of the brain through suitably positioned holes drilled in the skull. These wires are then connected either to instruments that record the electric potentials generated in the invaded tissue or to power sources that inject stimulating currents into the brain. Reference has been made in previous chapters to these techniques of electrical measurement and stimulation. However, in the investigation of the functions controlled by the older, centrally situated portions of the brain, the use of deeply implanted electrodes is so important that the technique itself justifies a short description before the results obtained by it are treated.

If, without previous background, we were for the first time considering an experiment involving the insertion of an electrode deep into the brain of a living animal, we would be understandably skeptical as to the probability of success. Our first fear would probably be that the act of forcing a stiff probe into the brain would do so much damage that it would invalidate the experiment, either by incapacitating the subject for normal behavior or by destroying the tissue near the probe and thereby rendering meaningless any electrical measurements. If such a fear were found groundless, we would still have other cause for pessimism. The brain structures that we want to test are not very large, particularly in rats, cats, and the other small laboratory animals we must work with; how can we accurately place the tip of an electrode where we want it? And if we get it inserted properly, how do we hold it rigidly in place and at the same time permit the animal enough freedom of movement to make observations on its behavior meaningful?

The only good answers to such questions are those supplied by actual experience. Fortunately for brain research, none of the obstacles to success has been found insurmountable. In particular, the problem that might have completely prevented the employment of the method—that of brain damage—has been found much less serious than might have been expected. The brain, whether that of a rat or of a human, appears to incorporate a great deal of redundancy; no individual neuron or small group of neurons seems to be essential to the performance of any important task. The design of nature's "computers" seems to have anticipated the likelihood that not all the components will function correctly and to have therefore provided an abundance of duplicate and parallel neuronal circuits. As a result, wire electrodes in considerable numbers can be inserted deep into the material of the brain without producing any observable change in the animal's capabilities or behavior. By anchoring the electrodes to the rigid mounting structure that nature has conveniently supplied for the purpose—the skull—they can be kept in place for months or years without damage to the subject.

In fact, electrode implantation has been found so harmless that in recent years the technique has increasingly been used on humans. In mental hospitals throughout the world, hundreds of patients have now been equipped with implanted electrodes for use in diagnosis or treatment. It is now customary, when this technique is used, for electrodes to be concurrently implanted in several of the deep-seated structures of the brain. Usually a dozen or more wire electrodes are implanted in each patient. These wires are connected to the terminals of an electric receptacle, generally similar in appearance to the sockets into which vacuum tubes are plugged in radio and television receivers. These receptacles are rigidly fastened by machine screws to the patient's skull. After the superficial scalp damage has healed, these electric appliances cause little inconvenience or discomfort. Human patients have worn such attachments with their associated implanted electrodes for more than two years without ill effects.

Whether the subject is human or animal, implanted electrodes provide the physician or research worker with an admirably flexible test arrangement. Connections can be made between the interior of the brain and external instruments simply by plugging in a flexible cable to the receptacle on the skull. Except for the restraint imposed by the cable, which can be minimized by overhead suspension and the use of long wires, the subject is free to move around and engage in more or less normal behavior during the observations. If the signals generated by the brain itself are simply to be recorded, plugging in the external instruments produces no sensation and has no effect of any kind upon the subject. If the procedure calls for stimulation by externally generated currents, the subject's freedom of movement permits his behavioral responses to be much more natural and meaningful than they would be under the restrained and artificial conditions of the operating room.

The rigid implantation of electrodes without discomfort or injury to the subject is a prerequisite to the success of the electric-probe techniques but does not necessarily constitute a complete solution of the experimental problems. It would still be possible for the local damage in the vicinity of the inserted wire to be so severe that the electrical measurements would only indicate the state of affairs in the surrounding abnormal tissue. Fortunately, this does not appear to be the case. Microscopic examination has shown that the layer of damaged tissue immediately adjacent to an implanted electrode is usually less than 0.02 inch in thickness. In addition, once healed, this damaged material is usually electrically "silent"; that is, it does not produce spurious indications on the measuring instruments. This is sometimes not true immediately after insertion of the electrode, but careful workers usually allow several days of postoperative healing time before attaching significance to measured small voltage effects.

Another problem—that of the precise placement of the electrodes—has been found harder to solve. The research worker or clinician usually employs a combination of methods in attempting to place the electrodes where he wants them. He starts by referring to three-dimensional charts that show the location and dimensions of the structures of the brain of the typical member of the species being worked on—human, cat, rat. . . . Nowadays such charts are prepared for use with *stereotaxis* techniques. A stereotactic structure possesses a rigid metal framework that can be clamped to the skull of the subject. This framework carries transport mechanism by means of which an electrode can be inserted through a previously drilled hole in the skull and its tip brought to a position inside the head that is exactly specified in three coordinates with respect to the rigid structure of the framework. If all members of a given species had exactly the same dimensions and configurations of skull and brain, such stereotactic methods, together with standard three-dimensional charts, would provide a complete solution to the problem of exact placement of electrodes. Unfortunately, individual variations cause the actual situation to fall considerably short of this ideal. Correction of the standard stereotactic maps for these variations is frequently attempted by means of preoperative X-ray examinations. After the electrodes have been placed, additional X-ray measurements provide further information as to their actual positions. The most accurate method of all, sometimes employed in animal experiments in which precise location of the electrodes is basic to an understanding of the results, is a post-mortem dissection of the brain and microscopic measurement of the actual geometry of the electrode placement.

Even if an electrode is placed exactly where the experimenter wants it, there still remain problems with respect to the localization of its electrical effects. This is especially true when the electrode is used, not for measuring the local potentials, but for injecting stimulating currents. The behavioral response elicited by an electric stimulus is not necessarily controlled by the particular point in the brain where the uninsulated tip of the electrode resides. The electricity travels out from this electrode tip through the surrounding tissue in a more or less diffuse manner. It may be remote tissue, rather than that immediately adjacent to the electrode tip, that responds and produces the observed effects. Careful research workers go to considerable pains to limit the effective spread of their injected currents.

Frequently they use an exceedingly fine electrode wire coupled with a remote large-area return electrode. Under such circumstances, the electric current density falls off rapidly with distance from the very fine electrode tip and therefore quickly becomes too small to produce neuronal effects. Sometimes, instead, a pair of fine electrodes is used side by side, with a spacing between their tips of only a few thousandths of an inch. In addition to these geometrical precautions, when precise localization of function is the objective, an attempt is usually made to employ minimum stimulating currents so as to diminish the likelihood that effects are produced at a distance from the electrode. By a series of measurements with stimulating currents of different magnitudes and a corresponding range of positions of the stimulating electrode in the brain structure of interest, it is usually possible to sort out remote from nearby effects, and to develop a reasonably accurate map of the effective centers, when such centers exist.

The kind of electric stimulus used has also been found to be of considerable importance. As pointed out earlier, because of the on/off nature of the electric communication code of the nervous system, pulses must always be used. However, this still leaves a wide variety of choices for the research worker. What should be the time duration of each pulse? What should the interval between the pulses be? How many pulses should be employed in a single stimulus? Should the pulses all be of one sign, or should positive and negative pulses alternate? Unhappily for the experimenter, the answers to all of these questions can be important. Perhaps not surprisingly, the most important parameter of the electric stimulus, aside from its magnitude, appears to be its frequency, the number of pulses applied per second. Different small structures of the brain appear to respond differently to different pulse frequencies. It is not uncommon for a single electrode to elicit quite different behavioral responses when the average stimulating current is held constant but the pulse-repetition frequency is increased from, say, 10 to 50 pulses per second. Because of the inevitable spread of the stimulating current, this phenomenon is not usually interpreted as indicating that a specific group of neurons behaves differently for different stimulating frequencies. Instead, it is frequently possible to account for the observed results on the hypothesis that different groups of neurons of different frequency sensitivities are selectively stimulated by the injected electricity as it spreads into the tissue in the vicinity of the electrode.

This rather detailed discussion of some of the difficulties associated with the technique of electrical measurements on the brain has been set forth here because the technique is central to the understanding that we now hope to gain of the localization in the brain of the control centers for emotion and consciousness. We need to know that the technique involved is a difficult one that is still being refined and developed, and that there are opportunities for error in its use. Different investigators sometimes arrive at conflicting conclusions. This happens in all frontier scientific research when the techniques as well as the phenomena under investigation are new and not completely understood. The test of the essential soundness of the body of research results obtained in a new field is whether there is a strong tendency, as the techniques are improved and better understood, for the differences in the results obtained by various experimenters to decrease and for the area of agreement to broaden. This is happening at quite a satisfactory rate in brain research. Improved appreciation of the effects of spreading of the injected stimulating current around the implanted electrode, for example, has explained why some observers reported that a given region of the brain appears to control rather diffusely a number of behavioral reactions, while others who happened to use smaller stimulating currents observed a more nearly point-to-point relationship between brain location and function. Other discrepancies have been cleared up through the discovery of the selective effect of pulse-repetition frequency, and so on.

Most of the material that follows is now believed valid by most of the workers in the field. This material strongly indicates that there exist sharply localized centers that control emotional responses, and that these centers are primarily found in the brainstem and associated structures that man shares in relatively unchanged form with many of the other animals. Let us now move on to a consideration of the evidence.

The Early Clues

It was a Swiss physiologist, W. R. Hess of Zurich, who developed the important electrode-implanting technique. Starting in 1924 he inserted fine tubings in the brains of cats and found that he could produce dramatic changes in their behavior by injection of suitable chemical substances. These observations encouraged him to continue his work by applying electric current for stimulation. For this technique, together with the new information about the brain he discovered with its use, Hess received the Nobel prize for medicine and physiology in 1949.

Hess, with his new technique, examined the regions in the upper part of the brainstem. He particularly investigated the thalamus and the hypothalamus, which we have already learned appears to be a control center for some of the most important of the body's automatic processes. In some of Hess's experiments, electrodes were implanted in the upper thalamic portion of what we would now call the diffuse reticular activating system. The results of stimulation through such electrodes were entirely consistent with the concept, described in Chapter 4, that the reticular system contains mechanism controlling the sensitivity and adjustment of the muscles of the body. By current injection through elecrodes placed in the thalamus and adjacent portions of the midbrain reticular formation of cats, postural-correction movements were frequently induced, apparently by shifting the normal balance or tension in the muscles involved. The head would be lowered, raised, tilted, or turned. Stimulation at one point would cause the cat to pivot continually in a small circle; another site of stimulation would result in rhythmic raising of the paws; still another electrode placement would cause the eyes to blink.

Stimulation of the hypothalamus, as might have been expected from other evidences of its role in visceral control, resulted in quite different types of behavioral manifestations. In this region, points were found where an applied stimulus would markedly increase or decrease the rate or depth of breathing; at the same time, the blood pressure and heart rate could be modified by the experimenter. Centers were found where electric stimulation induced vomiting. For other electrode positions, bodily elimination would result.

Work by other experimenters rounded out and confirmed the strong indications provided by Hess's work that the hypothalamus is the most important center for the control of the visceral processes of the body. We have already learned that the hypothalamus controls body temperature and that it plays a key role, in conjunction with the reticular activating system and the pituitary gland, in the regulation of glandular processes. In addition, certain regions of the hypothalamus have been found to be essential to the control of appetite and eating. One investigator, working with goats, found a place in the hypothalamus where destruction of a small amount of tissue would keep the animal from eating, no matter how hungry it became. Destruction at another spot in the hypothalamus would cause the animal to continue to make eating movements and to take food into its mouth over and over again, even when completely satiated. Probably similar mechanisms are involved in a rare condition observed in a few unfortunate humans who alternate between periods of fantastic and compulsive overeating and periods of complete starvation.

Hess, in his work on the hypothalamus, developed a concept of functionally related centers of nervous control. It seemed to him that the close grouping in the same brain structure of control points for heartbeat, respiration rate, blood pressure, elimination, and eating made a certain kind of natural logic. After all, the only practical response by the carnivorous animal to the pangs of hunger consists in hunting a victim that can serve as food; such combative behavior clearly calls for coordinated changes in heartbeat, respiration, blood pressure, and glandular secretion. The neural mechanisms grouped together in the hypothalamus to control these separate bodily functions might well constitute an interrelated system based upon the food-getting requirements for survival. Because of this hypothesis, Hess was not surprised when he discovered, in this region of inter-related neuronal control circuits, an area where the application of an electric stimulus would cause the animal to assume the bodily posture and facial expressions appropriate to hostility and antagonism. Such apparent manifestations of emotion were obviously appropriate to the hunt and were therefore suitable for control by a neuronal system designed for the coordination of the various bodily processes involved in the satisfaction of the basic urge of hunger.

In the early days of this work, the notion that there could be specific sites in the brain where electric stimulation would produce actual emotion was so alien to the then-prevailing theories of psychology and physiology that the term "sham rage" was employed by many (though never by Hess) to describe such electrically induced responses. This term reflected the prevailing view that all that an electric stimulus could do was to trigger the physical manifestations of the emotional reaction, but without the emotion itself; the basic motivations of pain, pleasure, rage, and so on were at that time commonly believed to involve excitation or activity of the whole brain in some obscure manner.

Closely associated with the phenomenon of electrically induced "sham rage" were certain fearlike reactions that, it was soon discovered, could be produced by stimulation in hypothalamic sites. With suitably located electrodes, injection of the stimulating current would cause dilation of the pupils, erection of the hairs in the body and the tail, frantic searching of the eyes, and the other external manifestations customarily displayed by an animal that is afraid and is preparing for flight. The investigators with most experience in the performance of such experiments gradually came to have a healthy respect for the reality of these states as they learned they could easily be clawed or bitten while the stimulating current was being supplied. Nevertheless, the adjectives "sham" and "pseudo" continued to be commonly applied to the emotional manifestations induced by stimulation through elecrodes implanted in the hypothalamus.

This was the general state of affairs during the early 1950s. In

1953, in an experiment performed at McGill University, an accident occurred that was to cast a new light on the relation between electric stimulation and emotion.

Discovery of "Pleasure" Centers in the Brain

The subjects were rats. The object of the experiment was to explore the operation of the midbrain reticular system. The principal research worker was James Olds. The work was under the guidance of the psychologist D. O. Hebb at McGill University. The technique of placing electrodes in the brain of the rat had not at this time been completely mastered by this group of experimenters. Consequently, in one rat the electrode tip missed the target and landed in a portion of the forebrain near the hypothalamus. Because of this lucky accident, a new phenomenon was discovered.

In the experiment then under way, the animal, equipped with an implanted electrode and plugged into the external circuits, was placed in a large box in which it could roam at will. One test routine called for the experimenter to close a switch and send a small current into the electrode whenever the animal happened to go to one particular corner of the box. With the rat in whose brain the electrode had gone astray, an unusual phenomenon was observed. The rat seemed to experience an enjoyable sensation from the injection of the current, and soon developed a consistent behavior pattern of coming back to the specified corner for more.

This was indeed something new. It appeared to be related to, but the reverse of, the earlier-discovered phenomenon of electrically induced "sham rage." In this experiment the animal could choose whether or not it wanted the electrical experience, and it deliberately made an affirmative choice. Under the circumstances, it was difficult not to believe that what was involved was a truly pleasurable experience, rather than just a superficial imitation.

All doubts as to the validity of this interpretation were soon removed when Olds put his rodents on an ingenious "do-it-yourself" basis. He installed a lever in the rat's cage and connected it to the external electric circuit so that, when the rat pressed the lever with its paw, the stimulating current was sent into its brain. Thus it was entirely up to the rat. Presumably, if it enjoyed the sensation, it would be motivated to learn to press the lever for its electric reward; if there were no actual enjoyment, its rate of lever-pressing should be no greater than the random rate characteristic of any ordinary rat running curiously around its cage and occasionally stepping on a lever that happened to be in its path. The results were immediate and indisputable. When the lever was disconnected so that pressing it had no effect, it was stepped on by the rat in its random peregrinations between 10 and 25 times per hour. When the current was turned on, the rat would press the lever several thousand times an hour! Moreover, there was no evidence of satiation. With suitably located electrodes, animals would stimulate themselves several thousand times per hour for 24 to 48 hours continuously, stopping only when physically exhausted. The subjective strength of the electric-reward mechanism was also measured in other ways. Food was withheld from rats for 24 hours or more, and they were then released in a cage containing food in one corner and the operating lever in the other corner. A rat with properly located electrode, which had previously taught itself the lever-pressing routine, would ignore the food, make for the lever, and indulge in a continued orgy of self-stimulation despite its hunger.

Olds has gone on to conduct a careful survey of the brainstem and associated regions in an attempt to make a three-dimensional map of the locations and relative effectiveness of the pleasure centers in the rat's brain. In this work, the number of times per hour the animal presses the lever is interpreted as a measure of the subjective intensity of the stimulus. Such measurements yield results possessing considerable internal consistency, in that the brain regions of high and low stimulus effectiveness determined in this way are constant for a given subject, and reasonably so from rat to rat. The resulting maps show pleasure centers in various regions of the rat's brain from the upper-middle portion of the brainstem forward, including the thalamus, the hypothalamus, and some of the so-called "basal ganglia" that are closely associated with the brainstem. Rates of self-stimulation as high as 7,000 per hour are achieved with certain favorable locations of the stimulating electrode.

Of particular interest are indications from recent work that different kinds of pleasure are represented to the rat by stimulation in different regions. Experiments have isolated a hunger reward system and a sexual reward system. With electrode implantation in a hunger reward center, the rat will stimulate itself energetically if hungry, but not otherwise; the electric current appears to have the same meaning to the animal as the satisfying effect produced by eating. The sexual aspect of other centers was established in a somewhat more complex way. Male animals were first made essentially nonsexual by castration. In such animals normal sexual behavior can be temporarily restored by hormone injection. With suitably implanted electrodes, these rats would stimulate themselves only after such injection, at a rate that would rise and fall in clear and immediate relationship to the hormone content of the blood. Incidentally, it was discovered that the hunger-sensitive and sex-sensitive centers were always different; an electrode placement for which self-stimulation rates were increased by hunger was never one for which rates were increased by hormone injection, and vice versa.

While rats are certainly the "old-timers" in this pleasure-center research, other animals have not been neglected. The monkey is coming along fast as a contender for honors in the field. In particular, a considerable amount of work has been done in locating the regions in the brain of the male monkey where electric-current injection elicits external evidence of sexual stimulation. One research group discovered a site for electrode placement where the pleasurable sensation was so intense that the monkey would stay awake to enjoy the experience, apparently without need for sleep, for up to 48 hours. Ordinarily monkeys, like humans, require a good eight hours of sleep a day.

All research groups, whether working with monkeys, cats, or rats, have reported generally the same findings. Many small regions can be found in the brainstem and associated portions of the old brain where injection of an electric current produces an obviously pleasurable sensation. Some of these small regions are much more effective than others. When the electrode is implanted in a good spot, the animal, if given a choice, will continue self-stimulation until physically exhausted, and after rest will repeat the performance, time and time again, without any evidence that satiation ever sets in. Usually, stimulation of the cortex does not produce pleasurable responses, although there are exceptions, probably explainable on the basis of the extensive neuronal connections between the cortex and the deeper brain structures. When a pleasure center is found in the cortex, however, its effectiveness is small by comparison with the better centers in the older brain. Moreover, cortical stimulation generally appears to have only a novelty value, since the animal tires of it quickly—a phenomenon that is not observed at all in the sensitive centers of the brainstem. In these deeper centers something fundamental to animal nature seems to be involved. Satisfaction of the basic drives of hunger and sex appears to be simply a matter of the presence of electric current in the proper neuron circuits of the brain!

The Punishment Centers

It must not be assumed that the work with deeply implanted electrodes has resulted only in the discovery of pleasure centers. This work has also confirmed and extended early observations on the existence of sites where electric stimulation produces manifestations of rage, fright, or pain. As in the case of the pleasure centers, stimulation in some of these punishment centers appears to provoke reactions of extreme intensity. There appears to be no further serious use of the terms "sham" and "pseudo" to describe the emotions induced in these experiments. When, upon application of a stimulating voltage, a monkey grimaces, shrieks, and obviously tries to escape, when its pupils dilate, its hair stands on end, it quivers and shakes, it bites and tears any object near the mouth hard enough to break teeth out of its jaw—it is now generally concluded that these are not meaningless or automatic physical symptoms; the monkey *is* fearful or in pain, or both. Such experiences are, of course, unpleasant not only for the subject, but also for the experimenters. They do not enjoy subjecting their animals to fright and pain, and do so as little as is consistent with obtaining the important information they seek. The justification for all such work is, of course, that the knowledge gained may ultimately make it possible to relieve human pain and suffering. Nevertheless, the unpleasant attributes of experimentation on the punishment centers are probably at least partially responsible for the fact that there appears to be less work of this nature done than the deliberate search for and stimulation of the pleasure centers in the brains of animals.

In punishment-center investigations, do-it-yourself experiments are sometimes performed in which the apparatus automatically applies an unpleasant stimulus that the animal then can turn off by operating a suitable lever. If such an experiment is continued for, say, three hours, with the animal continually working to minimize the amount of unpleasantness it experiences, there are likely to be aftereffects characteristic of severe illness. The animal remains irritable, biting or scratching when approached. It refuses to eat. Food in the stomach is vomited. Its skin becomes gray and pallid. It is apathetic and nonresponsive. Frequently, it dies. If, however, an animal that has been made ill in this way is then stimulated through an electrode placed in one of the effective pleasure centers in its brain, the whole picture is reversed rapidly; it revives in a few minutes, its appetite returns, it works cooperatively again with the experimenters; it is restored to health.

Knowledge of the existence of these centers of punishment in the brain and of their close proximity to neural circuits that control the visceral processes has led to a better understanding of certain psychosomatic diseases. For example, interesting work has been done on peptic ulcers, which have long been known to be associated with emotional stress. The hypothalamus contains punishment centers where current injection produces feelings of tension. It is therefore logical to assume that the actual experience of tension is accompanied by electric currents in these same centers. But very near by, another small hypothalamic region has been discovered wherein electric stimulation causes a large increase in the secretion of hydrochloric acid in the stomach and intestines. Prolonged stimulation through an electrode implanted in this region has been found to cause chronic ulcers in monkeys, although these animals are usually not prone to this disease of modern civilization. The implication of these observations is that peptic ulcers result from continuing emotional strain simply because of the overflow of electric currents from the emotionally activated neurons to the nearby circuits that control gastric activity.

In the development of the current understanding of the neurological basis of ulcer formation, an interesting series of experiments was performed by J. V. Brady, of the Walter Reed Army Institute of Research in Washington, D.C. He showed that ulcers can be developed in monkeys, as in men, by subjecting them to continuing stressful situations. In his work, a monkey was confined in a chair-type arrangement incorporating an electric circuit that would regularly apply an uncomfortable shock to the animal's sensitive feet. The monkey was then provided with a key which, if depressed with suitable timing, would prevent the shocks. The animal worked a regular schedule: for six hours it would steadily operate the lever to minimize the shocks, then would rest for six hours, then would work another six hours, and so on. After several weeks, the monkey would usually be found to have peptic ulcers.

A variation of Brady's experiment employed a pair of animals, both receiving exactly the same sequence of shocks but only one having a key connected so as to be effective in minimizing the shocks for both. Only the one with the effective key—the "executive" monkey —got the ulcers. The "employee" monkey received the same shocks and participated in the experiment in the same way as the other monkey except that it had no executive responsibilities. The employee monkey showed every evidence of relaxed good health at the completion of the experiment. This experiment was performed many times with different pairs of monkeys and with the same general result.

Interrelationship of Pleasure and Punishment Centers

Mapping of the pleasure and punishment centers in the brains of animals is by no means complete. However, certain findings are now well established. In general, pleasure and punishment centers have been found in the brains of all animals tested. They occur in various regions of the brainstem and associated noncortical structures. When proper account is taken of the inevitable spreading of the stimulating currents, the evidence seems to indicate that each center is quite small in extent, although there may be many such small centers in a given general region of the brain. Various observers have reported that the effect of stimulation can be shifted from extreme pleasure to extreme pain or fright by moving the stimulating electrode no more than 0.02 inch. The frequency with which this very close conjunction of pleasure and punishment centers is observed has led more than one worker in the field to suggest that the sensations of pleasure and pain may be produced by essentially the same mechanisms: an input to one terminal of the neuronal circuit produces an output signal that is interpreted as pleasure; an input to a different terminal of the same circuit produces an output signal that is interpreted as pain.

The experiments by Olds on the effects of hunger and sexual factors on self-stimulation rates of the rat correlate nicely with our subjective experience of different kinds of pleasurable sensations. Presumably, different types of punishment centers will ultimately be identified also. If subsequent work confirms the preliminary indications that pleasure and pain centers occur together, it will be interesting to learn what kind of pleasure is the negative of what kind of pain, in electrical neuronal terms.

Probably the exciting implications of the discovery of the commingled existence of pleasure and punishment centers in the brain were best expressed a few years ago on the occasion of a neurological research symposium when a newspaper reported on the meeting under the approximate headline, "Have Heaven and Hell Been Located in the Animal Brain?"

Deep Electric Stimulation of the Human Brain

Although depth electrodes were implanted in human patients as early as 1953, it has been only in the last several years that the techniques have been considered well enough developed to permit their extensive use on man. By now, several hundred patients have had their brains placed in direct electric communication with the laboratory instruments of neurologists. Because the tests made on humans are always directly related to the patient's condition and are never performed for purely experimental reasons, the amount of new information secured in this way on such matters as pleasure and pain centers is small by comparison with that obtained from animal experiments. Nevertheless, interesting confirmation has been secured by these tests.

Electric stimulation in various brain centers has produced sensations described by the patient as ease and relaxation, joy, and great satisfaction. For other centers, anxiety, restlessness, depression, fright, and horror have been reported. When arrangements are provided for self-stimulation in pleasure centers, patients have sometimes stimulated themselves into convulsions somewhat similar to those produced by electroshock treatment. After these self-stimulated convulsions, however, the patients are found to lie relaxed, smiling happily, contrary to the restless fighting frequently observed after shock treatment.

As with animal experiments, pleasure and punishment centers are frequently found situated close to one another, although the limited data on this subject suggest that in the human brain these related centers may be farther apart than in the brains of animals. As in animal experiments, suitable depth stimulation in humans produces marked changes in respiration, heartbeat, and blood pressure.

One of the most encouraging results of this work with human patients has been the discovery that stimulation through properly placed electrodes can sometimes produce prompt and dramatic relief of intractable pain. In such cases the application of the stimulating current seems to have the effect of turning a switch that immediately greatly diminishes or completely eliminates the pain. Unfortunately, while persistent stimulation stands off the pain for a time, the relief is temporary; it has not yet been found possible to effect a permanent improvement in these cases of intractable pain. Nevertheless, even temporary relief can be valuable, and with more knowledge it may be hoped that some measure of permanent alleviation can yet be effected.

Electric stimulation in pleasure centers has been used in attempts to improve the condition of patients possessing other forms of mental disorder. Several cases of schizophrenia have shown marked improvement after such treatment—to such an extent, in one or two instances, that the patient was permitted to leave the institution and rejoin his family. Unfortunately, these cures have not been permanent. As with intractable pain, it appears that more will have to be learned before electric stimulation techniques can be extended to permit the achievement of lasting improvement in the condition of the mentally ill.

Deep Brain Waves and Epilepsy

In the work with depth electrodes in human subjects, more has been done in the passive recording of brain-generated electric potentials than in the active stimulation of centers in the brain. This is easy to understand. Until more is known about the effects of electric stimulation, it can be employed only with extremely ill patients, and then only under conditions of great caution. In such work, for example, the discovery of a punishment center is an indication to the neurologist that he should not stimulate through that electrode again, unless the unpleasantness is so mild that the patient himself is willing to perform some self-stimulation and provide his own description of the effects. Even stimulation in the pleasure centers is typically at low current levels and with such surrounding precautions as to limit markedly the amount of useful information that is obtained. The recording of the potentials spontaneously generated by the brain itself, however, is quite another matter. Such recording does not do anything "to" the patient; it is like taking his temperature or blood pressure, but with even less sensation to the patient himself. All that is necessary is to insert a plug into the receptacle that has been permanently implanted in the patient's skull and turn on the recording instruments. The patient can be comfortably in bed, or sitting up, or moving around in his room while such recordings are made, and he feels no sensations of any kind arising out of the measurements.

The earlier observations on externally recorded brain waves naturally stimulated an interest in the relationship between the conditions of sleep, relaxation, and alertness and the patterns of voltage measured by deeply implanted electrodes. Are the patterns the same at lower levels as in the cortex? The answer appears to be "yes and no." Consider, for example, a human subject who is resting with eyes closed and developing a strong alpha pattern in the brain wave obtained with scalp electrodes. We have already noted that the alpha rhythms measured by pairs of electrodes placed over the left- and right-hand occipital lobes wax and wane in synchronism, indicating that a considerable portion of the brain is acting as a unit (Chap. 6). Therefore, it would be surprising if such synchronous alpha-wave activity did not extend to lower regions than those from which the scalp electrodes obtain their indications. And, indeed, this is found to be the case. Certain regions of the reticular activating system, in particular, appear to be closely associated with the cortical circuitry and to participate in the resulting electric synchronism. However, other regions of the brainstem show quite a different rhythm. In the hypothalamus, for example, the brain-wave pattern is roughly the inverse of that observed in the cortex; the relaxed, eyes-closed state produces a rapidly varying low-voltage signal, whereas alertness results in larger, slower fluctuations that look more like the cortical alpha wave. Several different rhythms have been identified and found to be more or less consistently produced by various portions of the brain in accordance with certain generally specified states of mind of the subject. However, there is considerable variation from individual to individual and from center to center of the brain; more work must be done before the significance of many of these lower-lying rhythms can be definitely determined.

There is one condition that produces extensive synchronization among the waves of voltage measured throughout the brain—an epileptic attack. While a major seizure is under way, the waves obtained from most or all of the electrodes, the deeply implanted ones as well as those attached to the scalp, swing up and down together, frequently through ranges of voltage variation that overload the recording instruments. An examination of these records leaves no doubt that most if not all of the neurons of the brain are for the time tightly coupled in one gigantic electric oscillatory circuit with the current at each point in the circuit swinging successively from the extreme positive to the extreme negative value permitted by the physical design of the component elements.

But recordings during major epileptic attacks are rare. Much more frequently observed are seizures of a more limited nature. In such episodes, the electric recordings frequently show that the wide-swinging "seizure" type of discharge is measurable by only two or three of the many electrodes that may be implanted in the brain. For these milder attacks, there may be no abnormal activity in the scalp measurements. Also, apparently, it is only when the runaway behavior of the neurons works its way up to the cortex that extensive behavioral disorder results. This is particularly true with disorders of consciousness; illusions, hallucinations, and loss of consciousness itself appear never to occur except in association with extensive involvement of the neurons of the cortex.

Frequently, in a patient with a record of epileptic illness, a deeply implanted electrode will display a seizure pattern without the concurrent appearance of any visible epileptic symptoms. This observation is not inconsistent with our general understanding of focal epilepsy, as developed in Chapter 6. We know that regions of damaged tissue can display abnormal electric discharges which do not affect the individual until for some reason the abnormal discharge spreads to surrounding healthy tissue. However, deeply implanted electrodes seem to provide a more sensitive means than surface electrodes of detecting the existence of these local abnormalities. This discovery is providing a new diagnostic technique for epilepsy.

On occasion, electric stimulation of an epileptic patient through an implanted electrode has been employed with interesting results. If the stimulating electrode is properly placed, the patient will have a seizure. The seizure so induced usually has the same general characteristics as those that occur without artificial stimulation. As we learned in Chapter 6, epileptic attacks are highly individual; the combination of symptoms and the sequence in which they appear is rarely the same for any two people. Of especial interest are the attacks that are preceded by a psychic aura—feelings of depression or exaltation, sometimes accompanied by illusions or hallucinations. These phenomena interest us because of their obvious involvement of whatever machinery is responsible for the emotional and intellectual processes of the brain. The possibility of inducing the typical epileptic attack of such a patient by stimulation through implanted electrodes would appear to provide a means of determining what portions of the brain are involved in these psychic phenomena. It would seem likely that the region of the brain responsible for the effects would also be the region wherein stimulation would induce the attacks. By such reasoning, it has been possible to conclude that the temporal-lobe structures—the material in and under the left- and right-hand lower surfaces of the brain—are principally involved in the psychic manifestations of epilepsy. Here an interesting correlation with depth of stimulation has been observed. If seizures are induced by an electrode implanted in the amygdala, a brainstem center lying under the temporal lobe of the cortex, they are likely to be characterized by such general effects as confusion, diminished awareness, amnesia, or automatic behavior. However, positive psychical experiences such as hallucinations or illusions seem to be elicited only if the seizure-inducing position for the electrode is closer to the surface of the brain—in the overlying cortex. Attacks produced by stimulation in this region sometimes possess a striking degree of hallucinatory detail. For example, Maitland Baldwin, of the National Institutes of Health, in Bethesda, Maryland, has told of one patient whose attacks always started with a hallucination in which he saw himself walking down a path toward a house and garage in the country. Not only would electric stimulation evoke this hallucination, but displaying a picture of the hallucinatory scene prepared by an artist from the patient's description was also sufficient to set off the seizure.

The observation that epileptic attacks with generalized effects on emotion and consciousness can be induced by stimulation through deeply implanted electrodes, but that cortical stimulation is much more effective in inducing attacks characterized by elaborate and detailed hallucinatory content, is consistent with our hypothesis as to the involvement of the brainstem mechanisms in basic animal responses and the importance of the cortex in intellectual elaboration and refinement. Unfortunately, from the clinical point of view, this work has not yet led to a technique for the cure or alleviation of the condition of epileptic patients, although it can be useful in diagnosis and localization of malfunctioning regions of the brain whose subsequent surgical removal does frequently produce a useful result.

For completeness, reference needs to be made to attempts to correlate the shapes of brain waves measured by deeply implanted electrodes with mental illnesses other than epilepsy. There does appear to be some correlation between the brain waves and the state of normalcy of the patient. During periods of great confusion and irrationality, there is more electric activity than when the patient is not behaving psychotically. In general, the waves deep within a deranged brain seem to display more spikes and large, slow variations than do those in a healthy brain. Again, these discoveries are useful in diagnosis, but not yet in cure.

The Control Center for Consciousness:
The Reticular Activating System

In Chapter 4, we were introduced to the extensive coordinating and control functions of the reticular activating system in the brainstem. We saw that this amorphous region of intermingled large and small neurons is stationed at the crossroads of communication among the major segments of the brain and also has "wire taps" on the afferent and efferent nerves connecting the brain with the periphery of the body. We learned that the nerve cells of the reticular formation perform various types of integration of the electric signals representing the sensory inputs and thereby choose specific modes of behavior from the repertory of response patterns available to the individual. We found that implementation of such a choice was effected by means of reticular control signals sent to other portions of the nervous system to inhibit certain sensory inputs with respect to others and strengthen and weaken the responses of the various muscles and glands.

Because of the nature of the subject matter of Chapter 4, our treatment of the reticular activating system was limited to a discussion of its role in selecting from among the various unconscious reflex responses available to the nervous system. It is now appropriate to enlarge the scope of this earlier discussion to include the influence of the reticular activating system on conscious activities.

The reticular activating system has been found to exercise control over the property of consciousness itself! Stimulation of its upper (thalamic) portion through an implanted electrode induces sleep in cats and dogs, provided that the stimulating voltage has a long, slow wave shape similar to the animal's sleeping brain-wave pattern. On the contrary, stimulation with higher-frequency wave forms, more nearly comparable with the alert pattern, always awakens the sleeping animal.

In general, direct electric stimulation in most regions of the reticular activating system arouses a sleeping animal. By itself, this is not impressive, since wakefulness can be elicited in so many ways—by a touch, a noise, a bright light, and so on. The interest arises from experiments indicating that the *only* thing that arouses a sleeping animal is electric activity in the reticular activating system—that other sensory stimuli affect consciousness solely through the collateral currents they send into the reticular formation, and not by means of their direct connections to the higher centers of the brain. For example, lesions confined to the reticular activating system of cats and monkeys will induce permanent coma; lesions interrupting the long sensory pathways from the body to the higher centers of the brain but sparing the reticular activating system permit a continuation of the wakeful state. It is now known that general anesthesia produces its effects by deactivating the neurons of the reticular system. A pinch on the foot, a sound in the ear, or a light in the eye will produce electric currents in the cortex of the brain that are as strong and clear when the subject is anesthetized as when he is conscious and alert. The patient is unaware of these sensations only because, under the influence of the drug, the reticular system is unable to send to the cortex and other higher centers of the brain the specific pattern of electric signals needed to "turn on" the sense of consciousness. Of course, the same absence of alerting input also inactivates the unconscious automatic reflexes that might otherwise be elicited by the sensory experiences of the operating table.

The persistence of substantial cortical activity during unconsciousness is also shown by the evidence that we can perform sensory discriminations in our sleep. A mother can sleep through a wide variety of miscellaneous neighborhood noises, yet be roused to instant alertness by the feeble cry of her child. A cat that has been trained to recognize one musical tone as heralding an unpleasant electric shock and another of only slightly different pitch as innocuous will be awakened by the one but not by the other. Its ability to discriminate between very similar tones is, if anything, better when it is asleep than when it is awake.*

While the reticular system turns consciousness on or off by sending suitable activating signals to the portions of the brain (whatever they may be) involved in conscious processes, it is itself urged into action by the sensory impulses it receives over its wire taps on the communication channels of the central nervous system. Incoming signals representing touch, pain, sound, or light are integrated by the reticular neurons to build up an output voltage to a threshold value for which the reticular system sends out its arousal commands. In the absence of such incoming sensory data, direct electric stimulation of the reticular formation by implanted electrodes will fool the mechanism into believing that there is something that requires conscious attention.

One kind of nervous activity employed by the reticular neurons in the summing process resulting in the arousal signal is that which goes on in the cortex. The reticular formation appears to consider such activity to be as indicative of the need for consciousness as external sensory stimuli. This is why, if we are aroused from sleep by a loud noise, we remain awake for some time after the noise has passed. The thought processes set in motion on our awakening create cortical currents which, by their collaterals into the reticular activating system, provide a continuing stimulus to the system that keeps the consciousness switch turned on. As we all know, occasionally to our sorrow, thinking alone can keep us awake. If, however, we can sufficiently diminish the intensity of our intellectual activity, the cortical currents alone will no longer be able to hold the reticular consciousness switch closed. Therefore, unless the cortical currents are aided by other reticular-activating-system currents produced by noise, pain, light, or other sensory stimulus, the consciousness switch opens, and we fall asleep.

The discovery of the role of the reticular activating system has cleared up some long-standing mysteries. Since antiquity it has been known that an animal can live and continue to perform some of its bodily functions after its spinal cord has been cut through. When investigated in the laboratory, such an animal is known as a *spinal preparation*. Although paralyzed with respect to many of its muscular functions, an animal prepared in this way appears to be awake and alert as judged by its expression and the apparently conscious responses it makes with its head, some of the muscles of which are still under its volitional control. However, in 1937, F. Bremer, a promi-

* Buendia, Sierra, Goode, and Segundo, in publication.

nent Belgian research scientist, on raising the point of the transection from the top of the spinal cord to the middle of the brainstem, discovered quite a different state of affairs. After such a section, the animal appeared to be asleep. This effect is now believed to result from cutting the fibers that carry, from the cortex above to the reticular formation below, the barrage of electric pulses produced by cortical activity. In general, it is found that a *decorticate preparation* —that is, an animal with all the nerve fibers that proceed from the cortex transected—can be awakened by intense sensory stimulation, but cannot long sustain a wakeful state. Evidently, normal sensory inputs alone, in the absence of cortical reinforcement, are not capable of holding the consciousness switch closed in the reticular activating system.

Through its ability to inhibit sensory stimuli, the reticular activating system is now believed to play an important role in mental concentration. We all know that when we focus our attention upon something, extraneous sensations appear to recede into the background. A person with unusual powers of concentration is sometimes oblivious to loud noises or other conspicuous sensory stimuli that would ordinarily attract his attention. It is now known that nerve signals produced by extraneous stimuli do not merely *seem* to be lessened when we concentrate; they *are* lessened. This was first shown in 1956 by a fascinating series of experiments (R. Hernandez-Peon, H. Scherrer, and M. Jouvet). In their work, an electrode was implanted in the *cochlear nucleus* of a cat, the center in the brainstem in which the signals from the neurons of the ears are sorted out and rearranged before traveling on to the cortex. As expected, a sharp noise made near the cat's cage would produce an easily identifiable spike in the pattern of voltage recorded from the implanted electrode. With a noise generator emitting a regular and continuing series of clicks, a correspondingly regular series of spikes would appear in the brain waves transcribed by the pen of the recorder. With these conditions established, the experimenters would suddenly present to the cat a stimulus of great feline interest. One such stimulus was a glass beaker containing live mice. Another was provided by blowing an odor of fish into the cage. Results were the same in both cases. The cat immediately exhibited alert attention to the new situation, and just as promptly the brain-wave spikes produced by the continuing series of clicks decreased dramatically in magnitude. Figures 7-2 and 7-3 are the voltage recordings obtained in such experiments; in the first the stimulus was the beaker of mice, in the second it was the odor of fish.

This and other experiments have led to the conclusion that the concentration of attention upon something of interest involves a behavioral response-selection process analogous to the selection from various possible automatic reflexes that, as we saw in Chapter 4, constitutes such an important function of the reticular activating system. In the conscious as well as the unconscious response-selection process, "volume-control" signals are generated in the reticular system to reduce our sensitivity to uninteresting or irrelevant stimuli and thereby permit us to achieve the peculiar but highly useful phenomenon of mental concentration.

An interesting practical application of this principle has recently appeared. Some dentists now equip their patients with headphones connected to magnetic-tape apparatus from which various recordings can be played as the dental work is done. For many patients, this

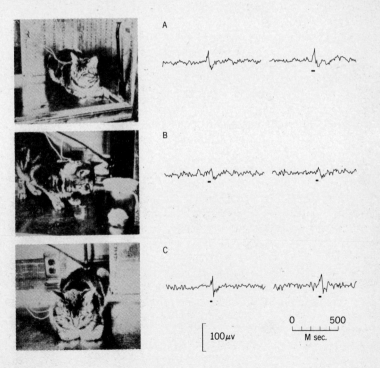

Fig. 7-2. Response of cochlear nucleus of a cat to serially repeated clicks of sound: *A,* when cat is inattentive; *B,* when its attention is attracted by mice in a beaker; *C,* when it is inattentive again. (*From R. Hernandez-Peon, H. Scherrer, and M. Jouvet, Science, vol.* 123 (1956), *pp.* 331–332. *By permission of the publishers.*)

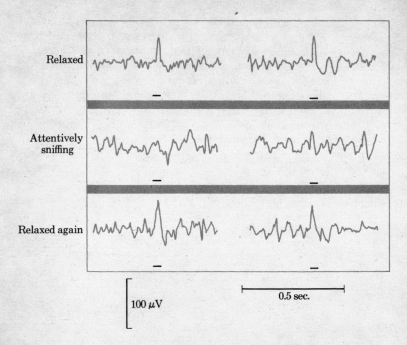

Relaxed

Attentively
sniffing

Relaxed again

100 μV

0.5 sec.

Fig. 7-3. Response of cochlear nucleus of a cat to serially repeated clicks of sound: *top,* when cat is inattentive; *center,* when it is attentively sniffing odor of fish blown into cage; *bottom,* when it is inattentive again. (*From R. Hernandez-Peon, H. Scherrer, and M. Jouvet, Science, vol.* 123 (1956), *pp.* 331–332. *By permission of the publishers.*)

reduces markedly the pain and physical discomfort that they otherwise feel in the dental chair. The recorded sound of waves breaking on the shore has been reported to be particularly effective. This kind of sound covers a wide range of the audible frequency spectrum. It is interesting to speculate that the resulting involvement of a correspondingly large number of neurons in the reticular activating system may be responsible for the unusual effectiveness of such a sound in turning down the "volume control" in the nerve circuits that conduct pain to the higher centers of the brain.

In this chapter we have ascribed considerable significance to the fact that the control centers, not only for automatic physical processes that support life, but also for the essentially animal-like passions and emotions, are found in the older part of the brain that we share in relatively unchanged form with lower animals. As was observed during our considerations of comparative anatomy, such a conclusion suggests that the higher intellectual processes that so sharply distinguish man from beast will be found to depend on the part of the brain that shows greatest difference between the human and lower species—the cerebral cortex. It is now time for us to direct our attention to the results of attempts to localize functions in this important region. If our deductions are correct, we may expect to find evidence of greater complexity in the performance of the cerebral cortex than in the behavior of the lower-lying regions of the brain. In this expectation, we shall not be disappointed.

BIBLIOGRAPHY

Baldwin, M., "Electrical Stimulation of the Mesial Temporal Region," in *Electrical Studies on the Unanesthetized Brain,* ed. by Ramey and O'Doherty (Harper & Row, Publishers, Incorporated, New York, 1960), pp. 159–176.

Bickford, R. G., H. W. Dodge, Jr., and A. Uihlein, "Electrographic and Behavioral Effects Related to Depth Stimulation in Human Patients," in *Electrical Studies on the Unanesthetized Brain,* ed. by Ramey and O'Doherty (Harper & Row, Publishers, Incorporated, New York, 1960), pp. 248–261.

Brady, J. V., "Ulcers in Executive Monkeys," *Scientific American,* October, 1958, pp. 95–100.

Bremer, F., "L'Interprétation des potentiels électriques de l'écorce cérébrale," in *Structure and Function of the Cerebral Cortex,* ed. by Tower and Schade (Elsevier Publishing Company, Amsterdam, 1959), pp. 173–191.

Buendia, N., G. Sierra, M. Goode, and J. P. Segundo, "Behavioral and Electrographic Study of Conditioned and Discriminatory Responses in Wakeful and Sleeping Cats," *EEG Journal,* in press.

Chapman, W. P., "Depth Electrode Studies in Patients with Temporal Lobe Epilepsy," in *Electrical Studies on the Unanesthetized Brain,* ed. by Ramey and O'Doherty (Harper & Row, Publishers, Incorporated, New York, 1960), pp. 334–350.

Chatrian, G. E., and W. P. Chapman, "Electrographic Study of the Amygdaloid Region with Implanted Electrodes in Patients with Temporal Lobe Epilepsy," in *Electrical Studies on the Unanesthetized Brain,* ed. by Ramey and O'Doherty (Harper & Row, Publishers, Incorporated, New York, 1960), pp. 351–373.

Delgado, J. M. R., and H. Hamlin, "Spontaneous and Evoked Electrical Seizures in Animals and in Humans," in *Electrical Studies on the Unanesthetized Brain,* ed. by Ramey and O'Doherty (Harper & Row, Publishers, Incorporated, New York, 1960), pp. 133–158.

French, J. D., "The Reticular Formation," *Journal of Neurosurgery,* vol. XV (1958), pp. 97–115.

French, J. D., "Brain Physiology and Modern Medicine," *Postgraduate Medicine,* vol. 27 (1960), pp. 559–568.

Heath, R. G., and W. A. Mickle, "Evaluation of Seven Years' Experience with Depth Electrode Studies in Human Patients," in *Electrical Studies on the Unanesthetized Brain,* ed. by Ramey and O'Doherty (Harper & Row, Publishers, Incorporated, New York, 1960), pp. 214–247.

Hernandez-Peon, R., H. Scherrer, and M. Jouvet, "Modification of Electrical Activity in Cochlear Nucleus during 'Attention' in Unanesthetized Cats," *Science,* vol. 123 (1956), pp. 331–332.

Hess, W. R., *The Functional Organization of the Diencephalon* (Grune & Stratton, Inc., New York, 1957).

MacLean, P. D., "The Limbic System with Respect to Two Basic Life Principles," in *The Central Nervous System and Behavior,* ed. by M. A. B. Brazier (Josiah Macy, Jr., Foundation, New York, 1959), pp. 31–118.

Magoun, H. W., *The Waking Brain* (Charles C Thomas, Publisher, Springfield, Ill., 1958).

Olds, J., "Pleasure Centers in the Brain," *Scientific American,* October, 1956, pp. 105–116.

Olds, J., "Differentiation of Reward Systems in the Brain by Self-stimulation Technics," in *Electrical Studies on the Unanesthetized Brain,* ed. by Ramey and O'Doherty (Harper & Row, Publishers, Incorporated, New York, 1960), pp. 17–51.

Penfield, W., and L. Roberts, *Speech and Brain Mechanisms* (Princeton University Press, Princeton, N.J., 1959), chap. II, "Functional Organization of the Human Brain, Discriminative Sensation, Voluntary Movement."

Sem-Jacobsen, C. W., and A. Torkildsen, "Depth Recording and Electrical Stimulation in the Human Brain," in *Electrical Studies on the Unanesthetized Brain,* ed. by Ramey and O'Doherty (Harper & Row, Publishers, Incorporated, New York, 1960), pp. 275–290.

Sherwood, S. L., "Stereotaxic Recordings from the Frontal and Temporal Lobes of Psychotics and Epileptics," in *Electrical Studies on the Unanesthetized Brain,* ed. by Ramey and O'Doherty (Harper & Row, Publishers, Incorporated, New York, 1960), pp. 374–401.

Sholl, D. A., *The Organization of the Cerebral Cortex* (Methuen & Co., Ltd., London, 1956), chap. IV, "Further Aspects of Cortical Organization."

van Buren, J. M., "Radiographic Localization of Depth Electrodes in the Human Temporal Lobe," in *Electrical Studies on the Unanesthetized Brain,* ed. by Ramey and O'Doherty (Harper & Row, Publishers, Incorporated, New York, 1960), pp. 177–191.

Wells, H. G., J. S. Huxley, and G. P. Wells, *The Science of Life* (Doubleday & Company, Inc., Garden City, N.Y., 1938), book eight, chap. III, "The Evolution of Behavior in Vertebrates"; book eight, chap. V, "The Culminating Brain."

THE FRONTAL LOBES

In searching for regions of the cortex that might contribute to the performance of the higher intellectual processes, we would not be inclined to pay too much attention to those cortical areas that have already been established to be terminal points for the peripheral nerves and that therefore are known to be primarily engaged in the receipt of sensory information or the transmission of motor commands to the outlying regions of the body. Of the several hundred square inches of surface area in the cerebral cortex, only about one-fourth is used for these sensorimotor processes (Fig. 7-1*i*). Included are the visual cortex at the extreme rear of the brain, the sensory and motor strips running down the sides of the brain, and a small region at the top edge of the temporal lobe which serves as the terminal area for auditory sensations. Of the remaining three-fourths of the cortical surface, nearly half is in the frontal lobes—the bulbous protrusions that lie ahead of the auditory receiving area and the sensorimotor strips. In the evolutionary development of the brain from the lower to the higher animals, nowhere has more growth occurred than in these frontal lobes. The expansion of the skull to accommodate them has given man the high forehead of which he is so proud. For hundreds of years, scientists, philosophers, and poets alike have agreed in assigning to the frontal lobes major credit for man's intellectual superiority over other animals. Therefore we shall start our search for cortical localization of the higher functions by examining the evidence that favors this region of the brain. As is not uncommon in the history of science, we shall discover that real progress began to be made when, by accident, evidence came to light that was completely incompatible with the generally accepted points of view. The evidence was supplied, convincingly though unintentionally, by a railroad foreman named Phineas Gage.

The Strange Case of Phineas Gage

In September, 1848, Phineas Gage, foreman of a road construction gang, had an iron rod blown through his head and achieved immortality. He did not become immortal in the usual way by going directly to his heavenly reward, for Phineas survived. In fact, it was the details of his survival that constituted the basis for the very considerable amount of fame that came his way.

It seems that Phineas had poured a charge of powder into a hole in a rock, prior to a routine blasting operation. The customary procedure was then for an assistant to cover the powder with sand. For some reason this was not done, and Phineas Gage neglected to check on the matter. Instead, supposing the sand covering to be in place, he dropped into the hole a heavy tamping iron. The result was catastrophic: the iron rod struck upon rock, produced a spark, ignited the powder, and took off for the stratosphere. On its way, the rod, which was nearly 4 feet long and 1¼ inches thick, passed cleanly through Phineas' brain, entering high in his left cheek and emerging from the top of his head.

Gage was stunned for an hour, after which, with some assistance, he was able to walk off to see a surgeon, talking on the way with composure and equanimity of the hole in his head. Eventually he recovered from the infection that developed in the wound, and lived for another twelve years. Gage eventually ended up in San Francisco, where he died under conditions that demanded an autopsy. Doubtless only because of this accidental circumstance were medical scientists able to verify the story by actual examination of the damaged brain. It was then found that not only had the left frontal lobe been severely damaged, but the damage had spread to the right frontal lobe also. Both skull and tamping iron are on view at Harvard University.

Gage's surprising survival of such a spectacular injury was followed by equally surprising aftereffects. The aftereffects were remarkable precisely because of their *non*spectacular nature. For Gage was still a competent individual: he displayed no loss of memory; he was still able to exercise the techniques of his vocation. For a man with such extensive damage of the very portion of the brain that had long been believed to be the seat of the higher intellectual processes, Gage displayed a disproportionately small decrease in his mental capacities.

There were some changes in Gage, but they were of quite a different nature from what would have been predicted by the prevailing theories. It seemed that his personality, rather than his intelligence, had been principally affected. Before the accident he had been considerate, efficient, and well-balanced; afterward he was fitful and irreverent, indulging frequently in gross profanity and manifesting little consideration for others. He had become obstinate, yet capricious and vacillating. With these new traits he could no longer be trusted to supervise others. In fact he showed little inclination toward work of any kind, but instead chose to travel around, making a living by exhibiting himself and his tamping iron.

Other Evidence of the Effects of Frontal Damage

The case of Phineas Gage, by dramatizing the relative invulnerability of the human animal to extensive damage of a portion of the brain that had previously been considered of overriding importance, stimulated the medical research workers of the late nineteenth century to be alert for further clinical evidence of the effects of major brain damage. The scattered clues obtained in this way were ultimately supplemented by a much greater mass of material arising out of the brain injuries of the First World War. Additional data were supplied by observations of the symptoms produced by brain tumors. While no two of these thousands of case studies were exactly alike, either in the nature of the brain damage or in the observed behavioral consequences, there is enough consistency among the various observations to justify certain fairly definite conclusions. To begin with, the evidence clearly indicates that the frontal lobes are not responsible for the control of any of the vital physical functions of the organism. Damage to this region does not affect breathing, heartbeat, blood pressure, temperature regulation, the operation of the visceral organs, or any of the several thousand automatic reflexes that contribute so much to health. With the possible exception of sphincter control, there is no evidence that the frontal lobes are directly involved in any of the physical processes of the body.

With respect to intellectual activities, the evidence is more difficult to interpret. Certainly frontal-lobe damage does not usually produce dramatic changes in intellectual capability. Past memories and skills are not lost. Scores achieved by the patient on various types of intelligence and aptitude tests, after frontal-lobe damage, are often lower than before, but occasionally they are higher. Only tests that measure capacity for dealing simultaneously with many concepts and performing judgments on abstract situations show a high correlation between frontal-lobe damage and decrease in score.*

* There is even some question as to whether impaired frontal-lobe function, as such, is responsible for these deficits. D. O. Hebb has made a case for

Most neurologists agree that the most conspicuous effects of frontal-lobe damage are personality changes. After 100 years of accumulation of evidence, the Phineas Gage case still appears reasonably typical. A person who has been ambitious, well-adjusted, highly motivated, and considerate will, after frontal-lobe damage, exhibit lack of drive, insensitivity to the feelings of others, diminished initiative and organizing ability, tactlessness, and frequently a general silliness and lack of responsiveness to ethical and moral considerations. There is often a feeling of euphoria. Physical restlessness and increased talkativeness sometimes occur, but completely unaccompanied by the imaginative thinking that might make such increased activity worthwhile. Not infrequent are childishness, naïveté, and emotional incontinence displayed in the form of bursts of laughter, temper, or rage.

Effects of Removal of Frontal Lobes of Chimpanzees

It was inevitable that the surprises arising out of the collection of data on the effects of frontal-lobe injury in man should have stimulated experiments on animals to test old hypotheses and generate new ones. The mid-1930s saw the initiation of considerable activity involving the selective removal of portions of the frontal lobes of the higher animals and determination of the resulting effects on their behavior. In experiments with chimpanzees, it soon became evident that removal of one of the frontal lobes produced little observable effect. If both lobes were removed, however, there was a considerable degradation in the ability of the chimpanzee to perform complex tasks, such as the solution of a problem calling for three different sequential actions. The results, in this important respect, were consistent with the observations on humans with frontal damage: there was impairment of the ability to hold in mind concurrently a number of different concepts.

There was an important side effect of some of this work. An adolescent female chimpanzee began to be greatly upset when she made an error. She started having violent temper tantrums and would throw herself about in uncontrolled fashion. Ultimately her displays of temper became so frequent that further testing was impossible. She was then operated on and both frontal lobes were re-

---

attributing much of the abnormal performance of frontal patients to the positive effects of scars and other damaged tissue left by the injury or surgical operation, rather than to the absence of frontal-lobe function per se.

moved. Upon recovery from the operation she was once again friendly, eager, and cooperative. She would go promptly to the experimental cage and attempt to perform what was expected of her. It was now quite impossible to evoke even a suggestion of her previous neurotic responses, although she made many more mistakes than before removal of the frontal areas. Her performance in the problem boxes, in fact, never approached her preoperative level. Nevertheless she remained a model of equanimity and relaxation. She made lots of mistakes, but they just didn't bother her.

Application to Psychotic Human Patients: Frontal Lobotomy

The studies on the chimpanzee were performed by Carlyle Jacobsen in the years 1933 to 1936 and were first reported at the International Neurological Conference in London in 1935. It was at that meeting that Egaz Moniz of Lisbon conceived the idea of using a similar operation on human patients. By the end of January, 1936, twenty operations had been performed at Lisbon on psychotic patients of the local mental hospital.

Out of his 20 cases, Moniz reported cures in 7 instances, improvement in 8, and no change in 5. In retrospect it seems likely that he was overly optimistic in his evaluation of results, but his accomplishments were sufficiently impressive that they stimulated many others to investigate the therapeutic possibilities of frontal-lobe operations on the mentally ill.

In his pioneering operations, Moniz did not remove the frontal lobes entirely but cut out of them several cores of material, largely from the central white matter on each side. His object was to transect the connective fibers running from the frontal cortex to the deeper structures of the brain. With the passage of time, modifications and improvements on the operative technique were made by various investigators, but the fundamental principle was always the same—the bundles of axons running down from the frontal lobes to the central regions of the brain (primarily the thalamus) were cut, thereby disconnecting the frontal lobes from the rest of the brain. The evidence obtained, both with humans and with animals, indicates that such a disconnection—called *frontal lobotomy* or *frontal leucotomy*—is as effective as actual excision of the frontal lobes, but runs less risk of major difficulties arising out of laceration of blood vessels with consequent hemorrhage.

In these operations, as with most work on the brain, the results were not completely consistent. Nevertheless, they followed a pattern. Ordinarily performed only on extremely psychotic patients, the operations usually resulted in patients who were less obsessional, less hypochondriacal, less self-critical, and less restrained, but more manageable. Introversion, preoccupation, and nervous tension were usually relieved and ordinarily did not recur. On the other hand, the operation also frequently produced general dullness, lack of initiative, disorientation, and apathy, as well as slowness, procrastination, psychomotor retardation, laziness, and lack of interest in life. Nonetheless, because of the deplorable preoperative condition of the patients on whom frontal lobotomy was used, they seemed to be more often benefited than handicapped by the operation.

The verification with humans of the result originally observed with chimpanzees—that removal of the frontal lobes or the transection of their connections with the rest of the brain would relieve feelings of tension and frustration—gave rise rather early to the concept that frontal lobotomy might also be of value in cases of intractable pain. And the severing of the connections to the frontal lobes was in fact found in a great many instances to give patients dramatic relief from pain.

However, the extensive observations made on victims of various types of frontal-lobe injuries have been asserted to reveal no direct connection between this portion of the brain and the purely physical processes of the body. The elimination of pain by severing of the connections from the frontal lobes would appear to be inconsistent with these observations. The explanation for this apparent inconsistency was discovered some years back in an interesting manner. In a postoperative interview, the examining physician asked the patient, as a matter of routine, if the pain had been relieved. He felt sure of an affirmative answer, since it was evident that the patient was much more relaxed and happy since the operation. The doctor was therefore surprised to hear her reply that the pain was still there, as intense as ever! Further interrogation brought out the important fact that what had been accomplished by the operation was not a diminution in the pain itself, but a change in the state of mind of the patient that kept the pain from bothering her, although it was still there. Interrogations of other patients have revealed that this is the typical pattern. Frontal lobotomy does not eliminate intractable pain; it merely changes the attitude of the patient so that he does not care very much whether the pain is there or not—just as he doesn't care very much about anything else. This appears to be quite a different phenomenon from the evidently genuine elimination of pain that we saw earlier can sometimes be effected by electric stimulation through electrodes implanted in the brainstem (Chap. 7).

The Role of the Frontal Lobes

What conclusions can we now reach about the part played by the frontal lobes in the day-to-day activities of the brain? There is of course little cause for surprise in the discovery that the frontal lobes are not directly involved in the control of physical processes; after all, many other parts of the central nervous system are available for such activities. On the other hand, our studies to this point have not prepared us for the difficulty of finding *any* specific functions—physical, emotional, or intellectual—that can be clearly attributed to this large portion of the cerebral cortex. If the precentral area of the brain is removed, the power of precise movement is lost. If the occipital area is destroyed, the subject cannot see. But if the frontal lobes are lost, no specific function is destroyed. To be sure, there may be partial impairment over a wide psychological field. But while there is reduction in many functions, there is loss of none.

Certainly the impairment that most consistently appears as a result of damage to or disconnection of the frontal lobes is of a motivational nature. Inhibitions, normally arising from the desire not to offend others, are released. The emotional drive that impels us to organize our thoughts and actions in an attempt to move toward some goal is diminished. In short, the evidence suggests that damage to the frontal lobes usually impairs the ability to couple the emotions to intelligence in such a way as to provide normal motivational drives and inhibitions.

The troublesome aspect of this assignment of primary function is that, in view of the great efficiency that nature has displayed elsewhere in causing small amounts of brain tissue to perform complex control functions, we would expect the large quantity of neuronal material in the frontal lobes to be capable of playing a considerably more important role. There is of course evidence that the frontal lobes are used in complex intellectual processes, as when a number of concepts must be held in mind at one time, or when abstract logic is involved. If it could be established unambiguously that such higher thought processes can never be carried out successfully by one whose frontal lobes are missing or disconnected, probably most of us would feel that the need for this large part of the cerebral cortex had been amply justified. For, while we do not yet understand very well what goes on in complex thinking, we have respect for the amount of data processing that it must entail, and would probably imagine that the considerable extent of the frontal lobes would not necessarily be disproportionate to the magnitude of such a task. Unfortunately, the evidence is not clear-cut. Part of the trouble, of course, is that it is difficult to devise intelligence tests that are adequately meaningful. There is so much difference in the abilities of normal individuals to deal with complex intellectual problems that one cannot use unoperated persons as controls against whose performance the scores of the frontal patients can be properly compared. The other obvious approach—comparing the performances of the frontal patient before and after his operation—could give meaningful results if normal, healthy persons could be operated on, but of course this is never done. The preoperative tests, when they can be conducted at all, must be given to patients who are mentally ill, sometimes desperately so. As a result of the practical difficulties it is not easy to arrive at definitive conclusions as to the precise effect of frontal lobotomy on the ability to deal with complex intellectual problems. All that we can be reasonably sure of now is that damage to or disconnection of the frontal lobes frequently appears to diminish this capacity.

An interesting analogy will suggest itself to the computer scientist. In some very large digital-computer installations a number of computer subsystems are flexibly interconnected in a sort of "telephone switchboard" arrangement, so that they can be automatically combined in various ways in order best to meet the requirements of different kinds of problems. Part of the time the various subsystems may be disconnected from one another, each solving a different problem, as presented to it by some portion of the input equipment. On other occasions, the equipment may automatically reorganize itself so that two or three of the subsystems operate together to provide the enhanced computing capacity required to deal with some complex problem that has been presented for solution. An installation of this type may incorporate some stand-by computing capacity that ordinarily is not used, but is activated only when a problem of unusual complexity is presented—perhaps a problem in which many concepts may have to be dealt with simultaneously, or one in which a high degree of abstraction may be involved. The possible analogy is obvious. Could it not be that the frontal lobes contain "stand-by" capacity, which is called upon by the computing circuits of the brain when matters of high logical complexity must be dealt with?

Such an analogy, of course, adds nothing substantive to the clues supplied by brain research, but it may make the computer scientist feel a little more comfortable about the frontal lobes if he can see a possible scheme for their employment that is similar to one familiar to him. Such a concept of stand-by capacity gives rise to an interesting prediction. While many adults do not appear to do much difficult thinking and therefore may not overwork their frontal lobes, this may well be less true of children. The most difficult mental activities that we engage in are usually those involved in learning something new, and we do most of our learning in childhood. It is also true that the ideas grasped and learned by children, when analyzed, are frequently found to involve quite a respectable level of complexity and abstraction, although in later life long familiarity with the concepts we learned so much earlier may make them seem simple. Therefore, if our idea about the frontal lobes is correct, we might expect damage to this part of the brain to have more profound and easily observable effects on a child than on an adult. Relatively few cases of brain damage to children are available for study, but the limited evidence provides some confirmation for our hypothesis. Children who are so unfortunate as to suffer major frontal-lobe damage frequently appear to lose their capability for further learning and remain mentally retarded for the remainder of their lives.

We may summarize what we have learned about the function of the frontal lobes as follows: They have no role in the control of the physical processes of the body. The closest thing to a full-time assignment they have may be some kind of mediation between our emotional desires and our intellectual activities; this may be responsible for the establishment of motivations that furnish the drive for us to organize our thoughts and actions to achieve our goals, and that also furnish the inhibitions which prevent our doing things that would be contrary to our long-range interests. On a part-time basis it is possible that the frontal lobes are called in by the rest of the brain to participate in our more difficult intellectual activities. Damage to the frontal regions may therefore be expected to be most serious in its consequences to those who most engage in difficult or abstract thought—to children, who are constantly learning new concepts, and to the relatively small number of adults who continue to learn, think constructively, and engage in creative work.

SPEECH

If there is any one capability that is uniquely human, it is the power of speech. Bees possess a sign language by which they can indicate to their fellows the type and approximate distance and direction of food; birds employ a variety of signs and sounds for indicating danger or sexual situations; high-IQ dogs can be taught to respond properly to several dozen verbal commands; apes can learn to associate numerous sounds with meanings. But these are simple, direct relationships. The responses by a well-trained dog to such commands as "roll over" or "play dead" clearly indicate the operation of intelligence, but are still of an entirely different quality from the competent employment by the average human of the system of symbols and meanings unprecedented in the animal world—language—by means of which we are able to call up and bring together the groups of associations we call "ideas" in a way that seems to be beyond the power of any other creature. And by the use of language a human can convey his thoughts to a kindred mind as no other animal can do.

Because of this clear human preeminence, it was inevitable that great interest should attach to speech-related phenomena. Not long after the spectacular adventure of Phineas Gage, observations began to be reported on the effects of brain damage on speech. The name of Paul Broca is outstanding in this pioneering work. A noted French surgeon, secretary of the Société d'anthropologie in 1861, Broca took advantage of several opportunities that came his way to perform post-mortem examinations of the brains of patients who had developed serious speech defects before death. These studies supplied the first indications that damage to specific portions of the brain can be responsible for speech disturbance.

"Forbidden Territory"

Following Broca's work, many investigators have contributed to the gradual development of understanding of the importance of various portions of the brain to the phenomenon of speech. In recent years, leadership in this field of research has been exercised by the Montreal Neurological Institute, under the direction of Wilder Penfield. This important work started thirty years ago, when Penfield and his associates embarked on the treatment of focal epilepsy by radical surgical excision of abnormal areas of brain. In those days, based upon the earlier discoveries of Broca and others, it was the general belief that the portion of the brain controlling speech was located along the side of the dominant hemisphere—the left side of the brain for right-handed persons, the right side for left-handed persons. Because of the extensive involvement of speech mechanisms with higher intellectual activities, it was the practice at that time to refuse radical operation upon the dominant hemisphere unless the tumor or other brain damage was located far forward in the frontal lobe or far to the rear in the occipital lobe.

But, by accepting such a large portion of the brain as "forbidden territory," the surgeons denied the benefits of their techniques to many patients with damage or tumors that produced chronic epileptic symptoms and, not infrequently, by spreading led to progressive degeneration and death. In the meantime, increasing numbers of patients were observed with focal epilepsy resulting from lesions and small tumors that happened to fall within the general area that earlier work had indicated was vital to the control of speech, and many of these patients did not have speech difficulties. This led Penfield and his associates to suspect that not all the territory that had been proscribed by earlier research workers should really be considered to be forbidden, and that a more precise delineation of the speech areas might lead to the possibility of extending the region within which operations could be performed for the removal of defective tissue and the relief of epileptic symptoms.

Mapping the Speech Areas

The tool chosen by Penfield for the more accurate mapping of the cortical speech areas was the modern technique of electric stimulation. Penfield's reasoning was about as follows: Insertion of an electrode and injection of a train of current pulses into a portion of the cortex that is responsible either for the receipt of sensory information or for the transmission of motor commands typically produces behavioral symptoms that permit the normal function of that portion of cortex to be identified. If the spot chosen for electric stimulation is in the visual cortex, the injected current in effect preempts a portion of the subject's field of view and fills it with flashes of light. Stimulation of the auditory cortex similarly blocks the normal receiving channels from the ears and produces an uncoordinated noise or clashing sensation in the brain; stimulation of a portion of the postcentral sensory cortex may produce a sensation of numbness in the right thumb, which at the same time is precluded from performing its normal function of touch discrimination. Penfield reasoned that something similar should happen if he were to stimulate the part of the cortex involved in the control of speech. Because of the complexity of the speech processes, he did not expect to be able to cause the subject to produce specific words or phrases, but he thought that the other, negative result commonly produced by stimulation might reasonably be expected to occur—the incapacitation of the particular aspect of the speech process controlled by the stimulated portion of cortex. By performing the brain operation under local anesthesia, with the patient fully conscious and cooperating, he hoped that the specific areas of the cortex where electric stimulation would interfere with speech could be accurately delineated.

In such a description as this one, in which the development of a new technique for obtaining improved understanding of brain mechanisms is the subject of immediate interest, there is danger of conveying an improper impression of the approach of such workers as Penfield and his associates to their patients. These men are physicians, not experimenters. Their objective in each operation is to apply their skill and knowledge in such a way as to maximize the probability of improving the condition of the one patient they are working on. When they insert probes in his exposed cortex, apply electric stimulation and record behavioral effects, it is always done for the purpose of localizing his specific abnormality, so that subsequent surgery may be most effective. For this reason, little can be done with one patient that has not been previously successfully checked out on others. Nevertheless, individual patients are different enough, both in inherent make-up and with respect to their lesions, that fresh application of a well-proved electrical exploration technique frequently leads to information about a previously undetermined aspect of brain function. When the surgeon is also a scientist, and when throughout the years he performs operations to relieve the suffering of many hundreds of patients, much new information can be secured. It was in this way that the Montreal Neurological Institute group slowly and cautiously developed what turned out to be a powerful new technique. For Penfield's method worked. Specific regions of the cortex were indeed found where application of the stimulus while the patient was talking would produce prompt and dramatic disturbance in his speech. The accurate mapping of the regions of the cortex within which electric stimulation produces such disturbances, and determination of the nature of the disturbances themselves, have provided important clues as to how the brain controls the processes of speech.

Nature of Electrically Induced Speech Disturbances

Penfield and his associates knew from the beginning that there was one kind of speech disturbance that they would certainly be able to produce and that would be of little interest to them. This was interference by incapacitation of the part of the brain that controls the muscles used in speech. Such a result, it was known, could easily be obtained by stimulation through an electrode inserted in the part of the precentral motor strip employed in the control of the muscles of lips, tongue, and throat. Such stimulation would indeed interfere with, or entirely prevent, talking by the patient. But it was purely a muscular effect; it would frequently be accompanied by uncontrolled twitching of the muscles and, upon termination of the stimulation, the patient would confirm that the only interference with speaking that he had been aware of was the inability to control his muscles.

This kind of interference was observed only as a result of stimulation in the well-established cortical motor regions. It was also only in such regions that occasionally stimulation produced positive effects. With the electrode in certain positions the injection of current would cause the subject to "vocalize," that is, to emit long-sustained vowel sounds. With such understandable exceptions, the effect of electrode stimulation was always negative; it interfered with the processes of speech, just as Penfield's preliminary working hypothesis had contemplated.

But electric interference with the thought processes underlying speech was Penfield's main interest. The inability of a patient to speak properly, even though he possesses adequate muscular control, is called *aphasia* by the workers in the field. And electrically induced aphasia was vividly demonstrated in many of Penfield's tests. On being asked to name the object in a picture while the speech area of his cortex was being stimulated, one patient said: "Oh, I know what it is. That is what you put in your shoes." After withdrawal of the electrode he said, "Foot." A little later he was unable to name the picture of a tree, although he knew what it was, naming it properly as soon as the stimulus was turned off. Another patient under electric stimulation could not think of the word for a comb, although when asked its use he said, "I comb my hair." When asked again to name it, he couldn't until the electrode was removed.

From descriptions by the patients of their sensations when these tests are under way, it is clear that what is involved is interference with only a part of the speech mechanism. The patient recognizes the object he is trying to name, can speak effectively in most respects, but for some reason no longer has access to the common words that ordinarily would come to him easily. He frequently tries to think of synonyms when he finds he cannot remember the word itself. On one occasion, the patient struggled unsuccessfully to answer a question during the electric discharge; afterward he said, "I couldn't get that word 'butterfly' and then I tried to get the word 'moth'." The test is evidently a puzzling and frustrating experience for the subject.

The blocking of access by the patient to the names of objects is typical of the effects produced by electric stimulation in suitable cortical zones, but it is by no means the only type of aphasia that can be induced. Hesitation, slurring, and distortion frequently occur. These effects can be produced by stimulation in the motor cortex, but they can also result from interference with the ideational speech processes as a result of stimulation in other areas of the brain. Sometimes repetition of words and syllables is caused by the electric stimulus. Confusion of numbers is frequently observed when the current is turned on while the patient is counting. In such circumstances the patient may jump from "six" to "twenty" and then back to "nine." Interestingly, the confusion is apparently of a limited nature, for nonnumerical words are not used; the patient displays the proper psychological "set" but is simply unable to give the correct numbers. In another kind of misnaming the patient may use words closely related in sound such as "camel" for "comb"; or he may use synonyms such as "cutters" for "scissors," "hay" for "bed," and "moth" for "butterfly." Sometimes an entirely unrelated word is used, such as "rink" for "scissors," or "comb" for "hammer."

While all of these results were obtained by the artificial injection of electric current into the exposed cortex of the patient, the behavioral effects were quite similar to those produced in the same and other patients when the stimulating current was injected into the speech cortex as a result of spontaneous epileptic attacks. Lesions in the cortical speech areas also were found to produce similar speech defects, although there was a tendency for a wider variety of symptoms to appear from natural causes than from artificial stimulation. As we shall see shortly, one of the cortical areas important for speech extends back from the temporal lobe almost to the associative area of the visual cortex in the occipital lobe. Lesions occurring in this region, close to the visual cortex, were sometimes found to produce much more severe disturbance of writing than of speech. Other cases were observed in which the patient could express himself adequately but could not understand what was said to him. Interesting though these special cases may be, they appear to be relatively rare. Until better understanding exists of the basic nature of aphasia, it is not likely that attempts to interpret these special situations will be fruitful. In most cases of aphasia, whether produced naturally or artificially, the phenomena are more general; they suggest a breakdown of the mechanism that we ordinarily use in going from a concept to a word.

Location of the Cortical Speech Areas

Figure 8-1 shows the three areas of the cortex that Penfield concluded from his tests are involved in the ideational processes of speech. No significant difference was observed between the kinds of disturbance elicited by stimulation in the three areas; instances were observed of production of all the kinds of disturbance described above by stimulation in each area.

Penfield's results, summarized in Figure 8-1, show that all the speech areas ordinarily are situated in the left hemisphere. He did not confirm the earlier belief that the dominant hemisphere, in terms of left- or right-handedness, controls speech. Some cases of speech control by the right hemisphere were observed, but these were rare and always appeared to be the consequence of special circumstances (to be discussed below). In the normal brain, the left hemisphere was found to control speech.

The existence of so nearly a standardized assignment of cortical tissue for the control of speech processes is rather remarkable. Speech is clearly an acquired function, with no hereditary overtones. The fact that the process of learning to speak, which must be a new and special experience for each individual, should automatically result in the involvement of a certain standardized portion of the cortex is probably replete with implications as to the detailed construction and operation of the brain. It is to be hoped that one day our knowledge will permit us to form the proper deductions from this significant evidence of speech localization. At present, only a few inferences can be drawn. Oddly enough, some of the most interesting speculation is suggested by the exceptions referred to above—the instances in which the assignment of cortex to the control of speech functions is *not* precisely in accordance with the map of Figure 8-1.

Fig. 8-1. The three speech areas of the cortex. (*Reprinted from Wilder Penfield and Lamar Roberts, Speech and Brain Mechanisms, by permission of Princeton University Press. Copyright 1959 by Princeton University Press. London: Oxford University Press.*)

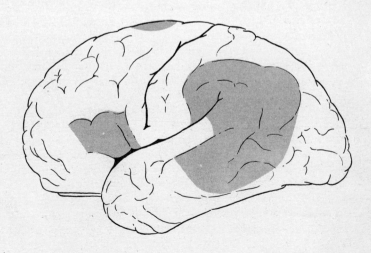

Plasticity of the Speech Cortex

When speech control by the right hemisphere was observed by Penfield and his associates, the individual involved was indeed usually left-handed, as had been noted by earlier investigators. However, they found that most people whose right hemisphere is dominant for handedness and who are therefore left-handed still employ the left hemisphere for speech. The right hemisphere seems to be used for speech only by individuals who, at birth or as very young children, sustain major damage to the left side of the brain. Under such circumstances, the brain appears to have enough plasticity to be able to transfer the control of speech to the undamaged hemisphere. This plasticity does not extend into adulthood; there is little evidence that speech defects caused by damage of the left hemisphere late in life can be overcome by training the other hemisphere to take over.

Another kind of exception to the standardized assignment of cortex to speech control was occasionally displayed by patients who presented themselves to Penfield without speech defects but with damaged tissue located in one of the three cortical speech areas. Upon investigation, these patients were found to have a characteristic history: some time previously, often years earlier, a head injury had been sustained; this injury had at the time resulted in severe speech disturbance; after weeks or months the patient had recovered most or all of his original facility with language. Again, the plasticity of the brain must have come to the aid of the patient. Apparently the functions related to speech that were normally performed by the tissue damaged in the head injury had been gradually taken over by some of the remaining healthy tissue of the cortex. This was not always accomplished without cost to the patient, however, for frequently the damaged tissue gave rise to epileptic symptoms. To relieve these symptoms, Penfield in many instances performed surgical excisions that therefore lay directly within the areas that in the normal brain would have been involved in speech control. These excisions did not result in aphasia.

In these situations there was no way of determining whether the speech functions normally exercised by the tissue before it was damaged had been taken over by adjacent areas of cortex or by one of the two intact cortical speech areas. There was good evidence, however, that the speech functions were never transferred to the opposite hemisphere. Once the hemisphere that was dominant for speech (usually the left) had been correctly identified, electric stimulation or surgical excision on the opposite side was never capable of producing aphasia. Evidently, the computing organization used by the brain makes it impractical for both hemispheres to be employed simultaneously in the control of speech. On the other hand, there is in the literature at least one instance of complete removal of the left hemisphere, for tumor, in a thirteen-year-old boy, with some subsequent return of language function. It seems possible that even at this relatively advanced age the right hemisphere can still be trained to perform speech processes.

This plasticity appears to be a property that is possessed by the brain tissue involved in all the higher intellectual processes, in marked contrast to the rigid assignment of specific areas of the brain for the receipt of sensory input data and for the control of the motor and reflex processes. Excision of part of the visual cortex produces blindness in the corresponding sector of the field of view, and no amount of future conscious or unconscious training can ever bring back the lost vision. The contrast involved in the shift from one hemisphere to another of the responsibility for speech control, in the case of a young child with a severe head injury, is indeed a striking one.

Redundancy in the Speech Cortex

The cortical speech areas exhibit another important property, that of redundancy. We have seen that not one single region, but rather three separate regions, of the cortex normally participate in the ideational processes of speech. Because of the similarity of the symptoms that can be elicited by electric stimulation in these areas, it is evident that they are all part of a single mechanism. In addition to the possibility that damage to one of these areas will result in its function's being taken over by nearby healthy cortex, it seems likely that extensive damage in one speech area may result in the transfer of its function to one of the two remaining areas. Penfield points out that the evidence for this hypothesis is convincing with respect to the uppermost speech area, for its complete excision has frequently been found to produce no more than a transient speech disturbance that clears up within a few weeks. Less convincing deductions can be made as to the dispensability of the lower forward speech area (Broca's area), but the evidence available is consistent with the conclusion that it too can be dispensed with, although with more difficulty to the patient. As to the large posterior speech area, however, Penfield has concluded that any major destruction there would be likely to produce such grave effects that, for an adult patient at least, there would be serious question as to whether normal speech would ever return.

It is probable that the properties of plasticity and redundancy are also possessed by the frontal lobes. This would help account for the surprising absence of major symptoms in many instances of frontal-lobe damage. The possibility that functions are duplicated in the left and right frontal lobes was suggested by the experiments on chimpanzees, referred to earlier, in which it was determined that little effect on behavior could be observed unless both frontal lobes were removed or disconnected at the same time. Obviously, the existence of redundancy and plasticity within the frontal lobes cannot upset in any significant way the conclusions we drew earlier as to the probable nature of their functions, for these conclusions were based almost entirely on the results of bilateral removal or disconnection.

In connection with the frontal lobes, it will already have been noted that one of Penfield's speech areas is located in this region of the cortex (Fig. 8-1). The fact that permanent disturbance to speech is not reported after frontal lobotomy is one of the indications that the normal functions of this speech area can in fact be taken over by the two remaining areas, as suggested above.

Integration of Speech Processes by the Brainstem

The employment by the brain of redundancy to provide greater invulnerability to accidental damage of an acquired characteristic such as speech is a most interesting discovery. An obvious question, to which considerable attention has been devoted, is how the three separate speech areas of the cortex are connected together. Penfield's work has thrown some light on this important question. As a cumulative result of operations on many different patients, there is no portion of the cortex surrounding the three speech areas from which brain tissue has not been removed. In no instance has such removal significantly interfered with speech. Therefore it seems clear that the connections that tie the three cortical speech areas together do not pass along the surface of the cortex itself; if so, some of them would surely have been interfered with by these operations. The interconnections, Penfield reasons, must be through the brainstem, to which all portions of the cortex are connected. Anatomical dissection shows, in fact, the existence of dense fiber tracts leading from each of the cortical speech areas to the posterior part of the thalamus, at the top of the brainstem. It is consistent with our general concept of the cortex as an organ of elaboration and refinement for us to imagine that the thalamus may do more than simply act as an interconnecting terminal board for the several portions of speech cortex: it may participate directly in the speech functions themselves. There is some evidence that this is true. In several cases described in the literature, patients developed extreme speech difficulties apparently as a consequence of lesions or tumors involving the thalamus alone. The fact that electric stimulation produces the same kinds of speech disturbance, whether applied to one or another of the cortical speech areas, is also consistent with the hypothesis that the principal function of the cortex in these experiments may have been simply to conduct the electric impulses to a central thalamic region where they could interfere with the main processes of speech control.

The Role of the Speech Cortex

It is not the intent of the foregoing discussion to suggest that the cortex is of little importance to the process of speech. The intellectual activities involved in speech must be fantastically complex. If ever an organ of elaboration and refinement, such as we assume the cortex to be, was called for, it would be here. We must bear in mind that, by comparison with the intricacy and delicacy that must somewhere be involved, we have been dealing with the grossest of effects. Neither the evidence from electric stimulation nor the observed effects of natural lesions or surgical excision of tissue are able to provide information as to where the memory of a word is stored or in what configuration of neurons is recorded the program for carrying out the syntactical processes of language. Aphasia—the improper functioning of the ideational processes of speech—appears to be some sort of breakdown of the information-retrieval machinery of the brain by means of which words are matched to concepts. The patient retains his normal intelligence, he recognizes and understands what is going on about him, but he is blocked from finding words to express his thoughts. This is usually a quite general type of blockage. To be sure, most electric-interference experiments, for convenience, employ spoken language. However, tests usually confirm that, when the patient cannot speak the proper word, he also cannot write it. And while the speech deficiency generally appears in these experiments as the inability of the subject to find a particular word for a particular object, the electric interference or damaged brain tissue responsible for the difficulty usually makes it hard for him to find words for many different objects. Electric stimulation has never given evidence of being so fine-grained in its effect as to interfere selectively with only one word or one small group of words in the patient's memory. Similarly, brain damage and surgical operation provide no evidence of such selective loss of vocabulary. This holds true even with respect to different languages. A truly bilingual patient who suffers a speech defect suffers the defect in both languages. A superficially learned second language, like other difficult conceptual mental skills, may be more vulnerable to mild aphasic damage than a native tongue that the patient speaks with ease, but careful investigation shows no evidence for any separate localization of function for different languages. This is an important point: it appears that there is a general capability for symbolic representation of thought that is interfered with in the abnormalities under consideration. This is further shown by the fact that a victim of severe aphasia not only is unable to express himself in speech, but is similarly handicapped in conveying meaning by gesture of head or hand. He may use the muscles of neck and hand for other purposes, but he cannot nod assent in place of the word "yes" or shake his head in place of the lost word "no." Gestures are lost as well as words; they too are symbols of conceptual thought.

SUMMARY

In the frontal lobes and the speech areas of the cortex, it is clear that we are dealing with phenomena that are considerably more subtle and diffuse than the reasonably precise one-to-one relationships that we have heretofore observed between brain and body function. Plasticity and redundancy appear to be important properties of these new areas.

With respect to the frontal lobes, our most striking observation is that they appear to display a direct correlation with personality—with the individual's drives, inhibitions, consideration for others, and adherence to moral and ethical principles. We can see in the effects on these characteristics of the severing of connections to the frontal lobes a relation with the specific neuronal configuration in the brainstem that seems to control our emotional responses. When these relationships between the frontal lobes and personality are supplemented by the frequently observed effects of frontal-lobe integrity on the performance of complex and abstract intellectual processes, we can feel that we may have succeeded in making a reasonably adequate assignment of function to the considerable and prominent neuronal material that comprises the frontal lobes.

With respect to speech, the conclusion that we all employ the same areas of the cortex must appear to us to be rather remarkable, in view of the obviously artificial and acquired nature of the function. The central integrative role of the brainstem in speech is a peculiarly satisfying discovery, in view of the concept we have already developed of the cortex as essentially an organ of elaboration and refinement of functions basically controlled by the phylogenetically older parts of the brain.

BIBLIOGRAPHY

Hebb, D. O., "Man's Frontal Lobes," *Archives of Neurology and Psychiatry*, vol. 54 (1945), pp. 10–24.

Jacobsen, C. F., "Studies of Cerebral Functions in Primates. I. The Function of the Frontal Areas in Monkeys," *Comparative Psychology Monographs*, vol. 13 (1936), p. 1.

Moniz, E., "Prefrontal Leucotomy in the Treatment of Mental Disorders," *American Journal of Psychiatry*, suppl. 93 (1937), p. 1379.

Penfield, W., and L. Roberts, *Speech and Brain Mechanisms* (Princeton University Press, Princeton, N.J., 1959).

Russell, W. R., *Brain, Memory, Learning* (Oxford University Press, Fair Lawn, N.J., 1959), chap. XII, "Hypothalamus: Frontal Lobes."

Russell, W. R., and M. L. E. Espir, *Traumatic Aphasia* (Oxford University Press, Fair Lawn, N.J., 1961).

Tow, P. M., *Personality Changes Following Frontal Leucotomy,* (Oxford University Press, Fair Lawn, N.J., 1955).

Triggering of Memory by Cortical Stimulation

It was not long after Penfield began his work on the localization of the speech areas in the cortex that, quite by accident, he stumbled upon a new and remarkable phenomenon. Electric stimulation in the cortex would sometimes suddenly force into the patient's consciousness detailed recollections of past events!

The first patient in which stimulated recollection was observed relived an episode of early childhood with such naturalness that she felt fear again as she had at the time of the original event. Another early patient seemed to see herself as she was while giving birth to her child, and in the surroundings of that original event. One young man saw himself with his cousins at their home in South Africa. It seemed to him that he could hear them laughing and talking. The scene was at least as clear to him as it would have been had he closed his eyes and ears moments after the event, even though it had occurred years earlier.

One woman heard the voice of her small son in the yard outside her kitchen, accompanied by the neighborhood sounds of honking autos, barking dogs, and shouting youngsters. One patient listened to an orchestra in the operating room, playing a number that she did not herself know how to sing or play, and that she only vaguely recalled having heard before. Another patient heard the singing of a Christmas song in her church at home in Holland. She seemed to be there in the church and was moved again by the beauty of the occasion, just as she had been on that Christmas Eve years earlier.

These electrically elicited experiences always appear to be real happenings out of the past. Nevertheless, they are usually not recollections that the patient has been consciously carrying in his memory. The episodes recalled frequently are trivial or inconsequential, without any attributes that make it likely that they ever were of great importance to the subject. It is as if the injected current had the effect of dredging up some random recollection from the memory storehouse.

Although the recalled events are often trivial, they are never vague. The vividness of the elicited experience always differentiates it from ordinary memory. According to Penfield, "the patients have never looked upon an experiential response as a remembering. Instead of that it is a hearing-again and seeing-again—a living-through moments of past time." Nevertheless, the patient does not lose contact with the present. If questioned during one of these electrically invoked experiences, he shows awareness that he is in the operating room and that the other events are related to recollection rather than to current reality. Discussion with those who have experienced the phenomenon has led to the use of the term "double consciousness" to describe the subjective sensation: the patient seems to have two concurrent existences, one in the operating room and one in the portion of the past that he is reliving.

There are other ways in which the experience induced by cortical stimulation differs from ordinary memory. In Penfield's words:

When, by chance, the neurosurgeon's electrode activates past experience, that experience unfolds progressively, moment by moment. This is a little like the performance of a wire recorder or a strip of cinematographic film on which are registered all those things of which the individual was once aware—the things he selected for his attention in that interval of time. Absent from it are the sensations he ignored, the talk he did not heed.

Time's strip of film runs forward, never backward, even when resurrected from the past. It seems to proceed again at time's own unchanged pace. It would seem once one section of the strip has come alive, that the response is protected by a functional all-or-nothing principle. A regulating inhibitory mechanism must guard against activation of other portions of the film. As long as the electrode is held in place, the experience of a former day goes forward. There is no holding it still, no turning back, no crossing with other periods. When the electrode is withdrawn, it stops as suddenly as it began.

A particular strip can sometimes be repeated by interrupting the stimulation and then shortly reapplying it at the same or a nearby point. In that case it begins at the same moment of time on each occasion. The threshold of evocation of that particular response has apparently been lowered for a time by the first stimulus. . . .*

* Reprinted from Wilder Penfield and Lamar Roberts, *Speech and Brain Mechanisms,* p. 53. (By permission of Princeton University Press. Copyright 1959 by Princeton University Press. London: Oxford University Press.)

It is worth pointing out that Penfield's suggestion of facilitation by repeated stimulation is consistent with a different kind of observation that has been made by another worker in this field, Maitland Baldwin of the National Institutes of Health. Baldwin has pointed out that memories are never elicited unless the patient has a past history of epilepsy involving damaged tissue near the part of the brain where stimulation elicits the experiential recall. He has inferred from this that the phenomenon is dependent upon a lowering of the normal threshold of the memory-recall process to electric stimulation, resulting from the current injected into the appropriate tissue by previous epileptic attacks.

The obvious direct involvement in these experiments of the important function of memory aroused great interest in attempts to determine the specific areas of the cortex where stimulation would be effective. After years of work by many observers, the degree of cortical localization of this phenomenon leaves little to be desired. Memory responses are obtained only when the stimulating current is injected into one of the temporal lobes, on the lower left or right side of the brain.

We have already learned (Chap. 7) that epileptic attacks arising from discharges in the temporal-lobe region, whether originating naturally or induced artificially by electrode stimulation, are characterized by what we called *psychic effects*. If the epileptic focus is in the deep layers underlying the temporal lobes, confusion, diminished awareness, amnesia, or automatic behavior is frequently observed. If the focus (or the stimulating electrode) is in the temporal lobe itself, we learned that the epileptic attack is likely to exhibit considerable hallucinatory content. It is also found that electric stimulation in this same area can sometimes produce illusions that suggest interference with some of the processes by means of which we classify our incoming sensations into various categories by comparison with past experience. We have little understanding of just what brain mechanisms underlie these complex processes. Nevertheless, there is at least a sense of orderliness about the discovery that the only cortical routes we can find to the memories of past events lie in the same regions of the brain that appear to be involved in other mental processes that must, by their nature, be strongly dependent upon employment of the content of the memory store.

Localization of the Memory Traces

The fact that the temporal lobes are the only areas of the cortex in which electric stimulation elicits experiential recall suggests, of course, that the actual memory recording may be located in that part of the cortex. On the other hand, such a conclusion is not necessarily required by the evidence. It could be only that current injected into the temporal lobe is conducted to some other region of the brain where the actual memory traces, whatever they may be, are stored. The surgical evidence on this point is not conclusive. Complete removal of one temporal lobe does not ordinarily appear to interfere with memory, although there is considerable evidence of memory deficit in the few instances of bilateral temporal-lobe excision available for study. If the temporal lobes are the actual repositories of whatever physical changes in the neurons constitute the basis for memory of past events, then it would appear at least that there is duplication of memory in the two lobes. Since we have seen (Chap. 8) that the brain employs redundancy in the mechanisms it establishes for accomplishing its higher intellectual functions, we should not be surprised at such duplication. Furthermore, it must be borne in mind that the evidence from bilateral excision is supplied solely by patients whose temporal lobes contain much damaged tissue. In view of the evidence for the recruitment of nearby healthy tissue to help out when speech functions are impaired by brain damage, the persistence of some memory capability even after bilateral excision of defective temporal lobes would not conclusively exclude this region of the brain as the normal repository of the memory traces.

On the other hand, it is quite conceivable that memory traces are not stored in the cortex at all. A cat or dog that has had all the connections between cortex and brainstem severed is still capable of learning simple tasks. Learning involves memory, and the memory trace established by a decorticate animal obviously cannot be in the cortex. We know too that the stored programs of behavior that determine our reflexes and guide our automatic bodily-control processes operate properly in the absence of the cortex. And considerations of simplicity might incline us to believe that the brain would employ the same general storage location for all its memory processes.

Such arguments do not answer any questions. They simply demand that, on the basis of the evidence so far presented, we maintain an open mind as to whether the tasks of elaboration and refinement assigned to the cortex include the storage of memories related to the functions it performs or whether all memories find their physical representation in the material of the brainstem.

In the laboratory of R. W. Sperry at the California Institute of Technology, a part of the answer to this question has been obtained. Sperry and his coworkers devised experiments to determine, among other things, where in the brain of a cat is stored the memory pattern that permits the animal to perform properly a discrimination chore that it has been taught.* The results obtained rank among the most important neurological discoveries of recent years and justify more than casual consideration on our part.

The Case of the One-eyed Cats

A cat can easily be taught certain types of visual discrimination. One practical teaching arrangement employs a long chamber, provided at one end with a pair of swinging doors, on each of which can be placed a test pattern. One door might, for example, display a circle, and the other a square. The goal might be to train the cat to open the door with the circle and avoid the door with the square. In such a case the experiment is arranged so that if the cat pushes through the proper door it finds a morsel of food; if it opens the wrong door it receives no food and possibly is reprimanded. After it makes its choice and opens one of the two doors, the cat is returned to the other end of the chamber, the circle and square are reaffixed to the same or opposite doors, according to some random sequencing program, and the animal is released for its next trial. After a number of days, on each of which about forty such training experiences or "trials" are run, an average cat will learn the routine to the extent that it will open the right door nearly every time.

The kind of learning involved here—discrimination between visual patterns—clearly requires employment of the visual cortex. Without this portion of the brain, the cat could distinguish between light and dark, but would not be able to detect detail. Since the cortex is employed in this kind of discrimination, it would seem that the memory traces related to this kind of learning would also be in the cortex, if indeed the cortex ever serves for memory-storage purposes. An experiment was designed to test this hypothesis.

An essential feature of the experiment was an eye patch that permitted the test animal to see out of only one eye at a time. With the right eye covered, for example, the cat would be trained to discriminate between two patterns such as the circle and the square. Once the animal had become expert in making the correct choice, the patch would be shifted, and the animal's batting average based upon the use of its untrained right eye would then be observed. With an ordinary, unmodified cat, there would be no difference in performance: even though the training had exclusively employed the left eye, the discrimination habit that had been learned would con-

* The first successes in this program were actually achieved by R. E. Myers, now at Johns Hopkins University.

trol the cat's performance just as accurately when the right eye was used. This, of course, was not surprising. From what has gone before, we all know now that we are not much different from cats in the way our nervous system works, and no reader would doubt that, if he were trained to perform some visual discrimination with his left eye, he would be able to perform the task equally well with the other eye.

But this was just the first step in the experiment. This first result would have been expected, not only by analogy with human experience, but also on the basis of anatomical considerations. In cats as in humans, the fibers proceeding from the retinal neurons of each eye divide so as to terminate on the occipital lobes of both hemispheres of the brain. Specifically, the optic nerves of the two eyes meet in what is known as the *optic chiasma*. From the chiasma, some of the fibers from the left eye continue on to the left hemisphere of the cortex and some from the right eye continue to the right hemisphere; but there is also some crossing over of left-eye fibers to the right hemisphere and vice versa. Such intermingling of the neuronal circuitry associated with the two eyes would be expected to prevent any such thing as the formation of pattern-discrimination memory traces available for use with one eye but not with the other.

The next step in the Caltech experiment was to attempt to eliminate this complicating intermingling of the cat's visual system. It was found possible to make a knife-cut through the optic chiasma, thereby producing the situation shown in Figure 9-1; the fibers from the left eye now terminated only on the left hemisphere of the cortex and those from the right eye terminated only on the right hemisphere. Tests (after the normal two or three weeks of postoperative recovery time) showed that the vision of the animal was less acute than before, but was still adequate to permit discrimination between the various optical patterns used in the experiment. A number of cats, after being operated upon, were put through the training course and taught typical visual discrimination routines, the combination of eye patch and chiasma section now ensuring clear control of the sensory traffic from the unbandaged eye to only one cortical hemisphere. If the learned memory pattern was stored in the cortex, it seemed that it would now have to be recorded in the hemisphere on which the incoming visual data terminated. Shifting the eye patch and use by the animal of the untrained eye might therefore produce a situation in which comparison of the incoming data with the previously stored pattern would be difficult or impossible. This would be reflected in quite a different degree of training transfer for chiasma-sectioned compared with normal cats.

But there was no difference. A cat's performance when using the untrained eye was still the same as that with the trained one. Obviously, wherever was stored the memory trace resulting from training of the left eye for the performance of a visual discrimination task, that trace was also available for comparison with the incoming sensory information from the right eye.

This result could have meant that the memory of the learned behavior pattern was stored in the brainstem rather than the cortex, and was thereby equally accessible for comparison with visual sensory patterns generated in either hemisphere. But it was still possible for the site of the memory storage to be in the cortex, provided that there yet remained connections by means of which the memory trace laid down in one hemisphere could be transferred to a corresponding site in the other or communicated with for comparison with sensory information arriving at terminal points in the opposite side of the brain. Anatomy provided clear evidence for such a system of interconnection—the *corpus callosum.*

The corpus callosum, shown schematically in Figure 9-1, is a bundle of tens of millions of axons connecting neurons of the left hemisphere with those of the right, and vice versa. Because of the symmetry of the brain, it has always been imagined that the individual fibers of the corpus callosum must interconnect neurons in corresponding locations in the left and right hemispheres. There is some evidence that this is so; for instance, a lesion placed in a particular spot in the left cortex will frequently give rise to abnormally functioning tissue in the mirror-image position in the right half of the brain. Nevertheless, the corpus callosum has always been something of a mystery. In view of its conspicuousness and its extremely large number of neuronal connectors, investigators have never been able to understand why cutting through it produces the remarkably small effects on the behavior of the subject that this operation usually elicits. Prior to the work in Sperry's laboratory, the evidence on the effect of sectioning the corpus callosum of various animals and even some epileptic humans was of an almost completely negative character.

Nevertheless, the experiment with the one-eyed cats seemed logically to call next for an elimination of the connections through the corpus callosum. Accordingly, several cats were subjected to an operation that not only eliminated the crossing over of the optic nerves by section of the chiasma, but also disconnected the major channels of intercommunication between the two hemispheres by complete section of the corpus callosum. After the normal convalescent period, these animals were then put through the standard routine.

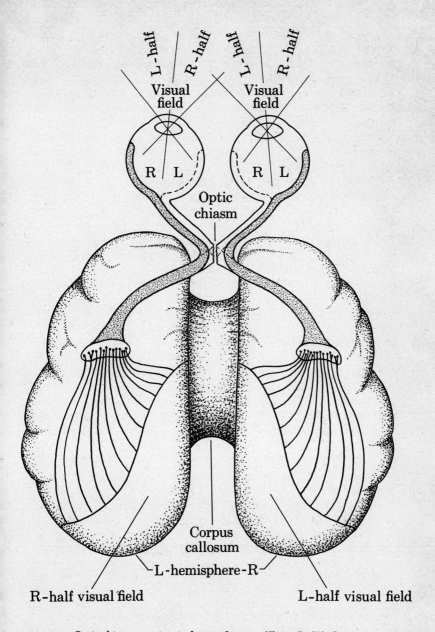

Fig. 9-1. Optic-chiasma section in brain of a cat. (*From R. W. Sperry, Science, vol. 133 (1961), pp. 1749–1757. By permission of the publishers.*)

This time the results were strikingly different. If the cat was trained to discriminate between two optical patterns to near perfection, using its left eye, and then the eye bandage was shifted, it was as though there had been a change in cats and not just in eyes: when using the untrained eye the animal had no more of an inclination to perform the proper visual discrimination than if it had never been exposed to the problem before! This result held even though overtraining of the initial eye was carried out to the extent of hundreds of excess trials. There was no transfer of experience from one eye to the other.

The matter went even deeper. These chiasma- and callosum-sectioned cats could actually be trained in contradictory discriminations with the two eyes. With the bandage over one eye, the cat could be trained to open the swinging door carrying the circle and to avoid the door carrying the square; using the other eye, it could be trained to open the door with the square and avoid the one with the circle. Shifting the bandage from one eye to the other would then automatically result in the corresponding change in the animal's behavior. The learning time for either eye was the same as that for an unoperated animal, and the fact that the left eye had been trained in one discrimination pattern before the beginning of right-eye training neither increased nor decreased the time required to train the right eye. By shifting the patch from one eye to the other after every few trials and concurrently changing the reward and punishment rules, the two eyes could be schooled during the same training session in their separate discrimination chores. Each eye required the same number of trials for the development of a given standard of performance as though only that eye were being trained; the interspersal of training episodes of a different type for the other eye appeared to have no effect. One of Sperry's associates, C. B. Trevarthen, was even able to devise a sophisticated type of experiment involving eyeglasses and polarized light by means of which the two eyes could be simultaneously trained to make contradictory discriminations. For example, on the panel associated with the food reward one eye would see an illuminated circle while the other at the same time would see an illuminated cross. Some animals could concurrently learn these conflicting discriminations with both eyes as rapidly as they could learn a simple habit with one eye alone!

The Cortical Location of the Discrimination Memory Traces

The Caltech work has been extended to include other types of sensory inputs than visual, and other animals than cats. For example, callosum-sectioned cats have been trained to perform tactile discrimination chores—to press one of two levers in accordance with the smoothness or roughness of the surface. The results were entirely consistent with those obtained with visual discrimination: there is no transfer of learning from the left to the right paw; different or conflicting response habits can easily be learned by the separate paws of the same animal. The experiments have also been performed on monkeys—with the same results.

These results go far toward providing an answer to our question as to the storage site of learned discrimination patterns. The memory trace representing a learned pattern of visual or tactile discrimination must be stored in the same half of the brain as that which receives the primary sensory data employed in the original establishment of the habit pattern. Once the habit has been formed, comparison between the incoming sensory stimuli and the stored memory pattern is effected by means of mechanisms involving only this one side. When the sensory input is shifted to the other half of the brain, it is then compared with whatever memory pattern has been generated and stored in that side, on the basis of what may have been an entirely different history of experience during the training period.

It also seems nearly certain that the memory trace for the discrimination pattern is located in the cortex, rather than in the brainstem. This is strongly indicated by the dramatic elimination of transfer of experience that occurs when the corpus callosum is cut. With the corpus callosum intact, that which is learned and stored in one hemisphere is available for purposes of comparison with the sensory input to the other side of the brain. With callosum sectioned, the memory/sensory comparison systems of the two hemispheres are separate and distinct. But the corpus callosum is a cortex-to-cortex communicating system. The observed results are reasonable only if we assume either (1) that some of the callosal fibers establish on one side of the cortex a sort of carbon copy of the memory trace stored on the other side, or (2) that the memory trace is laid down in only one hemisphere but that the sensory receiving neurons of the other hemisphere have access to the trace, for comparison purposes, through the corpus callosum. Either assumption strongly suggests cortical storage.

Another type of experiment has resolved the remaining question and shown that the interhemisphere communication of the corpus callosum actually results in the duplication of memory traces in both halves of the cortex, and not simply in the cross-comparison of sensory data arriving in one hemisphere with memory patterns stored in the other. For if a test animal with severed optic chiasma but intact corpus callosum is trained to make a visual discrimination with one eye and then the callosum is cut, the animal is able to perform the learned task while making use of the untrained eye. The copying of the original memory trace must have occurred before the cutting of the interconnection between the two hemispheres.

By an entirely different method, Jan Bures, of the Institute of Physiology of the Czechoslovak Academy of Sciences in Prague, has obtained additional information on the memory-duplicating function of the corpus callosum. Bures has developed a technique which he calls *reversible decortication*. When a solution of potassium chloride is applied to the exposed brain, a phenomenon is induced, called *spreading depression*, which temporarily puts the surrounding cortex out of commission. By this means, Bures was able to inactivate an entire hemisphere and keep it dormant for several hours while the other hemisphere maintained its normal activity. In experiments with rats, the animals were taught simple procedures while one hemisphere was kept inactive by the potassium chloride solution. On the following day, the other hemisphere was rendered inactive and an attempt was made to have the animal perform its previously learned behavior. Bures found that training had to be started all over again; there was no transfer of the learned memory pattern from the hemisphere in which it was initially recorded to the other half of the brain. The analogy with Sperry's results is obvious. However, Bures's experiments add a new piece of information: transfer of the memory trace does not occur between normally functioning interconnected hemispheres during the inactive interval after learning has been established in one hemisphere and before performance is called for by the other side of the brain. Presumably the interhemisphere transfer occurs at the time of the experience itself. Bures was able to confirm this deduction by having an animal perform the learned behavior a few times during the period when both hemispheres were active. Subsequently, when the initially trained hemisphere was deactivated, it was found that the other hemisphere was now partially trained, presumably due to the transfer of experience that occurred during the earlier practice session.

Not only have these experiments of Sperry and Bures established that sensory-discrimination memory patterns are located in the cortex, but they have in several instances provided indications as to just where in the cortex the memories are stored. For example, one of the split-brain cats was taught a pedal-pressing tactile discrimination routine with the left front paw; then all its cortex on the corresponding (right) hemisphere up to the somatic sensory and motor areas was removed. The isolated remnant of cortex was found to be still capable of controlling excellent performance of the learned routine, and was adequate to permit the animal to learn new tactile discriminations with the same left paw. To be doubly certain that there were no unsuspected cross-connections to the other hemisphere that were controlling the cat's performance, the sensorimotor regions of the other hemisphere were also cut away. Thus the cat retained the frontal portion of the right hemisphere for control of the tactile discrimination maneuvers of its left paw and the rear portion of the left hemisphere for control of its other visual and intellectual processes. Its memory and learning capabilities for tactile discriminations with its left front paw were found to be unimpaired. Sperry's conclusion was that he had cornered the memory traces for these new habits of tactile discrimination in the sensorimotor cortex of the corresponding cerebral hemisphere.

Bures, by a nice modification of his reversible decortication procedure, was also able to obtain evidence of localization of memory traces in rats. He found that a small spot on the cortex could be protected from the deactivation produced by potassium chloride by applying to the spot a solution of magnesium chloride of suitable concentration. In this way, Bures was able to preserve an island of active brain tissue in an otherwise deactivated hemisphere. This permitted him to conduct the following sequence: (1) Deactivate one complete hemisphere and train the rat to perform some new routine, presumably thereby making use of the unaffected cortical hemisphere. (2) Wait a day or so for recovery from the effects of the first step. (3) Deactivate all the previously trained hemisphere except for some selected island protected by application of magnesium chloride solution, and test the animal's ability to perform the previously learned routine.

Again, Bures's results were consistent with those of the Caltech group. If the rat's trained behavior was of a manipulatory nature involving use of the right paw, protection of the sensorimotor cortex of the left hemisphere not only preserved the animal's physical ability to perform the required delicate manipulations, but also kept active the pertinent memory trace, for the rat was under these circumstances fully able to perform the previously learned procedure. On the other hand, if the trick the rat had been taught involved visual pattern discrimination, protecting the sensorimotor cortex was ineffective, but insulating the primary and associative visual areas of the cortex against deactivation would preserve the animal's ability to perform the learned response.

The picture that emerges from all this possesses a pleasing simplicity and orderliness. When the elaboration and refinement capabilities of the cortex are called upon to permit the animal to learn some new behavior pattern too complex for mastery by the brainstem alone, the cortex is also assigned the task of storing a suitable memory trace of the learned discrimination; and the cortex uses for this purpose neuronal material in the same general part of the brain as that employed in the sensory recognition or motor control involved directly in the performance of the learned act. In the normal intact animal, all such memory traces are stored in duplicate; the massive communication system of the corpus callosum automatically lays down identical memory traces in both hemispheres even in the unusual situation in which the sensorimotor patterns of the learned behavior itself might appear to require the services of only one half of the brain. The carbon-copying of the memory trace from one hemisphere to the other takes place only during those times when the act is actually being performed; the evidence is against any kind of scanning mechanism that, when the animal is otherwise passive, continually reviews the contents of one hemisphere and duplicates them in the other side.

At this point it would be easy to conclude that, in these discrimination learning situations, we are dealing with matters wherein all the functions are performed in the cortex. With a split-brain animal, the sensory data on which a choice is based necessarily come in to one hemisphere only, and the learned memory of the desired pattern is stored nearby in that same hemisphere. In addition, at least in such tests as pedal pushing, the final muscular output dictated by the animal's choice is controlled by material in that same side of the brain. The simplest picture of the brain operations involved would certainly suggest direct interconnection within the cortex between the incoming data, the stored memory pattern, and the outgoing motor-control signals.

In the kinds of experiments described so far, it may indeed be true that the brainstem is not actively involved, but confidence in the generality of this conclusion is shaken by another of the Caltech experiments. In this instance the split-brain animal was trained to perform a more complex routine involving both visual and tactile discrimination. For example, a monkey would be required to pull the rougher of two levers when one visual pattern appeared, and the smoother of the two when another visual pattern appeared. Monkeys can, with some difficulty, learn such visuotactile discriminations. In these experiments, however, the arrangement was such that the monkey was forced to pull the lever, not with the arm controlled by the hemisphere receiving the visual pattern input, but with the arm on the other side of the body and thus controlled by the hemisphere that was separated by section of the corpus callosum from all visual input. Yet the animal was able to learn and perform the coordinated routine! In view of what has gone before it must be assumed that the incoming visual data were recognized as comprising one or another of the pertinent *visual* patterns by comparison with the memory traces of those patterns stored in one hemisphere, and that the incoming tactile data were analyzed as indicating a smooth or rough lever by comparison with *tactile* memory traces stored in the other hemisphere. Yet, despite the severing of the direct lines of communication between the two hemispheres, the tactile and visual identifications were brought together and a combined visuotactile pattern selection made on the basis of which orders were sent to the motor mechanisms to determine which lever the monkey would pull. The obvious conclusion is that this integration was effected in the brainstem. Here we have another example of how risky it is ever to assume that we have finally determined that a function is performed completely within and independently by the cortex. Our hypotheses consistently appear to agree best with the facts if they emphasize the role of the cortex as being that of elaboration and refinement, and not of a self-sufficient independent operator. If a cat is taught to discriminate between different musical patterns involving two simultaneous tones or precisely timed sequences of three tones, removal of its auditory cortex abolishes its learned responses. However, because of the remaining brainstem mechanisms, the cat is able to relearn and restore an appropriate memory trace for a simple one-tone pitch discrimination. Probably it is thus in general —the memory trace for a complex discrimination resides in the cortex, whereas the trace for a simpler routine, or perhaps even for the simpler aspects of the same routine, resides in the deeper structures of the brain.

Implications for Event Storage

In the storage of the memories of previous events such as those evoked by Penfield's electrodes, there would also appear to be room for participation by various parts of the brain. For the simpler elements of the experience, the deeper parts of the brain could easily be the sites of the memory traces. For the portions of the experience that consist of complex visual, audible, or tactile patterns, the cortex would appear to be the logical storage location. For such cortical storage, we might imagine that the visual content of a conscious recollection involves activity of neurons close to the visual cortex, that the recall of an audible note utilizes brain tissue close to that involved in the original sensation of hearing, and so on.

The simultaneous presence of different sensory qualities in the recollection of a previous event is a phenomenon that leads to an important conclusion concerning the memory mechanisms. If visual and audible stimuli, for example, occur simultaneously in the original experience, and this simultaneity is preserved in the recollection, it follows that the memory circuits must include interconnections between the presumably separately located sites of storage of the qualitatively different portions of a given recollection, these interconnections being suitable for enforcing temporal synchronization on the memory playback. The resulting picture of the memory store for past events is one of several parallel sequences of "snapshots" of the previous experience, each sequence pertaining to a different sensory modality, with the playback mechanisms so arranged as to preserve synchronization of the several parallel recording channels.

Although it does not necessarily take the same period of time to "live" a recollection as it did to experience the original event, the temporal ordering of the details is well preserved in the recollection. Penfield commented on this in his description of the inexorable, step-by-step fashion in which the recollections of his patients streamed through their consciousness under the influence of the stimulating electrodes. Indeed, in the recollection of a periodic stimulus the time scale itself may be preserved. E. Roy John, Director of the Center for Brain Research of the University of Rochester, has made some interesting observations that seem to have pertinence in this connection. He trained cats to perform certain instrumental reactions in response to the visual stimulus of a light that flickered on and off 4 times per second. When the trained cats were then subjected to a 10-per-second flicker, occasionally one of them would mistake this signal for the learned action stimulus and respond as it had been taught to do for the 4-per-second flicker. When this happened, electrodes implanted in the reticular formation or in the visual cortex of the cat would record an electric signal with a strong 4-cycle-per-second component—the flicker frequency that the cat had learned should evoke its instrumental response—even though it was currently being exposed to quite a different frequency of input stimulus! The cat was then taught not to respond to the 10-per-second flicker. After this differentiation, the 4-per-second component was no longer observed. The strong implication of the results of such experiments is that the memory mechanism can in some circumstances play back the previously stored data at precisely the speed of the original recording.

Changing One Individual into Two

Before we finally leave the Caltech work, we should take note of the rather spectacular split-personality implication of the split-brain experiments. While this implication is inherent in the results with cats, it was demonstrated in even more convincing fashion in later work with monkeys. First a monkey was subjected to a split-brain operation, in which its corpus callosum and optic chiasma were cut, just as in the cat experiments. But in addition, on one side of the monkey's brain, a frontal lobotomy was performed. It will be recalled that a result of this operation is the production of a relaxed, "I don't care" sort of animal. With a monkey prepared in this way, an arrangement equivalent to the cats' eye patches was employed by means of which the animal could be forced to use one eye or the other in viewing its environment. With the monkey employing the eye that was connected to the unmodified cortical hemisphere, a snake was displayed to the animal. Monkeys are normally deathly afraid of snakes and the split-brain monkey was no exception. It showed the usual fright and escape reactions. Then the conditions were changed so that the monkey had to employ the eye connected with the hemisphere that had had the lobotomy. Again the snake was displayed. This time, the monkey could not have cared less; the snake held no terrors for it. It was as though two different animal personalities now inhabited the body that had formerly been occupied by one!

Sperry plans to extend the present techniques to permit cutting most of the brainstem as well as the cortex into disconnected symmetrical halves. It is fascinating to contemplate the possibility of preparing an animal with essentially two separate brains, each capable of receiving its own sensations, recording its own memories, learning its own behavior patterns, developing its own emotional habits and personality attributes, and perhaps even sleeping and waking independently of the other. Fantastic though it seems, such a splitting of one into two separate individuals, both inhabiting and, from time to time, controlling the same body, may well be a consequence of the continuation of the exciting work that is underway in the biological laboratories of the California Institute of Technology!

The Multiple Memory Mechanisms

We do not always have to go to the laboratory or operating room to get information about the workings of the brain. All of us, in all our waking hours, all the days of our lives, are exposed to a continuous panorama of thought and sensation that, if interpretable, could undoubtedly provide great insight into the mechanism of the brain. So difficult is the interpretation of our subjective impressions that for the most part we are well advised to base our theories on laboratory and operating-room results instead. But of course we always check these objectively derived explanations of brain function against our subjective observations to make sure that nothing is being concluded by the scientists that is completely irreconcilable with what we seem to be observing in our own private little laboratories, sixteen hours a day, three hundred and sixty-five days a year. And occasionally, by such introspection, we may even be able to arrive at valid conclusions about the nature of some kinds of brain function. In any event, in a field where there is so much yet to be learned and where it is so hard to get direct answers to many important questions, we should not completely ignore any source of information, distorted though it may turn out to be. What do introspection and self-analysis tell us about memory?

If we think about it, we will probably all agree that there must be at least two different kinds of memory. There is, first of all, a long-term, permanent memory. Our own names and addresses, the words and grammatical forms of the language we speak, the addition and multiplication tables, important episodes in our early life—these memories, once established, are with us to stay. To be sure, our memory-recall system is less than perfect; all of us occasionally have mental blocks for particular words or the names of acquaintances. Yet even in these circumstances we never doubt that the memory is still there somewhere; we just can't lay our hands on it. We may suspect that our memories fade with the passing of time, and some probably do, but this is a very slow process. Also we know, through observation of our more senior acquaintances, that sometimes the old, long-standing memories even appear to become more vivid as a person grows older. In any case, we know that there is a large inventory of recollections that stays with the average person until he dies.

Clearly, there is also another kind of memory. It is of a fleeting, short-term nature. The universality of this kind of memory is attested by a current television advertisement of the telephone company that exhorts subscribers not only to look up, but also to write down, the number that is to be called so that the dialing can be done digit by digit with reference to a written record. Although, despite the telephone company's appeal, many of us can hold in mind the seven characters of the typical metropolitan phone number long enough to get it dialed, the number frequently does not stay with us well enough that we can manage the circumstance of a busy signal that calls for a second dialing two or three minutes later.

There is much evidence of the fleeting character of short-term memory. It is not unusual for a beginning language student, in attempting to read a sentence of foreign text, to have to look up the translation of the same word twice when it appears twice in the same sentence! And when we are introduced to someone at a party, our auditory receptors may clearly pass along to our brains the name that is pronounced, but if we are inattentive or are thinking of something else, the name does not stick. There is an interval of a few seconds after the introduction during which, by exercising conscious effort, we can retrieve the name from our fast-decaying short-term memory; but if we do not focus our attention on the matter within such a very short interval, the information that once appeared upon our sensory cortex is vanished beyond our power of recall.

Concentration of attention over a period of time usually is required to transfer sensory-input data into the permanent memory. When we deliberately try to memorize a telephone number, a stanza of a poem, or a mathematical formula, we consciously force our minds to go over the material many times in order to fix it in our memory. When, as frequently occurs, an event is remembered without conscious effort, introspection usually reveals that there was something very special about the event that caused our attention-focusing apparatus to concentrate upon it for a time, at least to concentrate upon the particular elements of the event that later recall indicates were stored in our memory. The events that really get set in our memory usually have an attached interest that causes us to recall them frequently after their occurrence; even though the event occurs only once, its long-term implantation in our permanent storage system seems to be associated with the frequent reliving in our imagination of the original experience.

These subjective impressions about short- and long-term memory are consistent with a number of physiological observations. Some of the clearest evidence for the existence of multiple memory mechanisms comes from the study of brain concussion. A standard clinical definition of *concussion* (Trotter, 1924) is "a transient state due to head injury which is of instantaneous onset, manifests widespread symptoms of a purely paralytic kind, does not as such comprise any evidence of structural cerebral injury, and is always followed by amnesia for the actual moment of the incident." The neurologist W. Ritchie Russell, of Oxford University, has made statistical studies of these amnesic effects resulting from concussion. The length of the *permanent retrograde amnesia*—the period before the blow that is never again remembered—shows considerable variation from incident to incident, and in general is greater for the more severe injuries. However, usually its duration is several seconds. This period suggests a relationship with the subjective phenomenon involved in the ease with which many of us fail to "get" the names of persons introduced to us at a party. It was earlier suggested that this phenomenon indicates that the memory of a currently occurring event fades away rapidly, within a few seconds, unless some attention-focusing mechanism singles out some of the elements of the incoming sensory information for emphasis and retention. It would seem likely that such attention focusing is controlled by some portion of the reticular activating system, in view of what we have learned earlier about its other functions. In any event, the evidence from studies of retrograde amnesia is consistent with the hypothesis that it takes the attention-focusing mechanism a few seconds to operate and that the interruption of this process by a blow on the head is what accounts for the permanent retrograde amnesia that is associated with concussion.

In addition to a short-term memory, probably associated with some sort of natural decay of the nerve currents established in the brain by the incoming sensory impulses, there is evidence for what we might call a "medium-term" memory mechanism. This is suggested by the peculiar kind of memory deficit sometimes exhibited by patients with lesions in the amygdaloid-hippocampal structures that underlie the temporal lobes. Their memory is not impaired for events that occurred before the surgical operation or the pathological development that resulted in damaged brain tissue; they can carry on a normal conversation and can remember telephone numbers or other information for a few minutes; but five or ten minutes later these patients not only will have forgotten the numbers, as most of us would have, but will have no recollection that there had even been a conversation on the subject! One epileptic patient had his hippocampus removed on both sides. After the operation, in marketing for the family at a store directly across the street, he could remember quite well what he had been told to buy. Yet, sent on a similar mission to another store ten minutes away, he couldn't remember by the time he got there why he had come.

With these patients, memories seem to get started in the normal way and to continue properly for a few minutes, but then disappear entirely. Apparently there is some kind of neuronal circuitry in the deep brain structures underlying the temporal lobes that is normally involved in converting a medium-term recollection, which can persist unaided for a few minutes, into a truly long-term memory trace.

There is additional evidence for a separate medium-term memory mechanism. If, a few minutes after completing a series of training runs on some new learning situation, a rat or hamster has electric current passed through its brain adequate to produce convulsions, partial or complete cancellation of the effect of the training results. If the shock follows the training experience by only five minutes, learning is completely lost; after fifteen minutes, the loss is considerable; after an hour the loss is small; electroshock administered several hours after completion of the training experience has no observable effect upon the animal's retention of the memory and ability to perform the learned procedure. Evidently, in these experiments the current sent through the brain is not capable of interfering with the memory once it is established in the permanent memory store, but is able either to destroy the medium-term memory trace or to incapacitate whatever mechanism is involved in converting to long-term memory. Whichever effect is produced, the experiments seem to indicate that, for the animals tested, the time normally required to establish a record in the long-term memory store is minutes, but not hours.

Work recently performed by Reginald Bickford and associates at the Mayo Foundation, a part of the Graduate School of the University of Minnesota, suggests an interesting additional link between the results obtained with rats and hamsters and the observations of memory deficit in human patients with hippocampal lesions. The Mayo Foundation group, while applying electric stimulation below the cortical surface of the temporal lobes of epileptic patients in an exploratory procedure prior to operation, produced in two of the patients a syndrome of amnesia for recent events, with normal recall for events preceding the amnesia. This amnesic condition continued for as much as two hours after termination of the electric stimulation that induced it. It is easy to imagine that the situation with the rats and hamsters was similar—some of the current coursing through the brain during electroshock deactivated the memory-transfer mechanism, which then took so long to recover its normal ability to establish records in the permanent memory store that the medium-term memory trace had by then disappeared, whether or not it had been directly destroyed by the electroshock current.

Thus a combination of subjective impressions and objective observations has led us to a three-stage concept of memory. The brain automatically preserves for a brief interval the description of the immediate external environment provided by the nerve impulses coming in over the external neuronal receptors. In the absence of selection and reinforcing activities, this input information fades away quickly—probably within a few seconds. Normally, however, partly consciously and partly unconsciously, an attention-focusing mechanism, which may be the reticular activating system, performs an initial sorting operation on the incoming data, some of which is earmarked as being of special interest and thus is preserved in what we have called the medium-term memory. Once reinforced by this attention-focusing process, the memory trace can apparently persist in the medium-term-memory status for a period of some minutes. In a brain incapacitated by lesion, surgical excision, or electric stimulation, the memory trace may be incapable of fixation and be permanently lost after a few minutes. In a normal brain, however, some kind of process goes on by means of which the memory is made permanent. Here again, attention focusing, perhaps by the same mechanism that selected the original sensory data, seems to cause some recollections to go into the permanent memory in indelible fashion, and others to be stored so tenuously that, if they are not later reinforced by repetition or subsequent recall, they may drop out of the storage system altogether.

The Strength of Old Memories

There is considerable evidence that memory traces, once well installed in the permanent storage mechanism, strengthen with time. In cases of severe concussion, in addition to the brief interval just before the blow that is never recalled by the victim, there is often a much longer interval that is temporarily erased from the memory. After a moderate blow on the head, memories may be temporarily lost for the events of several hours preceding the injury; after a harder blow, the preceding days or weeks may be blank; on the initial recovery of consciousness from a very severe blow, the victim may give the date as several years previously, with no recollection of the intervening period. As the patient recovers, the period of retrograde amnesia shrinks, but always from early to late. The older memories are the hardest to eliminate, and they are the first to return. With continued recovery, the amnesia shrinks until it finally reaches the minimum period of a few seconds beyond which further recovery of memory is not possible.

The greater strength of the older memories is also exhibited by the effects of electroshock treatments of the mentally ill. In a series of such treatments, amnesia for past events is gradually induced, progressively from the present working back into the past. When the shock treatments are terminated, the patient gradually recovers the lost memories, from the past working up to the present. The forgetfulness of the aged has similar characteristics. An old person frequently appears to have an unusually vivid recollection of early events; it is recent occurrences that he cannot remember. Again, when a young child with a total vocabulary of, say, fifty words suffers a severe brain concussion, he may lose half his vocabulary, and the words that are lost are always the ones last learned.

The peculiar strength and invulnerability of the old memories has led Russell to put forth some interesting speculation. He starts with the rather generally accepted idea that the establishment of a memory trace in the permanent storage system involves some kind of change in the effectiveness of the synapses that interconnect the neurons participating in the storage of that trace. Such increase in synaptic strength must make it easier for a nerve impulse, once set in motion, to follow the circuit determined by the new pattern of facilitated connections. Russell suggests that the nature of the electrochemical processes that occur when a pulse passes from the axon of one neuron into the dendrite or body of the next is such as further to strengthen the synapse employed. This idea, in fact, is often advanced in partial explanation of why memories, as of the learned motor processes involved in a golf swing, are strengthened by repetition. But Russell goes a step further in his speculation. Calling attention to the fact that most neurons occasionally fire spontaneously in the absence of a stimulating signal, Russell suggests that the resulting randomly generated currents continually traverse the neuronal circuits of least resistance and thereby automatically strengthen the memory traces that have already been established. In this way, the longer the memory has been installed in the storage mechanism of the brain, the stronger its trace is likely to become.

In addition to explaining the curious persistence of old recollections, this hypothesis would appear to provide a physiological basis for other subjective observations about memory. As college students cramming for examinations, many of us have found that what was difficult and confusing the preceding night seems clear and simple the next morning, after a good night's sleep. Athletes frequently observe improvement in their performance on returning to practice after laying off training for a while. If Russell's ideas are correct, these observations are readily understandable. Once the correct memory patterns are established in the brain, they will be automatically strengthened by the passage of time, because of the tendency of the randomly generated discharge currents of the neurons to traverse, and thereby strengthen, the established synaptic connections. Therefore, if what has been crammed tenuously into the memory storage system is correct, more progress may be made in strengthening that learning by laying off the subject entirely for hours or days than by continuing the training process. This is especially true if fatigue has progressed to the point where continued practice or study is likely to generate errors that may actually diminish the quality of the stored memory trace.

Quantity Requirements on the Memory Store: Implications as to the Storage Mechanisms

The sheer magnitude of the storage capacity that must exist in the human brain to account for the observed memory capabilities poses one of the most severe problems faced by any theory of brain function. Consider the implications of Penfield's observations that, under electric stimulation, a patient may relive what appears to be an insignificant episode of his remote past, and that, furthermore, he frequently is able to recall a degree of detail going far beyond what we customarily associate with normal memory. This sort of observation lends credibility to reports, long prevalent in the literature, of unusual feats of memory performed under hypnosis. A report that has been discussed in several brain-research symposia concerns a bricklayer in his sixties who, under hypnosis, was able to describe specific bricks in a wall that he had laid in his twenties. The bumps on the surfaces of the bricks he described under hypnosis could be checked, and they were there! Another example cited by psychologists is that of an adult who was asked to recall some details of a classroom in which he sat when six years old. Although initially unable to do this, even under hypnosis, he readily described the details when the hypnotist suggested that he was once again six years old!

Such hints of the possible existence in the brain of a permanent record of past events far transcending in completeness that which is normally available for conscious recall has led some research workers to give serious consideration to the possibility that all sensory data that we receive during our lifetime are accurately and permanently stored somewhere in the memory. What this assumption would mean in terms of the storage capacity called for in the brain was calculated by John von Neumann in his pioneering book, *The Computer and the Brain* (1958). His calculation certainly leads to the maximum possible requirement, for he assumed not only that throughout an entire lifetime (taken to be sixty years), a complete record is made of the electric signals generated in all touch, retinal, and other input receptors, but that all the approximately ten billion neurons in the brain constitute receptors in the sense that their detailed electric activity is stored somewhere in the nervous system. This calculation led to a memory-capacity requirement of 2.8×10^{20} bits of information. On the basis that one on/off switch can store a single bit, this means that each neuron in the nervous system has associated with it the equivalent of 30 billion on/off switches of memory capacity!

This is a most extreme calculation; it does not really seem necessary to go so far. A somewhat more modest result is obtained by confining the calculation to the amount of input information provided by the sensory receptors alone. By far the largest part of the input data that we receive is visual; a calculation of storage requirements based upon the electric activity of the fibers of the optic nerves would not fall far short of specifying that required for recording all incoming stimuli. Assuming 2 million retinal receptors for the two eyes, 14 action pulses per second as typical of the output of a stimulated retinal neuron, and 2×10^9 seconds, or 60 years, as the lifetime, we find that the memory-capacity requirement is reduced to 6×10^{16} bits. This is the equivalent of 6 million on/off storage units for each neuron. Although appreciably smaller than von Neumann's figure, this number still does not afford us much comfort.

But calculations such as these probably represent an overreaction to the surprise that was aroused by the discovery that our memory has considerably more content than had previously been suspected. Despite the vividness of the "reliving" of past experience described by Penfield's patients, there was no suggestion that the elicited recollections had anything like the complete information content of the original scenes. Even the observation that an event several years in the past is relived with the same distinctness as though the subject had recalled it only moments after the actual occurrence gives us no reason to think that the amount of detail involved is more than a small fraction of that assumed in our calculations. In fact, this is subject to a simple test. All the reader has to do is to enter an unfamiliar room, study it intently for a few minutes, and then close his eyes and try to compare his recollection with the eyes-open direct vision. Although a few specially noticed details of the original scene will be present in the mental image, the vast majority of the details of texture, brightness, and color that constitute the exceedingly fine-grained original picture seen with our eyes open will not have been remembered. As Penfield has pointed out, the memory has registered in it "all those things of which the individual was once aware—the things he selected for his attention in that interval of time. Absent from it are the sensations he ignored, the talk he did not heed." Even though our memory may store some form of record of trivial past events that we would not have thought worth retaining, there is no evidence of anything approaching photographic detail in the quality of such storage. And it is quite an extrapolation from the double handful of observations of the eliciting by cortical stimulation of detailed records of unimportant events to the conclusion that *all* events are recorded in the memory. It seems more likely that there may have been associated at the time with each of these seemingly trivial events some element that caused them to be remembered, while other events that today would seem as important were not recorded. It does not really seem necessary to conclude that the sixty-year-old bricklayer referred to earlier has stored in his memory the surface details of *every* brick he has laid in *all* the buildings on which he has worked in his forty-year career!

To the author, at least, it seems likely that we record in our permanent storage system only a small fraction of the events that we experience and, moreover, that we abstract and record only a tiny fraction of the originally present sensory data in the events we do remember. It is not easy to reduce this kind of subjective feeling to an objective and quantitative basis, but there is one kind of calculation that may be pertinent. Various psychological tests lead to the conclusion that the amount of information that a person can take in through his receptors and pass on immediately to another person is quite small; the best estimate is about 25 bits per second under the most favorable conditions. This is consistent with the observation we have all made that we can apprehend only about 5 or 10 chunks of information at a time, where a "chunk" is the name of an item, an entry in a list, or the like. Such an item might involve 15 bits of information on the average—a total of perhaps 75 to 150 bits that we can consider at one time. These numbers are tremendously smaller than those corresponding to the vast amount of information that comes in through our sensory organs and that therefore is available to, but usually not recognized by, our sense of consciousness. If we perform our calculation of memory-storage capacity on the basis of an "apprehended" information rate of 25 bits per second, we come out with something like 50 billion bits as our storage requirement—corresponding to four or five storage flip-flops per neuron, instead of the millions or billions yielded by the earlier calculations.

We can even push our memory-capacity requirements below the figure of four or five binary elements per neuron by assuming that the memory devices work at the rate of 25 bits per second for only a fraction of the twenty-four hours of the day. Additional substantial reduction in storage requirements results if we assume that a large proportion of what gets recorded in our "permanent" memory is not really permanent at all—that many of the recorded patterns decay through disuse so that in hours, days, or weeks the associated storage elements are freed from their pattern fixations and rejoin the "pool" of elements available for storage of new information. To be sure, to differentiate from memory effects lasting a few seconds or minutes we have in preceding pages emphasized the relative permanence of what we have called the "long-term" memory trace. And we have seen that some of these traces are indeed of a very permanent nature, even tending to become stronger with the passage of time. But in general we have preserved a concept of the strengthening of a memory trace by frequent recall of the memory; we imagine that the neuronal currents occurring during the process of recollection, in retracing the paths involved in the original perception, tend to continue and strengthen whatever physical changes in the neuronal material resulted in the establishment of the stored pattern in the first instance. In spite of Russell's interesting hypothesis of the continual strengthening of well-established memory traces through the action of random neuronal currents, and without the intervention of conscious recall, the evidence seems strong that such automatic unconscious processes alone are not adequate to tie down firmly all memories for all time. Even though, if we could somehow empty out and observe the entire content of our memory store, we would probably be amazed to discover the record of many past events that we had thought were long forgotten, it is also quite possible that we would find missing many memory traces that would have been present in a similar inventory of cerebral content taken five years earlier. A fifty-year-old man who could recall one-tenth of the episodes of his nineteenth year that he remembered vividly at the age of twenty would still impress most of us as a person with a good memory. Yet, he could maintain this ability with only one-tenth of the neuronal storage material that would otherwise be called for.

When our answers can differ by factors of millions, depending upon the specific assumptions we make, what is the point of wasting time on these calculations of memory-storage capacity? It is because of the hints that such calculations might give as to the basic nature of the memory mechanism. While there is general agreement that the establishment of a memory trace involves physical changes in neuronal material, it is not yet known just what these physical changes consist of. One very important question, to which storage-capacity calculations are directly pertinent, has to do with whether the neuron itself is the basic storage element. Clearly, this is possible only if the number of bits of required storage is less than the number of neurons in the brain. As we have seen, we can just barely satisfy this requirement by stretching all steps of the calculation in the direction of low storage needs. However, such a borderline result does not carry much conviction, especially when account is taken of such factors as the memory requirement for the control of the automatic bodily functions and of redundancy considerations, which may lead to duplication of the memory traces in more than one location.

Fortunately, the whole neuron is not the only possible candidate for designation as the basic storage element. Each neuron in the brain has many input terminals. Estimates range as high as one thousand for the average number of synapses made on the body and dendrites of each neuron by the axons of other cells. Most investigators feel that memory resides in the strengths of these synaptic connections. This provides one thousand times as many storage elements as the number of neurons—a number of elements that seems more comfortably related to the storage requirements.

There is another possibility. It is not necessarily true that the neurons and their interconnections are solely responsible for the unique properties of the brain. In the interstices between the neurons there are packed many so-called *glial cells*—so small that there are approximately ten of them for each neuron in the brain. To this point these cells have been ignored, in accordance with classical neurological doctrine that attributes to them only "housekeeping" functions related to some of the chemical processes needed to support the metabolism of the neurons. But not all research workers are convinced of this interpretation. For example, W. R. Adey, of the University of California at Los Angeles, argues convincingly that some of the integration or data processing of the brain may be due to the local variations in impedance to electric current flow throughout the tangled forest of dendrites that characterizes most of the neuronal material of the brain. On this thesis, the dendritic structures would comprise both the "inputs" and "outputs" of the basic computing elements of the system, with the on/off action-potential sequences of the axons relegated to the role of transmission of processed data to remote locations. With such an interpretation, the glial cells, which crowd to within a millionth of an inch of the bodies and dendrites of the neurons, could participate in memory storage. Permanent changes in the efficacy of their electric conductivity to local spots on the neurons could modify the resulting dendritic currents and thereby yield the basic attributes of the memory function. This hypothesis, in common with the one that assigns the basic memory function to dendritic synapses, leads to a storage capacity many times greater than that characteristic of an arrangement in which one neuron can store the equivalent of only one binary bit of information.

One of the most important goals of present-day neurological research is the determination of the essential physical characteristics of the memory trace—the location and the nature of the permanent changes that underlie memory. Meaningful experiments are difficult to devise and perform. The cross-sectional area of an average synapse in the brain is only 10^{-8} square centimeter. Microscopic observation of a particular synapse before and after neural activity to determine whether its physical dimensions have changed slightly (one hypothesis of memory-trace formation) has not yet been found practical. The analogous process of analyzing the detailed electrochemical properties of the synapse before and after learning is even more difficult.

Fortunately, scientists can often find an indirect way of getting at a problem when the direct approach does not lie within the capabilities of existing techniques. Such an indirect approach, for example, consists in the comparison of the chemical composition of neuronal samples that have been removed from adjacent areas of an animal's brain after one of these areas has been subjected to unusual activity by electric stimulation. Any resulting chemical differences between the stimulated and unstimulated material might then be related to the only permanent functional change that the normal brain is known to undergo with use—establishment of memory traces.

The work of this kind done so far strongly indicates that neuronal activity increases the amount of RNA in the nerve cells. RNA is the genetic material that determines the amount and types of proteins formed in any living cell. It requires no great stretch of the imagination to visualize a possible connection between protein synthesis and changes in synaptic strength. This kind of thinking about the chemical nature of the memory trace is today highly speculative, but is illustrative of the research trends from which, in the next several years, positive answers may be confidently anticipated.

Summary

Evidently there is much yet to be learned about memory. We are still in the dark as to the microscopic neuronal mechanism of the memory trace. It has not even been possible to identify any specific volume of brain tissue that, like the memory unit of an electronic digital computer, can be clearly identified as the repository of stored information; no surgeon has yet been able to remove the recollection of a single event or the remembrance of an isolated habit by the manipulation of a scalpel. Nevertheless, there is unmistakable evidence of the existence in the brain of specific memory mechanisms. Penfield's dramatic elicitation of vivid recollections from the past by electric stimulation of the temporal lobes clearly implies the existence of specific neuronal circuitry for memory of past events. The results obtained by Sperry and Bures can hardly be accounted for on any other basis than that the recollection of learned patterns of tactile and visual discrimination is stored in regions of the cortex close to the tissue that serves as the terminal area for the related sensory inputs. Other evidence suggests that it is only the higher discrimination patterns that are stored in the cortex, and that the memory traces related to the less complex aspects of learned behavior are probably recorded in the more primitive portions of the brain. We have inferred that a similar dichotomy could well pertain to the storage of recollection of past events as well as learned behavior patterns—the more complex sensory portions of the original observation being stored in the cortex, the simpler features being recorded in the brainstem.

We have seen that there is evidence for different types of memory mechanisms. Either by accidentally formed brain lesions, by surgical excision, or by electric stimulation, conditions can be induced in which medium-term memory is good, long-term memory is good, but there is no transfer from one to the other. This hardly permits explanation except on the basis of separate medium- and long-term memory mechanisms—at least in the sense of an additional process being required to establish a long-term memory. In this connection it seems significant that the deep structures underlying the temporal lobes appear to be the site of the memory-transfer mechanism, while the temporal lobes themselves are the only regions wherein electric stimulation will elicit recollections of past events.

Particular interest attaches to the evidence, supplied both by subjective observation and by studies of brain-concussion effects, that an attention-focusing process is probably involved before information supplied by the sensory receptors gets established even in the medium-term memory. We have here a picture of input devices continually serving up to the control centers of the brain a series of panoramic representations of the state of the outside world, with each snapshot in the series persisting for only a few seconds and then fading away, except in so far as the attention-focusing mechanism of the brain selects some portion of the submitted information for retention. The suggestion has been made that the same attention-focusing mechanism may be responsible for the final stage, conversion into a long-term memory trace.

In Russell's suggestion as to the strengthening of the established traces by the random discharge of the neurons we have found an appealing explanation of the curious strength and persistence of old memories, and a logical basis for the usefulness of "sleeping on it" in the fixation of newly learned information or patterns of behavior.

Thus, while much is unknown about the phenomenon of memory, it is also true that a good deal is known about it. And more is on the way. Such hypotheses as the current suspicion that neural-activity-enhanced RNA-triggered protein synthesis is basic to memory-trace formation may or may not prove correct. Nevertheless, the magnitude and competence of the effort underway would appear to justify the expectation that, within a few years, the site and physical nature of the microscopic changes in the neurons that constitute the building blocks of the memory will be identified. This, in turn, is almost certain to suggest new directions to those who are seeking to relate the larger-scale characteristics of the nervous system to observed brain function. There should be no lack of progress in the foreseeable future.

BIBLIOGRAPHY

Adey, W. R., "Recent Thoughts on the Neuron Model Based on Brain Wave Analysis," paper given at Biomedical Engineering Symposium, San Diego, Calif., April, 1961.

Bickford, R. G., et al., "Changes in Memory Function Produced by Electrical Stimulation of the Temporal Lobe in Man," in *The Brain and Human Behavior,* ed. by Solomon, Cobb, and Penfield (The Williams & Wilkins Company, Baltimore, 1958), pp. 227–240.

Bures, J., "Reversible Decortication and Behavior," in *The Central Nervous System and Behavior,* ed. by M. A. B. Brazier (Josiah Macy, Jr., Foundation, New York, 1959), pp. 207–248.

Burns, B. D., *The Mammalian Cerebral Cortex* [Edward Arnold (Publishers) Ltd., London, 1958], chap. V, "The Problem of Memory."

Galambos, R., "Changing Concepts of the Learning Mechanism," in *Brain Mechanisms and Learning,* ed. by Fessard, Gerard, Konorski, and Delafresnaye (Charles C Thomas, Publisher, Springfield, Ill., 1961), pp. 231–242.

Galambos, R., "Glia, Neurons, and Information Storage," in *Macromolecular Specificity and Biological Memory,* ed. by F. O. Schmitt (The MIT Press, Cambridge, Mass., 1962), pp. 52–54.

Gerard, R. W., "The Fixation of Experience," in *Brain Mechanisms and Learning,* ed. by Fessard, Gerard, Konorski, and Delafresnaye (Charles C Thomas, Publisher, Springfield, Ill., 1961), pp. 21–36.

Hebb, D. O., *Organization of Behavior* (John Wiley & Sons, Inc., New York, 1949).

Hebb, D. O., "Distinctive Features of Learning in the Higher Animal," in *Brain Mechanisms and Learning*, ed. by Fessard, Gerard, Konorski, and Delafresnaye (Charles C Thomas, Publisher, Springfield, Ill., 1961) pp. 37–52.

John, E. R., "Neural Mechanisms of Decision Making," paper given at Symposium on Information Storage and Neural Control, Houston Neurological Society, Houston, Tex., Mar. 9, 1962.

Konorski, J., "The Physiological Approach to the Problem of Recent Memory," in *Brain Mechanisms and Learning*, ed. by Fessard, Gerard, Konorksi, and Delafresnaye (Charles C Thomas, Publisher, Springfield, Ill., 1961), pp. 115–132.

Lorente de No, R., "Circulation of Impulses and Memory," in *Macromolecular Specificity and Biological Memory*, ed. by F. O. Schmitt (The MIT Press, Cambridge, Mass., 1962), pp. 89–90.

Miller, G. A., "A Note on the Remarkable Memory of Man," *Institute of Radio Engineers Transactions on Electronic Computers*, September, 1957, pp. 194–195.

Morrell, F., "Lasting Changes in Synaptic Organization Produced by Continuous Neuronal Bombardment," in *Brain Mechanisms and Learning*, ed. by Fessard, Gerard, Konorski, and Delafresnaye (Charles C Thomas, Publisher, Springfield, Ill., 1961), pp. 375–392.

Morrell, F., "Electrochemical Mechanisms and Information Storage in Nerve Cells," *Macromolecular Specificity and Biological Memory*, ed. by F. O. Schmitt (The MIT Press, Cambridge, Mass., 1962), pp. 73–79.

Myers, R. E., "Corpus Callosum and Visual Gnosis," in *Brain Mechanisms and Learning*, ed. by Fessard, Gerard, Konorski, and Delafresnaye (Charles C Thomas, Publisher, Springfield, Ill., 1961), pp. 481–506.

Penfield, W., and L. Roberts, *Speech and Brain Mechanisms* (Princeton University Press, Princeton, N.J., 1959), chap. III, "The Recording of Consciousness and the Function of Interpretive Cortex."

Quastler, H., "The Complexity of Biological Computers," *Institute of Radio Engineers Transactions on Electronic Computers*, September, 1957, pp. 192–194.

Russell, W. R., *Brain, Memory, Learning* (Oxford University Press, Fair Lawn, N.J., 1959).

Sperry, R. W., "Cerebral Organization and Behavior," *Science*, vol. 133 (1961), pp. 1749–1757.

Trevarthen, C. B., "Double Visual Learning in Split-brain Monkeys," *Science*, vol. 136 (1962), pp. 258–259.

Trotter, W., "On Certain Minor Injuries of the Brain," *British Medical Journal*, (1924), pp. 816–819.

von Neumann, J., *The Computer and the Brain* (Yale University Press, New Haven, Conn., 1958).

Automatic Learning

Learning by Classical Conditioning

If food is put in a dog's mouth, saliva flows. This is entirely automatic; the substance in the mouth acts on taste organs in the tongue and palate, and the action of the glands is regulated through the nervous system in accordance with the information thus supplied. The odor of food can produce the same salivary reaction. It is possible that this is a similarly automatic, chemically mediated response. But salivation can also be stimulated by the sight of some particular food that the dog relishes. This is not an innate, unlearned reaction. It does not occur with a naïve puppy: for a dog to react in this way, previous experience is required connecting the sight of the food with subsequent gustatory enjoyment.

Ivan Petrovich Pavlov, professor at the Medical Academy at St. Petersburg, first comprehended the far-reaching implications of these well-known behavioral characteristics of dogs and other animals, and upon them based a series of investigations that, after a half century, still ranks as a unique tour de force in modern psychology. Interestingly enough, Pavlov started these psychological investigations after he had already been awarded a Nobel prize, in 1904, for his pioneering work on the physiology of digestion.

To the extent to which these matters were thought about at all in the early years of the twentieth century, a dog's salivation at the sight of food was interpreted, in anthropomorphic terms, as an indication that the animal had "learned" that the visual image meant food and that the salivary response was the result of the animal's thoughtful contemplation of the ensuing consequences. But Pavlov was distrustful of such phrases; he was not sure what the words meant. In any event, he set out to design experiments to give as much insight as possible into the mechanisms involved when repeated experience, such as the visual perception of a platter of food, ultimately resulted in the stimulation of a normally automatic bodily response, such as salivation.

Pavlov's experiments were essentially uncomplicated. A dog that was kept restrained but comfortable in the quiet surroundings of the laboratory would be subjected to the sound made by a metronome or buzzer; shortly thereafter, a door in front of the dog would open and a tray of food would appear. The simple but far-reaching consequence of the experiments was the discovery that, after a number of trials, the sound of the metronome or buzzer alone would automatically start the salivary process. In Pavlovian terms, the dog had been *conditioned*. The audible signal, the *conditioned stimulus*, had come to have the same effect on the automatic physiological activities of the dog as that produced by the *unconditioned stimulus*, the food itself. Pavlovian conditioning is frequently called *classical conditioning*, to differentiate it from *operant*, or *instrumental*, *conditioning*, to be discussed later.

Classical conditioned responses were quickly recognized as representative of a common ingredient in much animal and human behavior. When a horse breaks into a trot in response to the crack of a whip, it is because it has been conditioned to the point where the audible stimulus produces the same muscular response as does the automatic unlearned reaction to the painful stimulus of the whip across the animal's flanks. When a child displays a chronic fear of the dark because of having been frequently punished at an early age by being shut in the closet, it can be said that the child has been conditioned so that the normally neutral stimulus—the absence of light—is capable of arousing the emotional reaction associated with the unpleasantnesses that had at one time coincided with darkness.

Conditioned responses might have been considered to constitute no more than an interesting sidelight on the complex and poorly understood processes of higher reasoning if they had been observed only in humans and such intelligent mammals as dogs and horses. The endurance and importance of the field opened up by Pavlov's experiments resides in the fact that conditioned-response learning has been found to occur so widely that it appears to constitute a fundamental property of the basic neuronal organization possessed in common by most creatures. The same is true of *operant* conditioning, to be discussed in the next section, which possesses many features in common with classical conditioning but is even more advanced in its "intellectual" implications. We shall defer to that section the examination of evidence for the widespread applicability of learning by conditioning to low as well as high forms of animal life. For now, we shall consider other observations that lead to the same conclusion—that conditioned reflexes can be of an entirely automatic, unthinking character.

Consider, for example, one of Pavlov's early variations of his experiments with dogs. He had established that salivation could be conditioned to any kind of neutral stimulus detectable by the animal—not only to sounds of metronomes and buzzers but also to lights, to touches of the finger applied to the animal's side or leg, and the like. Then he sought to determine whether the salivary response could be conditioned to a normally painful stimulus. The stimulus chosen was an electric shock, initially so weak as to be a barely perceptible tickle, but increased in strength with the progress of training. Ultimately it was found that the application of a surprisingly powerful shock produced no sign of pain or displeasure, not even the quickening of pulse rate and breathing that usually accompanies an unpleasant surprise. Instead, it was followed by mouth-watering, tail-wagging, and the other physical accompaniments of pleasurable anticipation. Other dogs were conditioned to identify a prick of the skin, deep enough to draw blood, as a welcome signal of approaching food!

Much more recently, J. P. Segundo and associates, at the Instituto de investigación de ciencias biológicas, in Montevideo, have reported experiments that seem closely related to Pavlov's removal, by conditioning, of the painful effects of noxious stimuli. In the Uruguayan experiments, cats were conditioned to the point where an audible tone appeared to "turn off" the painful sensation associated with a subcutaneous electric shock. In this case the conditioning procedure was one in which the sounding of a musical tone was followed, a few seconds later, by cessation of the electric current that was making the animal uncomfortable. Ultimately, the tone alone would cause the cat to exhibit the same behavioral symptoms of relaxation and ease normally accompanying cessation of the painful stimulus, even though the punishing current had not been turned off! Figure 10-1 shows a test animal during various phases of these experiments. The upper pictures (left to right) display the appearance of the cat before the shock, while receiving the electric shock, and just after it has been turned off. In the lower trio of pictures, the shock was being applied when the middle and right-hand photographs were taken, but the right-hand photograph displays the animal's apparent ease and relaxation in response to an audible tone that, in previous conditioning experiences, had heralded the removal of the painful stimulus. The oscilloscope tracing under each photograph is the concurrent EEG record. These tracings also show that, in the conditioned cat, the electrical effects of the noxious stimulus in the brain are turned off almost as effectively by the audible tone as though the shock had, in fact, been discontinued.

Of course, we are all aware of evidence for the existence of some kind of "switch" in the nervous system that is capable, under certain circumstances, of turning off the sense of pain. Most of us have had the experience of sustaining some form of physical injury in the course of a highly exciting or otherwise emotionally tinged episode and not being aware of it until after the excitement has died down. This is common among those who are injured in battle or in automobile accidents. Nevertheless, these demonstrations of techniques for deliberately conditioning an animal, in the quiet of the laboratory, to lose its feeling of pain or even develop a response of pleasure to what would normally be an intensely painful stimulus, are striking to say the least. These conditioning techniques seem to involve "getting hold of" responses of the nervous system ordinarily considered to be automatic and entirely outside the range of external control, and molding them into something quite different from what they had been before.

Some of the most interesting examples of the manner in which conditioning can permit the establishment of connections between simple stimuli and bodily responses normally inaccessible to conscious control come from experiments on humans. In the work of C. V. Hudgins, the conditioned stimulus was the sound of a bell. The bell was rung; then a bright light was directed into the eyes of the subject, thus producing the natural contraction of the pupils through the operation of the pupillary-control reflex discussed in Chapter 4. After many training sessions, the sound of the bell alone produced pupillary contraction.

The experiment was further refined. In the conditioning sessions, as the bell was rung, Hudgins sharply spoke the word "contract." Ultimately it was possible to dispense with both light and bell: the sound of the word alone acquired the ability to force an involuntary and substantial contraction of the pupils of the human subjects.

Yet another step was found possible: the subjects could be taught to replace the experimenter. Before long they learned to produce their own pupillary contraction without the aid of bell, light, or Hudgins, merely by saying or thinking the word "contract."

Hudgins's experiments are not unique. R. Menzies´ employed similar techniques to train subjects to produce a change in their body temperature by saying a suitable code word to themselves. It is a neurological fact that when one hand is suddenly chilled, the other will become somewhat chilled also, owing to a bilateral reflex action. Therefore Menzies was able to use, as the unconditioned

Fig. 10-1. "Turning off" of painful sensation by audible tone, in conditioned cat. (*From J. P. Segundo et al., in Brain Mechanisms and Learning, Charles C Thomas, Publisher, Springfield, Ill., 1961. By permission of the publishers.*)

stimulus that through normal physical processes produced a drop in temperature of the *left* hand, the immersion of the *right* hand in ice water. Ultimately, the lowering of the temperature of the left hand that had originally been produced by the ice water was achievable at the will of the subject.

The possible relevance of such experiments to the bodily control occasionally displayed by followers of yoga and other occult practices is obvious. There is also a possible relationship to hypnotism. In fact, Andrew Salter (1955) makes a convincing case for the explanation of most of the phenomena of hypnosis in terms of classical conditioning. Apparently, many normally involuntary bodily functions can be linked to voluntary actions, or to the neuronal activity produced by words, simply by giving the subject training of the same basic nature as Pavlov's original conditioning of his salivating dogs.

In a way, the automatic and mechanical nature of learning by conditioning is more vividly demonstrated by experiments with human subjects than by the evidence we shall examine in the next section for learning among very low forms of animal life. For the human subjects who participated in the experiments of Hudgins and others did not at any time develop an awareness of what processes they were controlling to achieve their effects. Evidently the experience was always a mysterious one. When Hudgins asked the subjects, "What did you do when I said 'contract'?" their answers were, "I did nothing." A conditioned reflex, once established, requires no conscious effort. It merely happens.

Although conditioned reflexes can be "forgotten" if not used, in most respects they have the same outward attributes as the innate, permanently wired-in reflexes of the animal. This observation led early investigators to seek evidence as to whether a well-established conditioned reflex could itself be employed as a natural or "unconditioned" reflex in a typical classical conditioning experiment. It was found that this was indeed possible. For example, once Pavlov's dogs had been trained to the point of copious and prompt salivation on the sounding of a metronome, the animals could be further trained to associate a visual symbol such as a large black square with the imminence of the audible signal; as a result, after training, display of the black square alone would produce salivation. This result could be achieved even though at no time during the training had the presentation of the visual signal followed by the audible signal been in turn followed by a food reward.

Because of the phenomenon of *extinction,* which we shall refer to later, such double conditioning experiments are not easy to perform successfully. Recently, the modern techniques of direct electric stimulation of the brain have permitted more highly controlled demonstrations of the generality of the classical conditioning process. At the University of Michigan, for example, R. W. Doty and C. Giurgea essentially manufactured their own unconditioned reflexes by sending stimulating current through electrodes implanted in the motor cortex of a dog or monkey. Depending on the exact position of the electrode, the resulting "unconditioned" response might be lifting and extension of the right hind leg, curling of the tail, rotation of the head, or, with a monkey, lifting of an arm. These motor responses were of course the analogs of salivation in the Pavlovian experiments, while the electric stimulation of the motor cortex took the place of the food stimulus. The equivalent of the clicking of the metronome or the ringing of the bell was supplied, in these experiments, by electric stimulation in another area of the cortex, remote from the motor cortex itself.

The results of the University of Michigan work were positive and convincing. After a number of trials per day for several weeks, it was found that the application of the conditioned stimulus would cause the animal to commence the expected physical response, before current was sent into the electrode implanted in the motor cortex. An important aspect of this work, emphasized by Doty and Giurgea, was the absence of motivational aids in the establishment of the conditioned response. Although the animals presumably experienced some kind of sensation from the conditioned stimulus, various tests indicated that the sensation was of a neutral kind—neither especially pleasant nor unpleasant.

The Michigan work does not stand alone. Other investigators have even established that physical reactions produced by electric stimulation of brainstem formations can be conditioned to audible tones.

The principle underlying all this work seems clear: if stimulation of a specific pattern of sensory neurons in the brain is followed by a specific pattern of activity of motor- or glandular-control neurons, however produced, repetition of the sequence will ultimately lead to the formation of neuronal connections by means of which the sensory pattern alone can directly drive the motor or glandular response. This seems to be an automatic process, not involving the intervention of consciousness or higher intelligence. Although it is not certain that all motor actions possible to the body can be connected in this way to ordinarily irrelevant sensory stimuli, it has certainly been established that much muscular and glandular activity not normally subject to the control of the individual can be so connected. We shall henceforth refer to this neural principle by the term *automatic pattern interconnection.*

Learning by Operant Conditioning

In Pavlovian, or classical, conditioning, a normally irrelevant stimulus is gradually caused to elicit a motor or glandular response that is ordinarily the uncontrolled reaction to an entirely different kind of input stimulus. In *operant,* or *instrumental,* conditioning, the irrelevant stimulus is gradually made to elicit a motor response of a kind that is normally under the voluntary control of the animal. Roger Sperry's Caltech cats had undergone operant conditioning in learning to open the swinging door bearing the correct symbol. Since operant conditioning can be successfully employed with a wide variety of animals, let us extend our understanding by consideration of a primitive example—the education of an earthworm.

It has been known for fifty years (R. M. Yerkes, 1912) that the earthworm can learn a simple spatial maze. If started at the base of a T-shaped tunnel, the worm can learn to turn right, when it reaches the crossbar of the T, and thereby achieve the reward of a bed of succulent mud, and not turn left to be punished by the unpleasant stimulus of electric shock or sandpaper. This kind of learned behavior appears to differ from that of Pavlovian, or classical, conditioning, only in that the motor response involved is of the kind which we customarily regard as more "volitional" than the automatic, built-in reflexes involved in the classical experiments. Of course, for an organism as primitive as a worm, a good case can be made for the thesis that all motor responses are simple automatic reactions to the environmental conditions. Nevertheless, in the course of training the worm to make the proper turn at the crossbar of the T, there is no means of ensuring that the same motor response will always occur —part of the time the worm will turn left and be punished, part of the time it will turn right and be rewarded.

The elements of reward or punishment seem to be essential in operant conditioning, whereas these ingredients need not be a part of the classical conditioning routine. In classical conditioning, as established by such experiments as those performed at the University of Michigan on corticocortical coupling, or in the training of human subjects to control pupillary contraction or body temperature, there was no question of motivational stimuli: the connection between the sensory pattern and the ultimate motor response was a simple and direct consequence of a large number of repetitions of a consistent stimulus/response experience. But in conditioning an earthworm to turn right instead of left, two motor responses are possible to whatever kind of sensory input indicates to the worm the presence of the crossbar of the T. The development of a selective pattern of behavior requires some kind of neuronal mechanism that establishes a connection between the triggering sensory pattern and the two possible motor-response programs, with the connection being established more strongly for one of the two possible responses than for the other. In all operant conditioning experiments it has been found that the response that is strengthened is the one that best fulfills some physiological need of the organism, such as hunger, sex, or physical comfort.

The phenomena of operant conditioning contain an interesting implication with respect to the memory processes. After the worm has made its turn at the crossbar of the T, either toward the right or toward the left, it must proceed for a while before it is either rewarded or punished for its choice. Clearly therefore the sensory and motor patterns related to the episode in question must persist for some time so that their interconnections can be available for relative strengthening or weakening after the animal's score has been indicated to it by the pleasantness or unpleasantness of the sensation it finally experiences. This after-the-fact strengthening or weakening, by emotional input, of neuronal connections that have previously been tentatively established would appear to have something in common with the earlier-discussed effect of attention focusing in retrieving from the decaying short-term memory detailed information that would otherwise be lost.

Operant conditioning techniques are by no means limited to the training of animals to choose between only two possible responses. Consider, for example, the training of an animal to press a lever when a light is turned on. This is accomplished by taking advantage of the natural curiosity and restlessness of the caged animal. The lever is positioned so that it will occasionally be stepped on while the animal aimlessly wanders around its cage. If the light is on when this happens, the subject is "reinforced" by being presented with a morsel of food. With the passage of time, the behavior follows a "learning curve" which ultimately results in prompt and consistent lever pressing whenever the light is turned on. When such performance is exhibited by a monkey, we might be inclined to say the animal "gets the idea" and employs thinking procedures in controlling its subsequent behavior. When the same kind of performance is exhibited by a rat or even lower animal, it is much easier to imagine that what is involved is an automatic mechanical process, not associated with what we would call "thinking."

The argument in favor of the automatic, mechanical nature of operant conditioning is strengthened by comparison of the rates of learning of higher and lower animals. An earthworm learns its T-maze performance in 100 or 200 trials. A cat requires a similar number of trials to learn to respond to a visual signal by hitting a lever and thereby avoiding having an unpleasant blast of air blown into its ear. And experiments have been reported with a six-month-old baby to determine how many trials would be necessary to condition it against reaching out to touch the flame of a lighted candle. (The experiment of course was so arranged as to block the child's hand each time before injury was sustained.) The number of trials required was the same as for training the earthworm, approximately 150!

The existence of a primitive, automatic ingredient in learning is also suggested by the ability of decorticate animals to learn, as long as the task to be performed does not require sensory discrimination capability that has been removed by elimination of the cortex. Hernandez-Peon even found that a decorticate cat learns to lift its paw to avoid an electric shock, when warned by a buzzer, as quickly as does an intact animal! Most spectacular of all are some recent experiments on planaria. If a flatworm is cut in two, the front end will regenerate a tail, the tail end will regenerate a head, and, in about three weeks, there will be two self-sufficient worms where only one grew before. The pertinent point is this: if an educated worm is used in the experiment—one that has been taught an operant response such as a T-maze performance—the new worm formed from the tail end, as well as the new head-end worm, will both perform correctly as soon as put to the test! This result obviously is tied in with the existence in various segments of the worm of similar aggregations of neurons that constitute the closest thing these primitive organisms have to a brain, and indicates that nature has provided for redundancy in its method of storing the memory of past experience in the neural anatomy of the worm. But the result also supports the concept that the basic processes involved in operant conditioning are primitive in the extreme.

It must not be thought that, because the worm has been a star performer in these experiments, it possesses some accident of neural configuration that makes it unusually susceptible to operant conditioning. Wherever in the animal kingdom the psychologist looks, he finds that patient experimentation is rewarded by additional evidence of the universality of learning. If moist filter paper is placed at 24-hour intervals on the same groups of tentacles of a sea anemone, the paper will at first be carried to the mouth by the tentacles, but after a few repetitions of the stimulus it will be rejected, and the habit so formed will be retained for a week or more. However, the learned response applies only to the specific tentacles that have been trained; the untrained tentacles will accept the filter paper even while the trained tentacles reject it. And even microscopic organisms can learn. J. W. French, in 1940, observed a measurable decrease with practice in the time required for paramecia to find their way through a glass tube into their individual culture medium. It is in fact not even clear that man is any more adept than the lower animals at the formation of a simple conditioned response. By operant conditioning methods, pigeons are taught to peck out tunes on chimes, seals to blow horns, and bears to ride bicycles. It probably takes the average human a comparable number of trials to develop proficiency in a new golf stroke, which is an extension of the normal motor patterns no greater than that required for the tricks learned by the animals.

To be sure, man can learn a much more complex and involved series of motor patterns than the lower animals can; he is also able to generate internally his own systems of rewards and punishments for the operant conditioning process. Whereas a pet animal, on being taught a new trick, has a correct performance reinforced by an affectionate word or a pat on the head from its master, the golfer who is learning a new stroke provides essentially the same input to his neural system by comparing how his club or ball has actually traveled with respect to his objective and generating his own rewarding or punishing emotion of approval or disapproval in accordance with the closeness of the comparison. It is doubtless this internally generated signal that reacts back on the still-sensitive patterns of sensory and motor neurons activated during the just-completed stroke to strengthen or weaken their interconnections and make it more or less likely that similar neuronal relationships will govern performance on the next occasion. Of course, the sensory pattern to which motor action is being tied is in this case a combination of visual inputs, showing the position and motion of the golf ball, club, and parts of the body, and proprioceptive inputs relative to balance, rate of motion, and tension and configuration of the various muscles. When a golfer learns a new stroke, or when a bear learns to ride a bicycle, an entire series of successive conditioned responses must be established. Patterns must be stored, in the memory system, of the specific configurations of the sensory data that constitute the triggers for the initiation of corresponding stored subprograms of motor response by the muscles. The determination by the coincidence circuits of the brain that the actual configuration of incoming sensory information adequately matches one of the stored trigger patterns must send a suitable implementing signal to the appropriate stored subprogram of motor control. It is by the automatic electrochemical processes of operant conditioning that these connections are gradually established between the successive memory patterns that represent the sensory content of the ultimately standardized golf stroke and the corresponding stored patterns of motor control. It is by the connection-strengthening and -weakening effects of the emotional signals of approval and disapproval that correction of the stored motor-control programs is gradually brought about until the desired performance is finally achieved.

It must be admitted that, even when broken down in this way, the learning of a new golf stroke is not quite completely described in terms of a series of operant conditioning processes exactly analogous to that involved in the T-maze conditioning of the earthworm. This is because of the feedback aspect that causes the detailed sequence of sensory stimuli observed by the golfer to be itself dependent upon his motor responses to those stimuli. Therefore, as learning progresses, there is a gradual modification of the sensory stimuli to which motor responses are being conditioned. This continual changing of the problem that is presented for solution undoubtedly increases the difficulty and may help account for the fact that it takes a golfer much longer to perfect a new stroke than it does an earthworm to learn to run a T-maze properly. Nevertheless, there appears to be no need to invoke any basically new learning principle. We are not dealing with absolutely precise stimulus and response patterns in any of these situations; there must always be a certain tolerance between the trigger pattern stored in the memory and the configuration of incoming sensory data that will be identified by the coincidence circuits as being adequately similar to the anticipated implementing pattern. As long as the sequence of sensory patterns experienced by the golfer does not change too rapidly from trial to trial, the normal operant conditioning process should continue to apply and gradually bring about convergence of the motor-response patterns and therefore of the input-stimulus patterns upon an adequately standardized set of representations. In fact, the existence of such convergence is one of the conditions that is influential in the establishment of the ground rules for any sport. A game of tennis could be devised to be played with square balls, a rough court, and a racquet with a wavy stringed surface. The unsuitability of such a game for serious consideration can be described by the statement that it does not lend itself well enough to the processes of operant conditioning. There is no way for the player to devise a series of maneuvers and strokes that will ultimately converge to a reasonably small number of standardized situations wherein a successful play involves a reproducible, and therefore conditionable, sequence of interrelated sensory stimuli and motor-response patterns.

Extinction of a Conditioned Response

In our discussion of classical conditioning, reference was made to the probability that a conditioned reflex involves neuronal arrangements very similar to those that control the innate reflexes with which the animal is provided at birth. Such an observation would appear to be equally true of a conditioned response of the operant variety. But, whether or not conditioned- and unconditioned-reflex mechanisms are essentially the same, it is certainly true that the conditioned variety rarely if ever becomes as firmly established as the automatic reflexes. The learned habit can be partially or completely forgotten with the passage of time, if there are no intervening practice sessions. In addition, conditioned responses are subject to a process, called *extinction*, that will have to be explained by any satisfactory theory of brain function.

While extinction applies equally to operant and classical conditioning, we may conveniently demonstrate it by calling once again upon Pavlov's salivating dogs. If a dog first develops a habit of salivation when a tone is heard, as a result of many successive experiences of hearing a buzzer and then receiving food, and if then the experimenter starts withholding the food, the dog's salivary secretion starts to diminish. After only six or eight such "nonreinforced" trials, a few minutes apart, salivation in response to the buzzer may disappear entirely. The obvious interpretation is that the electric connection established earlier between the sensory pattern of the buzzer and the motor pattern controlling salivation has been broken as a consequence of the emotional response to the withholding of the food. But this interpretation cannot be entirely correct; for if the dog is allowed to rest for a period, the conditioned response to the buzzer returns, even though no reinforced trials have intervened. To be sure, if these extinction exercises follow one after another, with no intervening instances of food reinforcement, the conditioned response ultimately disappears permanently. However, this is a much slower process than the temporary extinction of the response that occurs after a small number of nonreinforced trials.

The common-sense interpretation of such results is that, after the food fails to appear two or three times, the dog "gets the idea" that the buzzer may no longer be a signal for food, and when it "realizes" that food is less and less likely to appear, the anticipation aroused in it by the buzzer diminishes and so does its salivation. After a rest, the dog may forget the recent unpleasant episode and revert to the earlier habit of interpreting the buzzer as heralding an imminent feast; or the last experience may be remembered, but not vividly, so that the dog gives more weight to the cumulative evidence of the past than to immediately recent experience.

Such would probably be the thoughts of a human subject in a conditioning experiment, and possibly of Pavlov's dogs. But it is hard to believe that an earthworm would figure things out like this. Yet the phenomenon of extinction is observed with the lowly organisms as well as with the higher animals. For these lower creatures, extinction, like conditioning itself, must arise directly out of the properties of the neuronal networks. In the higher animals the same automatic extinction process probably occurs, although similar results may also occasionally be produced by the operation of the much more complex neuronal processes of higher reasoning.

One-trial Conditioning: Imprinting

A curious exception sometimes occurs to the normal rule that animal learning of a new behavior pattern requires many training repetitions. The name *imprinting* has been given to the phenomenon whereby a very young animal, usually only hours or days old, is able to form a highly specialized kind of habit as a consequence of a single experience. Most of the quantitative studies of imprinting have been made on birds. This is partly because birds exhibit the phenomenon more strongly than most other animals. In addition, complete isolation from other animals from the instant of birth, which is required for these experiments, is easiest to achieve when the subject can be hatched from an egg and subsequently be cared for in an incubator.

Imprinting is easily demonstrated. Half of the eggs laid by a goose are removed to an incubator for hatching, and the other half are left with the nesting mother bird. The goslings hatched by the mother will, in the normal way, immediately follow her around the barnyard. The goslings hatched in the incubator will similarly follow the first moving thing they see—the attendant who moves them from incubator to exercise area, for example. But this is not just a matter of following the attendant because no proper mother is available. For, if the two groups of goslings are now differently marked for identification and placed together under a large box, with the mother goose and the incubator attendant standing nearby, removal of the box will then be the signal for an automatic sorting-out process: the incubator babies will ignore the goose and stream to their human "parent"!

It is not even necessary that the foster parent be a living creature; inanimate objects pulled along ahead of the young birds can also serve as parents. Young Canada geese and mallard ducklings have been "adopted" in this way by a small green box containing a ticking alarm clock. Other ducklings and goslings have been induced to respond to a football.

The phenomenon of imprinting is made even more curious by the fact that there appears to be only a brief interval of time in the life of the very young animal when such imprinting can occur. In an extensive series of experiments performed by Eckhardt H. Hess, of the University of Chicago, it was established that ducklings are most strongly imprinted between the thirteenth and seventeenth hours after hatching. If their first experience in following a moving object occurs within five or six hours after leaving the egg, they form a noticeable attachment for whatever "foster mother" is presented to them, but it is tenuous and easily broken by comparison with the exceedingly strong fixation formed by a sixteen-hour-old duckling. On the other hand, if the first following experience is deferred until the duckling has reached the ripe old age of thirty hours, little evidence of imprinting is detected.

Imprinting has been observed, not only with geese and ducks, but with guinea pigs, sheep, turkeys, pheasants, quail, and chickens. Since the phenomenon has only recently been brought into the realm of controlled measurement, its extent and importance remain undetermined. However, the breadth of possible applicability of imprinting is indicated by investigations that are under way into whether the smiling response of human infants may involve similar brain mechanisms.

Imprinting obviously is not an example of ordinary learning by conditioning. The acquisition by the young animal of the habit of following is much too rapid for this. The narrow time interval during which imprinting can be effected also indicates the operation of some special mechanism. For some peculiar reason, the pattern of neuronal interconnections that enables the young bird to follow its mother and thereby stay out of trouble is incomplete at the time of hatching. Apparently the genetic mechanisms are able to supply a wiring diagram for the neurons that will automatically cause the young animal to follow a moving object, but cannot build into the neural equipment a stored sensory pattern representing the mother, as a trigger mechanism for the following response. Instead, the young animal has been equipped with an inherited stored "program" which, during a narrow interval of time no doubt defined by some aspects of the baby's physiological state, completes the almost-innate following-response reflex. Under the control of this imprinting program, the neural mechanisms seize upon the sensory stimulus pattern associated with the first moving object presented in the critical interval, store it in the memory, and tie it with strong and permanent connections to the inherited system of neuronal interconnections that provide for the muscular activities involved in following a moving object.

One day, when we know much more about the detailed nature of the neuronal interconnections that determine behavior, we may understand the practical circuit problems that have in these instances resulted in the curious incompleteness of nature's provision for what ought to be completely innate behavior patterns provided at birth to the young animal. For now, we should probably not allow the peculiar characteristics of one-trial imprinting to distract our attention unduly from the attributes of the much more general phenomenon of learning by conditioning, which always appears to require the cumulative effect of many successive episodes.

The Electrical Concomitants of Learning

Inevitably, many experimenters have turned their attention to measurement of the electric activity of the brain that is associated with learning experiences. It seems impossible at this time to draw sweeping conclusions from the results of this work, but the electrical measurements do provide interesting corroboration of some of the deductions from behavioral observations, as well as additional clues that must ultimately be valuable in the development of a comprehensive theory of brain function.

By the use of external electrodes in man and of internally implanted electrodes in animals, regions in the cortex and brainstem have been found in which electric potentials develop in response to either audible, visual, or tactile sensations. In human EEG measurements, these nonspecific responses are most likely to appear when the electrodes are placed close to the vertex, or top, of the head. In electrodes implanted in the deeper brain regions of animals, the reticular activating system provides strong signals, as might be expected from its general attention-focusing and response-control functions discussed in previous chapters. Similarly, the amygdaloid nucleus and other related portions of the so-called *limbic system,* which is known from other experiments to be involved in emotional processes, readily exhibit nonspecific electric indications of the receipt of outside sensory stimuli.

If monotonously repetitive stimuli are provided, such as a regular

series of clicks or staccato tones, the nonspecific-brain-potential measurements will display the property of *habituation*: the pulse of brain
potential induced by each audible stimulus will, with continuing
repetition, gradually diminish and ultimately disappear. If we consider these nonspecific brain potentials as being somehow related to
the degree of attention the subject is paying to the stimulus, their
gradual decline correlates nicely with subjective experience: noises
that initially interfere with concentration or keep us awake may
ultimately recede into the background of our consciousness and lose
their effectiveness if they are monotonous and repetitive in character. Such habituation must be regarded as another basic form of
learning. It is in effect a kind of negative learning, perhaps anton-
ymous to the essentially positive learning of conditioned responses.
Habituation is found throughout the animal scale, from protozoa to
man. The indication is that, as in the case of learning by conditioning, habituation derives from some fundamental property of nerve
tissue and does not necessarily require special complex neuronal
circuits.

Robert Galambos, of the Walter Reed Army Medical Center, has
shown that in other respects the behavior of the nonspecific brain
potentials appears to correspond to subjective attention phenomena.
He habituated a rhesus monkey to audible clicks, until the voltage
pulses induced by the audible stimulus in electrodes implanted in
several positions in the brainstem faded into the general brain-wave
background. Then he suddenly changed the rules: he accompanied,
or "reinforced," each click with a puff of air to the animal's face. This
immediately caused the evoked potential associated with each click/
air-puff episode to become very large at all electrode positions. And
after a number of conditioning episodes during which the click was
always followed by the annoying puff of air, a large response was
then evoked by the click acting alone, in accordance with the established principles of learning by conditioning.

The brain processes involved in Galambos's experiments on monkeys probably are similar to the mechanisms underlying the variations
of the EEG records with conditioning observed with human subjects
by Vladimir Sergeivich Rusinov, of the Institute of Higher Nervous
Activity of the Academy of Sciences of the U.S.S.R. The subject
was asked to press a rubber bulb every third time that an audible tone
was presented. The tones were all of the same duration and initially
followed one another at regular intervals. After enough bulb-pressing
episodes to habituate the subject and remove indications from his
EEG record, the experimenter surreptitiously arranged, in the next
sequence, to withhold the third tone—the one calling for the bulb to

be pressed. The absence of the expected signal triggered off spikes in the EEG record similar to those observed by Galambos on reinforcement of a habituated acoustic signal by an annoying puff of air. Further, just as in the case of the monkeys, the reinforcement caused EEG responses to be picked up by electrodes placed some distance away from the position on the head ordinarily most responsive to these nonspecific, attention-signaling impulses.

Such results, although not extensive, are encouragingly consistent with the general nature of the conclusions we have been led to, by entirely different evidence, relative to the memory and learning processes. It is satisfying to have evidence for nonspecific nerve currents that diminish in the same way as our subjective sensations seem to fade, when the stimulus is monotonous and persistent. The sudden increase in these electrical effects induced by a kind of "punishment"—a blast of air in one case, and the necessity to refrain from performing an anticipated bulb-pressing operation in the other case—also provides evidence for the physical reality of the motivational effects of reinforcement on memory and learning that have been deduced from behavioral observations. The fact that such a reinforcing stimulus causes the nonspecific currents not only to increase in magnitude but also to spread and appear in areas of the brain where they were not detectable before is also suggestive. If learning involves the interconnection of neuronal circuits that are widely separated in the brain, as we have decided it must, we might expect a learning situation such as that produced by unusual sensory stimuli, particularly when reinforced by suitable emotional motivation, to be accompanied by wide-ranging electric currents that sensitize or otherwise implement the necessary neuronal-connection processes.

These same interpretations appear to apply to the brain potentials measured when an animal is undergoing operant conditioning. In such a case, the conditioned stimulus is likely to be an audible or visual signal that indicates to the animal that pressing a lever will prevent shock or supply food. As the animal learns, habituation causes the initially high nonspecific brain activity to decrease and possibly even disappear entirely. The stimulus-produced brain potentials return promptly, however, if the animal is frustrated in its learned response as, for example, by moving the lever out of reach or by disconnecting it.

Brain-wave "Signature" of Memory and Learning Mechanisms

W. R. Adey, of the UCLA Brain Research Institute, appears to have discovered a kind of brain wave possessing phase properties that provide specific indication of the correctness of performance of a learned response. The wave also seems to be an essential ingredient of the electric activity accompanying operation of the memory mechanisms.

Because of the indications from earlier work that the temporal regions of the brain play an important role in memory (see Chaps. 7 and 9), Adey suspected that these regions would probably also play an important role in learning processes. He therefore implanted electrodes deep in the temporal lobes of cats and recorded their brain-wave patterns during conditioning sessions in which they learned to perform an operant response. A form of T maze was employed, wherein the animal had to choose the correct path, in accordance with the visual cues supplied to it, in order to receive a food award.

Adey's results were consistent and reproducible. For the resting, nonperforming animal, the brain waves measured by the deep temporal electrodes were of an irregular pattern, characterized by a spectrum of frequencies ranging from about 4 to 7 cycles per second. When the cat was traversing the maze in search of a food reward, however, the irregular pattern was replaced by an almost-single-frequency burst of 6-cycle-per-second waves. This was true for both untrained and trained animals, but training produced a pronounced change in the intensity distribution of this 6-cycle-per-second "approach" rhythm over the various regions of the temporal lobe in which electrodes were placed. Furthermore, by cross-correlation measurements, it was found that learning resulted in major changes in the phase relationships among the single-frequency approach waves picked up on the various electrodes. These phase, or time-of-arrival, variations were also consistent with the conclusion that learning results in permanent changes in the spatial patterns of neuronal currents.

Occasionally a trained cat would choose the incorrect response. The associated brain-wave pattern was most interesting. While an error was being made, the phase relationships among the 6-cycle-per-second waves picked up by the various electrodes would change extensively. Apparently an incorrect path could be taken through the cortex by the single-frequency currents of the approach rhythm, and when this happened, an error was made by the animal.

Although Adey concentrated on the temporal regions of the brain, he also implanted electrodes in other areas of some of his test animals. In this way he found evidence of the 6-cycle-per-second approach rhythm in both the upper portion of the reticular formation of the brainstem and the primary visual cortex. In the visual cortex, at least, the single-frequency rhythm appeared only after training, but ultimately was sharp and clear. It seemed to Adey that this spreading of the 6-cycle-per-second rhythm to other parts of the brain with the progress of training might be related to the role played by the temporal regions in memory. This thesis received some confirmation from the results of experiments in which small lesions were placed in the brainstem of trained cats in such a way that the approach rhythm was blocked from both the visual cortex and the upper reticular formation. While this blockage persisted, the animals would continue to traverse the T maze in hope of receiving a reward, but apparently without any ability to use visual cues to distinguish between right and wrong paths. When the lesions healed, in eight to ten days, the 6-cycle-per-second approach rhythm reappeared in the reticular formation and visual cortex, and at the same time the cats recovered the ability to make correct choices!

Thus it appears that Adey's "approach" waves must constitute the electrical signature of some kind of brain mechanism that is basic to the processes of memory and learning. This work is continuing, on monkeys as well as cats. The Brain Research Institute is installing extensive new electronic equipment to speed up and extend the application of the cross-correlation and other modern data-processing techniques that have proved invaluable in this work. We may expect to hear more in the future about Adey and his 6-cycle-per-second waves.

BIBLIOGRAPHY

Adey, W. R., C. W. Dunlop, and C. E. Hendrix, "Hippocampal Slow Waves," *AMA Archives of Neurology,* vol. 3 (1960), pp. 74–90.

Adey, W. R., "Studies of Hippocampal Electrical Activity during Approach Learning," in *Brain Mechanisms and Learning,* ed. by Fessard, Gerard, Konorski, and Delafresnaye (Charles C Thomas, Publisher, Springfield, Ill., 1961), pp. 577–588.

Asimov, I., *The Intelligent Man's Guide to Science* (Basic Books, Inc., Publishers, New York, 1960), chap. 16, "The Mind."

Asratyan, E. A., "Some Aspects of the Elaboration of Conditioned Connections and Formation of Their Properties," in *Brain Mechanisms and Learning,* ed. by Fessard, Gerard, Konorski, and Delafresnaye (Charles C Thomas, Publisher, Springfield, Ill., 1961), pp. 95–114.

Beurle, R. L., "Storage and Manipulation of Information in the Brain," *Journal of the Institute of Electrical Engineering,* February, 1959, pp. 75–82.

Brazier, M. A. B., K. F. Killam, and A. J. Hance, "The Reactivity of the Nervous System in the Light of the Past History of the Organism," in

Sensory Communication, ed. by W. A. Rosenblith (The MIT Press and John Wiley & Sons, Inc., New York, 1961), pp. 699–716.

Bullock, T. H., "The Problem of Recognition in an Analyzer Made of Neurons," in *Sensory Communication,* ed. by W. A. Rosenblith (The MIT Press and John Wiley & Sons, Inc., New York, 1961), pp. 717–724.

Doty, R. W., and C. Giurgea, "Conditioned Reflexes Established by Coupling Electrical Excitations of Two Cortical Areas," in *Brain Mechanisms and Learning,* ed. by Fessard, Gerard, Konorski, and Delafresnaye (Charles C Thomas, Publisher, Springfield, Ill., 1961), pp. 133–152.

Eccles, J. C., "The Effects of Use and Disuse on Synaptic Function," in *Brain Mechanisms and Learning,* ed. by Fessard, Gerard, Konorski, and Delafresnaye (Charles C Thomas, Publisher, Springfield, Ill., 1961), pp. 335–352.

French, J. W., "Trial and Error Learning in Paramecium," *Journal of Experimental Psychology,* vol. 26 (1940), pp. 609–613.

Galambos, R., "Some Neural Correlates of Conditioning and Learning," in *Electrical Studies on the Unanesthetized Brain,* ed. by Ramey and O'Doherty (Harper & Row, Publishers, Incorporated, New York, 1960), pp. 120–130.

Galambos, R., "Changing Concepts of the Learning Mechanism," in *Brain Mechanisms and Learning,* ed. by Fessard, Gerard, Konorski, and Delafresnaye (Charles C Thomas, Publisher, Springfield, Ill., 1961), pp. 231–242.

Garcia-Austt, E., J. Bogacz, and A. Vanzulli, "Significance of the Photic Stimulus on the Evoked Response in Man," in *Brain Mechanisms and Learning,* ed. by Fessard, Gerard, Konorski, and Delafresnaye (Charles C Thomas, Publisher, Springfield, Ill., 1961), pp. 603–623.

Gerard, R. W., "The Fixation of Experience," in *Brain Mechanisms and Learning,* ed. by Fessard, Gerard, Konorski, and Delafresnaye (Charles C Thomas, Publisher, Springfield, Ill., 1961), pp. 21–36.

Harlow, H. F., "The Evolution of Learning," in *Behavior and Evolution,* ed. by Roe and Simpson (Yale University Press, New Haven, Conn., 1958), pp. 269–290.

Hebb, D. O., *The Organization of Behavior* (John Wiley & Sons, Inc., New York, 1949).

Hebb, D. O., "Distinctive Features of Learning in the Higher Animal," in *Brain Mechanisms and Learning,* ed. by Fessard, Gerard, Konorski, and Delafresnaye (Charles C Thomas, Publisher, Springfield, Ill., 1961), pp. 37–52.

Hernandez-Peon, R., and H. Brust-Carmona, "Functional Role of Sub-cortical Structures in Habituation and Conditioning," in *Brain Mechanisms and Learning,* ed. by Fessard, Gerard, Konorski, and Delafresnaye (Charles C Thomas, Publisher, Springfield, Ill., 1961), pp. 393–412.

Hess, E. H., " 'Imprinting' in Animals," *Scientific American*, March, 1958, pp. 81–90.

Hudgins, C. V., "Conditioning and the Voluntary Control of the Pupillary Light Reflex," *Journal of General Psychology*, vol. 8 (1933), pp. 3–51.

Lehrman, D. S., "Varieties of Learning and Memory in Animals," in *Macromolecular Specificity and Biological Memory*, ed. by F. O. Schmitt (The MIT Press, Cambridge, Mass., 1962), pp. 108–110.

Menzies, R., "Further Studies in Conditioned Vasomotor Responses in Human Subjects," *Journal of Experimental Psychology*, vol. 29 (1941), pp. 457–482.

Morrell, F., "Lasting Changes in Synaptic Organization Produced by Continuous Neuronal Bombardment," in *Brain Mechanisms and Learning*, ed. by Fessard, Gerard, Konorski, and Delafresnaye (Charles C Thomas, Publisher, Springfield, Ill., 1961), pp. 375–392.

Rowland, V., "Conditioning and Brain Waves," *Scientific American*, August, 1959, pp. 89–96.

Rusinov, V. S., "EEG Studies in Conditional Reflex Formation in Man," in *The Central Nervous System and Behavior*, ed. by M. A. B. Brazier (Josiah Macy, Jr., Foundation, New York, 1959), pp. 249–310.

Russell, W. R., *Brain, Memory, Learning* (Oxford University Press, Fair Lawn, N.J., 1959), chap. III, "Memory—the Capacity to Repeat"; chap. XIV, "Brain: Learning: Character."

Salter, A., *What Is Hypnosis?* (rev. ed., Farrar, Straus & Cudahy, Inc., New York, 1955).

Segundo, J. P., C. Galeano, J. A. Sommer-Smith, and J. A. Roig, "Behavioural and EEG Effects of Tones 'Reinforced' by Cessation of Painful Stimuli," in *Brain Mechanisms and Learning*, ed. by Fessard, Gerard, Konorski, and Delafresnaye (Charles C Thomas, Publisher, Springfield, Ill., 1961), pp. 265–292.

Sholl, D. A., *The Organization of the Cerebral Cortex* (Methuen & Co., Ltd., London, 1956), chap. VI, "The Mode of Operation of the Cerebral Cortex."

Wells, H. G., J. S. Huxley, and G. P. Wells, *The Science of Life* (Doubleday & Company, Inc., Garden City, N.Y., 1938), book 8, chap. VI, "The Cortex at Work," pp. 1288–1317.

Yerkes, R. M., "The Intelligence of Earthworms," *Journal of Animal Behavior*, vol. 2 (1912), pp. 332–352.

Higher Learning

A Working Hypothesis on Consciousness

As we move up the scale of intellectual complexity beyond the kinds of phenomena that we have somewhat arbitrarily categorized as "automatic learning," we come face to face with a formidable philosophic problem—the sense of consciousness. This subject is awkward and embarrassing to a mechanist. Of course, the problem has been with us in earlier chapters, but to this point has not become acute; so far it has been possible to keep consciousness well in the background of our discussions. But we are now about to concern ourselves directly with some of the phenomena of conscious mental processes and also with speculation on the kinds of purely mechanistic schemes of brain function that might underlie these processes. Before doing this, logic requires that we be clear as to our attitude toward the troublesome property of consciousness.

The subjective phenomenon of consciousness—the sense of awareness that is more real to the individual than anything else—has qualitative attributes that render it completely incapable of being derived from or accounted for by any combination of physical principles known today. This inadequacy of currently available physical science to explain consciousness can be either catastrophic or relatively insignificant in its implications as to the probable pertinence of mechanistic models of brain function. If the phenomenon of consciousness is an active and directly controlling part of the brain process under investigation, then mechanistic explanations are not likely to be in accordance with the observed facts of behavior. If, on the other hand, consciousness is purely a passive property, a kind of window through which we can observe a small part of the workings of the brain without interfering with the orderly operation of the machinery we are watching, then we can hope for pertinence of our theoretical models to conscious as well as to unconscious activity.

It is doubtless clear to the reader that we have been implicitly subscribing to the passive theory of consciousness. We shall continue to do so. However, this does not mean that we are entirely ignoring the property of consciousness. An engineer assigned the task of deciphering the details of construction and operation of a new and strange computer, unequipped with instruction handbook or maintenance manual, would not ignore any cathode-ray oscilloscopes, flashing lights, or meters that he found on the control panel, fragmentary though their indications might be. In what has preceded, and in what follows, we are considering consciousness in a similar way—as a sort of display device of unspecified calibration and distortion-producing characteristics which is connected in an unknown way into the complicated circuits we are trying to understand, but which nevertheless provides clues that may help us find solutions to some of the mysteries with which we must deal.

In the upcoming considerations, therefore, our concern with consciousness will reduce to the necessity of recognizing its display-device features, especially when, as in the evocation of the memory of an event or a concept, the end product of the neural activity appears to be solely the stimulation of our sense of awareness. Our mechanistic treatment of this kind of situation will be to bypass the problem by simply assuming that the sense of conscious recollection is automatically produced when specific groups of neurons in the brain are activated. At this stage of our ignorance, the best assumption is probably the simplest one—that the activation of a stored sensory pattern results, without the intervention of further machinery, in our conscious awareness of the contents of that pattern. Such activation will be our concern, but we shall not be concerned with the means by which it produces our subjective sensations.

For those to whom the idea of a completely passive sense of consciousness is unacceptable, there is nothing in this treatment that is logically inconsistent with an ultimate determination that some small degree of conscious control exists. Our working hypothesis, for all practical purposes, is simply that known physical principles are adequate to explain the brain processes to the depth of detail to which present knowledge makes speculation reasonable. A small perturbation in the operation of these physical principles, which could be of great philosophic importance, might not be observable by the computer or brain scientist for many years to come. As to such a possibility, we can preserve an open mind.

Memorization

The storage and recall of events is a consciousness-related phenomenon that has been slipped into the discussion of earlier chapters. Let us attempt to remedy our logical delinquency, not by a second treatment of event storage, but by discussion of a very similar process of conscious learning. When we attempt to fix in our minds, or "memorize," the contents of a room in which we find ourselves, all we appear to be doing is attempting to aid the normal processes of event storage and recall. Let us consider the subjective sensations associated with conscious memorization; they may help us understand how some of the machinery of the brain works.

Effective memorization is usually accompanied by the sensation of concentration of attention on the subject being memorized. We should probably not be surprised at this, in view of our several past observations on the importance of attention focusing in providing some electrical or chemical ingredient that is necessary for the permanent fixation of transient memories. However, our powers of concentration are not employed just to exclude irrelevant noises and thoughts from our consciousness; instead, our attention is "focused" successively on the various small pertinent details that we wish to imprint in our memory. This slow, laborious, step-by-step inventory operation that most of us have to perform if we are later to be capable of accurate recall is consistent with other evidence we have examined suggesting that the memory mechanism is not able to operate effectively at a very high data rate. Certainly such a conscious aid to memory would seem unnecessary if our storage system were capable of automatically recording and preserving for future use an accurate representation of all the data arriving over our sensory inputs.

It is probably correct to think of the memorization process as involving primarily the normal event storage and retrieval mechanisms, aided by an abnormally high level of attention focusing. The successive episodes of focusing the eyes and attention on the various objects in a room whose contents are being memorized would then be linked together in the memory by a form of the automatic-pattern-interconnection principle operating to tie together, for later recall as a group, the various sensory patterns that were originally experienced at about the same time. However, this cannot be quite the whole story. Temporal relations are less strongly involved in memorization than in most everyday activities of event storage and retrieval. The original memorizing activities may involve concentration first on a chair, then a table, then a book, and so on, but the future evocation of the scene may not preserve the same time sequence. Furthermore, the fact that a considerable period of time was spent in staring at one object and a briefer period in concentrating on another does not appear to be a part of the recollection that is later retrieved from the memory. It is as though some mechanism in the brain recognizes the essentially static nature of the memorization situation and sends suitable signals to turn off the sequencing circuits that must ordinarily be employed in event storage to permit successive "snapshots" of the changing external conditions to be independently recorded in separate matrices of neuronal material.

Such an ability of the brain mechanisms to "stop the camera" helps explain other aspects of the memorization process. Even when we have selected a small detail that we propose to fix in our memory as one of the pieces out of which the entire mosaic of the memorized recollection is to be formed, we know that we must keep our attention focused upon it for some little time if it is to stay with us. This seems understandable if the visual input remains connected to the same storage elements while a given detail is being concentrated on; thus, whatever electrochemical changes in the storage elements are involved in the fixation of a memory pattern, they would continue strengthening during the memorization process.

Another aspect of memorization is suggestive: the fact that we frequently do not lay the pattern down in one continuous effort. After we have partially established in our minds the picture of the chair we are trying to remember and have gone on to concentrate for a time on the table, we may then come back to the chair and, by further concentration, improve the accuracy of our memory trace by increasing the detail that we shall later be able to recall. Evidently the matrix of storage elements containing the partially formed memory pattern can be reconnected to the sensory inputs a second or third time around, for correction and further strengthening of the tenuously established connections.

Here, as in all aspects of visual perception and storage, there must be involved some complex transformations of the sensory data of the kind discussed in Chapter 3. In memorizing the contents of a room, we can move around and view the objects from different directions and angles without unduly disturbing the memorization process. In this discussion we evade the complexities of this difficult matter of perception invariance simply by assuming the existence of suitable transformations that in some way stabilize the incoming visual pattern against such distance, direction, and attitude changes before it is connected to the neuronal storage elements to reinforce or correct the trace that has previously been laid down.

The concept of a memory-storage system that can operate as a recorder of either "motion pictures" or "stills," with the recording mode being selected by some kind of circuit that detects the rate of change of the sensory pattern on which our attention is focused, is consistent with other evidence from experience. Although in Chapter 9 we saw some evidence that temporal sequencing and sometimes even absolute timing intervals can be preserved in the memory, this is certainly not always true. Our subjective judgments of time are often unreliable. All of us have been surprised on occasion to learn in how short an interval, as measured by the clock, a sequence of fast-moving events has occurred. Conversely, a long period relatively devoid of sensory, mental, or emotional activity is likely to be recorded in the memory, if it is recorded at all, as a few "stills," possibly supplemented by one or two short strips of "motion pictures." Incidentally, the computer scientist will not overlook the great reduction in the storage-capacity requirements that is occasioned by such a memory mechanism—one that records only when significant data are being received, and that even then spends much of its time in the correction and improvement of existing traces, rather than in the establishment of new records.

Associative Recall

Any theory of memory and learning, if it is to accord with compelling subjective experience, must provide a mechanism by means of which an event that is presently being seen, heard, smelled, or tasted can "remind" us of some previous happening in which similar sensory elements were present. It seems necessary to assume that the continually changing representation of current events played on our primary sensory screens is not only being connected to uncommitted neuronal storage elements for the establishment of new memories, but is also being passed to the input terminals of the many patterns of previously facilitated interconnections that represent our storage of past events. We must conclude that when a sufficient proportion of the input terminals for one of these stored patterns is activated by incoming sensory stimuli, the entire pattern is fired, as a consequence of the system of interconnection among the storage elements that had been established in the original recording. There then comes into our consciousness the recollection of the past event that was similar in some important respect to the current event that evokes it.

The absence of complete chaos in our conscious thought processes implies the existence of a strong inhibiting mechanism that filters only one chain of recollections at a time out of the memory store. Nevertheless, it seems reasonable to imagine that this inhibiting process is to some extent countered by a facilitating process that maintains a relatively low threshold for evocation of other recollections that share important sensory elements in common with what is currently either being experienced or recalled. Recollection of a past event related to a red balloon can easily be followed by another memory featured by a red apple.

The Formation of Concepts by Means of the Automatic-pattern-interconnection Principle

The ability to formulate and employ complex concepts is without doubt one of the principal bases for man's claim of intellectual superiority to the other animals. As the deepest penetration into the field of mental phenomena that we will make, let us see how far the mechanistic point of view that characterizes our approach to all such matters can carry us toward an understanding of the simplest type of concept formation—the establishment in the mind of a list of properties that together define a class of objects.

Consider a formal training program, with a hitherto uninformed child as the pupil. Suppose that we begin by showing the child a shiny red apple and at the same time distinctly pronouncing the word "ap-ple." We would expect an adequate number of repetitions of this performance, particularly if strengthened in each case by success in getting the child's attention, to result in the building of a permanent stored pattern in the brain. This pattern would possess both auditory and visual components which, by the operation of the automatic-pattern-interconnection principle that characterizes conditioned learning, would be tied together in the memory. As a result, ultimately the sight of the apple alone would be enough to trigger the entire stored complex and bring into the child's mind the recollection of the sound of the word; similarly, the spoken word would elicit the visual image.

Now let us add another sensory modality to our training routine. Suppose we allow the child to touch the apple and feel its smoothness each time it is presented. Because of the earlier training, the sight of the fruit now activates the previously stored audio-visual pattern, thereby qualifying its neuronal elements for participation in further interconnection activities. Thus, the automatic-pattern-interconnection processes can begin to build a bridge between a newly forming tactile representation of the apple and the better-established audio-visual pattern.

In a similar way we can add a memory trace for smell, and one for taste, to the growing assemblage of interconnected patterns in the child's memory circuits. At this point an interconnection will probably automatically be established to another part of the brain in which a memory trace for "pleasure" gets recorded, and we may as a consequence find that future recall of the package of memories associated with "apple" is suitably emotionally colored.

We can also make motor-control programs a part of our stored package. The child can be taught to say the word "apple" as he sees it, feels it, or eats it. Since this is operant rather than classical conditioning, there is the usual requirement for reinforcement, perhaps by parental approval or by more apple to eat when correct sounds are made.

Thus the child gradually builds up the "concept" of "apple." On our theory, the concept consists physically of a set of memory traces, in different and perhaps widely separated regions of the brain, one for each sensory modality that has been repetitively present during the learning experiences. The automatic-pattern-interconnection principle has seen to it that these separate memory traces are interconnected so that when one is activated, the others also fire. As a result, a child that has become sophisticated in the ways of apples can be caused to "think" of an apple by the aroma from a neighboring orchard. In such a case the sequence of neuronal activity is triggered by the activation of the odor component of the package of stored memory traces, resulting from the near identity of the incoming olfactory stimulus with the stored olfactory pattern. In our terms, the resulting "thought" consists simply of the subjective conscious effect produced by the simultaneous activation of the whole package of stored memory traces constituting the child's concept of "apple."

The development and employment of complex concepts doubtless is basic to most intellectual activity. This must be especially true of creative thought. In this connection there may be particular significance in the feature of our postulated storage mechanism whereby the activation of one stored memory pattern lowers the threshold of all other patterns containing similar sensory content. An essential ingredient of creative thought is the ability to move quickly and easily from one concept to a related one. It seems possible that the principal difference between the creative and the unimaginative individual is simply that the feedback or other mechanism involved in this threshold-lowering process is more effective for the one than for the other.

It is also easy to see why the possession of language gives man a great advantage over other animals. When words are "conditioned" to concepts they become symbols, the thinking or speaking of which can evoke the entire package of properties that constitute the concept. We would surely be greatly limited in the number of properties that we could combine into a single concept if we did not have a system by means of which a written or spoken label can automatically connect our sensory inputs for the addition of new information to the proper package of stored patterns.

Insensitivity of Thought Mechanisms to Brain Damage

In previous pages we have had a number of opportunities to observe the peculiar invulnerability of man's memory and, for that matter, of his general intellectual capacity, to surprisingly large amounts of brain damage. It is therefore encouraging that the conclusions at which we have arrived by our considerations of the memory and learning processes are not inconsistent with this observed diffuseness of higher brain function. We have come to expect the memory traces for either a concept or an event to be widely dispersed in the brain, with the visual part of the memory package in one location, the auditory part in another, and so on. And the interconnections between these related traces of different sensory modalities must clearly be multiplexed. The automatic-pattern-interconnection process that ties together the auditory and visual representations of an apple in the child's memory store would also connect the visual and the olfactory trace, the auditory and the taste, the taste and the olfactory, and so on. If a lesion or surgeon's knife were to interrupt one of these connecting paths, others would remain that could be physically quite remote from the one cut, because of the entirely different routes traversed among the storage locations for the various sensory modalities.

In addition to this diffuseness associated naturally with the memory processes, we are entitled to imagine that a degree of redundancy exists in the elemental memory traces themselves, as well as complete duplication, in some instances at least, of the stored patterns in more than one location of the brain. (Sperry's split-brain work, described in Chapter 9, led to this conclusion with respect to the visual discrimination patterns learned by his animals.) A combination of these factors of diffuseness and redundancy may well be capable of providing an adequate basis for an explanation of the inability of brain-research workers to localize the higher intellectual processes.

The Higher Intellectual Processes

The closer our explorations approach the field of complex mental phenomena, the smaller becomes the quantity of available and relevant physical measurements. This was noticeable in the last chapter and has become glaringly evident in this one, as our discussion has come to depend more and more on nonquantitative subjective and behavioristic observations, and less and less on supporting measurements made directly on the brain and nervous system. Clearly we have come to the end of the line in our treatment of the observed facts of brain construction and performance.

There is something unsatisfying about stopping just as we are coming to the higher thought processes. It seems as though this is where the story would really begin to get interesting, if we could only go on. And of course there is a way of traveling at least a short distance beyond the explored frontiers of our field: We could put some of the facts we have learned in our studies together with other ideas that we think are likely to be true and allow ourselves to be carried by the resulting theoretical model of brain function toward an explanation of higher intellectual processes that so far lie outside the realm of direct measurement.

To be sure, there are difficulties. While the material in the preceding chapters has revealed a great many hints and clues as to how the brain works, there isn't a great deal that is known with certainty. This means that an undesirably large number of unverified assumptions must be used as the basis for any model that attempts to go very far toward explanation of the more complex thought processes. But the very difficulty and uncertainty of the field that makes model-building riskier than usual also enhances its opportunities for major accomplishment. Theory, even when less solidly based than we would like, does turn up suggestive clues; and such clues are badly needed in brain research. Therefore many theoretical models of various aspects of brain function have been devised, and others are continually being invented. Probably there is something wrong with all of them, and a great deal wrong with many of them. Nevertheless the trend is good, not bad. Knowledge will come from it.

The theory of higher brain function is outside our scope, and we shall not undertake it. We should note, however, that the considerable amount of theoretical work now underway, although necessarily highly speculative, is making good progress in relating the general kinds of physical mechanisms that have been discovered in the brain and nervous system to observed mental characteristics. This inspires confidence in the essential soundness of the present trend of theory and experiment. If such confidence is not misplaced, we may hope that a physical model of brain function may one day be developed that *is* worthy of being taken seriously, in its detailed predictions as well as in its philosophic implications.

BIBLIOGRAPHY

Bruner, J. S., "Neural Mechanisms in Perception," in *The Brain and Human Behavior,* ed. by Solomon, Cobb, and Penfield (The Williams & Wilkins Company, Baltimore, 1958), pp. 118–141.

Hebb, D. O., *Organization of Behavior* (John Wiley & Sons, Inc., New York, 1949).

Sholl, D. A., *The Organization of the Cerebral Cortex* (Methuen & Co., Ltd., London, 1956), chap. VI, "The Mode of Operation of the Cerebral Cortex."

Computers and the Brain

Not long ago nearly everyone subscribed to the concept of brain/mind dichotomy. According to this concept, even the most complete and detailed understanding of the physical structure and operation of the brain could never suffice to explain mental activity. The mind was considered to be something nonphysical, outside the realm of the natural sciences; it was believed to make use of the brain as the agent for some of its activities, but was thought to possess properties and powers that could never be interpreted on the basis of any conceivable organization of cells and tissue.

In recent years the dualistic brain/mind concept has steadily lost ground to the mechanistic point of view. The development of machines capable of performing thoughtlike processes has aided this trend, although it would be unfair to attribute too much influence to electronic computer developments. The fact is that the change is mostly to be attributed to the successes of the traditional approach of medical research workers. Throughout the years they have learned that, whatever their philosophy, they make consistent progress in learning how living organisms operate by assuming that they are subject to the physical laws of nature and by painstakingly applying the techniques of scientific investigation. As a result, the history of medical research largely consists in repetitions of a single theme: the removal of one after another of the organs and functions of the body from the realm of the physically unknowable and unexplainable to which all living processes were once assigned. In former times the idea that the heart is no more than a complicated pump, which would one day be replaceable by a man-made device during a lengthy surgical operation, would have seemed as shocking to most people as the modern discoveries that the brain, too, operates in accordance with the physical laws of nature.

The practical approach to understanding a complex system of inter-related structures, whether it be a living organism or a man-made device, is to try to simplify the problem by breaking it down into smaller parts. This is why so much attention has been paid by research workers to the localization of functions in the brain. If it were impossible to find portions of this complex organ that are responsible for certain of its functions and other portions that seem to be related to other functions, not only would progress be impossible, but serious doubt would be cast on the validity of the mechanistic point of view. This is the reason for the importance of the discoveries that nervous tissue possesses neuronal building blocks whose individual properties largely account for the communication characteristics of the peripheral nerves, and that there are localized and determinable points of connection of the peripheral nerves to the cortex. Of similar importance are such developments as the isolation in the brain of the temperature-control mechanism and of neuronal circuits responsible for other reflex actions. Every time the control of some additional bodily process is traced to a specific part of the brain, there is a reduction by just that much in the amount of function that must be attributed to the "nonmaterial mind" and a corresponding increase in what can be accounted for by the machinelike brain.

Most impressive of all, of course, are the observations that reveal the physical basis of the "higher processes" of emotion and intelligence. The discovery of pleasure and punishment centers in the brain—discrete, localized, stable aggregations of neurons in which an electric current means a sense of well-being, hunger, sexual gratification, rage, terror, or pain—made it difficult for those whose thinking emphasized the dichotomy of the brain and the mind. This difficulty was further increased by the evidence for the controlling effect on personality of the integrity of the neuronal connections to the frontal lobes, as well as by the clear relationship established by Penfield between stimulating cortical currents and the "mental" processes of speech and memory. And evidence for the automatic, machinelike nature of some of the learning processes has further aggravated the plight of the brain/mind dualist.

In short, all the material of the preceding chapters has consisted of evidence for the applicability of the established physical laws of nature to the activities of the nervous system. The underlying thesis throughout has been, in essence, "The brain is a machine."

But if the brain is a machine, the next question is "What kind of machine?" Or, in more practical terms, "Is the brain so similar in its construction and operation to some known type of man-made machine that studies made on one are extensively pertinent to the other?"

Nowadays it is commonplace to emphasize the analogy between

the human brain and electronic digital computers. Such popular terms as "artificial intelligence" and "electronic brains" underscore their real or imagined similarities. On the other hand, there are dissenting opinions. Competent life scientists sometimes point out that the brain is not electronic, only partially digital, and not really a computer at all. These divergent points of view lead to different conclusions as to the importance of collaborative work between the computer and brain scientists. There is practical value in a realistic appraisal of the essential similarities and differences of the two fields.

No one denies that many of the end results of the activities of computers and the brain are similar. Every chapter in this book has provided instances of brain or nervous-system performance that have operational characteristics analogous to those exhibited by man-made devices. And even when no evidence has been available to support a detailed computer analogy to brain function, the attitudes and kind of language that characterize computer science have seemed to be applicable; in spite of the present impossibility of completely accounting for the more complex operations of the brain in terms of established physical principles, there is a comfortable feeling about them—they seem to be the kinds of operations that we may hope to observe in later generations of more sophisticated computers.

Although there may be little argument about the existence of operational similarities, there is much less than complete agreement on the implications of such similarities with respect to the mechanisms involved. If we look only at the end result of the transport of passengers across the Atlantic Ocean, much is to be said for the resemblance between a steamship and a jet airplane. The two vehicles convey passengers from New York to London at a similar cost and at about the same rate, in terms of average number of passengers moved across the ocean per hour of travel time; in each case schedules must be set, tickets must be sold, reservations must be made, and passengers must be transported to and from terminal points. Yet, nearly identical though these operational features are, no one would suggest that the machinery employed is so much alike that steamship and jet-aircraft designers could profit extensively by looking over each other's shoulders. Could it be the same with computers and the brain? Is it possible that the similar operational results they achieve are obtained by mechanisms that are so dissimilar as to preclude any extensive usefulness of cross-fertilization of the two fields?

The differences are obviously great. Visual comparison of the brain and a modern computer would not be likely to suggest a strong family resemblance. But we should be as wary of placing undue weight on structural differences that may turn out to be superficial, as we are of being overly impressed by what may be superficial similarities in their operational results. We must recognize that the physical characteristics of an existing electronic digital computer are largely determined by economic considerations associated with the present and entirely transient limitations of the state of the art. In a modern computer installation, for example, there are likely to be motor-driven magnetic drums, complex tape-driving and -reeling mechanisms, two-dimensional arrays of magnetic cores, and the like. But it is only considerations of cost and size that prevent all these mechanical devices from being replaced by large numbers of electronically operated on/off switches, essentially similar to the "gates" and "flip-flops" employed for the actual computation and logical manipulation. In fact, it can be shown that a general-purpose electronic digital computer could be comprised in its entirety of suitably interconnected, electrically activated on/off switches. In such a computer, some of the switches would serve as storage elements for data and programs, and others as logic elements for the performance of the data-processing operations; certain combinations of switches would be employed to provide the necessary temporal sequencing of the circuit to cause the computer to go through the large number of elemental steps specified by its program for the accomplishment of its assigned tasks. But the result would be a network possessing all the computing and logic-processing capabilities of the most complex modern machines—all done with on/off switches, nothing more. And no great stretch of the imagination is needed to see a resemblance between a vast assemblage of tiny switching elements interconnected by wires and a vast assemblage of neurons interconnected by nerve fibers.

Thus we must search at a deeper level if we are to find really basic differences between computers and the brain. Let us consider one clear-cut difference: the principles of construction of nature's neuron and those of the computer engineer's transistorized electronic switch. Complex chemical processes in the one obviously have no close analogy in the other. But here again, the apparent importance of such a difference disappears under analysis. The computer scientist is essentially uninterested in the details of construction of his components; he is concerned primarily with their over-all performance characteristics. There is at least one "electronic-digital-computer" research program under way in which the computing elements are entirely hydraulic. Nevertheless the same general principles of design, analysis, and assembly govern this work as apply to all other work in "electronic" digital computers. To be sure, electronic components are employed in most computers, but only because no one has yet invented nonelectronic devices that can compete in size, weight, reliability, cost, and speed. If someone could devise a practical way of preparing organic neuronal material so that it possessed the over-all operating properties called for by digital-computer theory, it would find a ready market. In the term "electronic digital computer," the adjective "electronic" is essentially incidental.

If we cannot find differences between computers and the brain that we accept as essential by comparisons of their over-all system configurations or of the principles of construction of their components, we must move our investigations from the anatomical to the physiological level. Are the functions performed by the neurons in the brain closely similar to those performed by the component switches in the computer?

This question is more difficult to deal with than those we have considered. We know that the neuron possesses not only some of the characteristics of an on/off switch, but also other properties. As described in Chapter 1, the all-or-nothing-response feature of the neuron is exhibited only by its axon. The body of the neuron, in electronic terms, is more like a summing amplifier that adds the effects of a number of inputs and compares the sum with a threshold value to determine whether the axon is to fire and, if so, what is to be the frequency of its output pulse train. And the threshold value is usually adjustable by chemical or electrical changes in the surrounding tissue.

This is a description of a much more complex and sophisticated device than the simple on/off switch of the computer designer. A computer engineer, presented with such components for use in the construction of a control system, would have a choice to make. In implementing the pupillary-reflex mechanism, for example, he could arrange his circuit inputs and voltages so as to operate the neurons as simple on/off switches, wired into a configuration equivalent to a general-purpose digital computer, including suitable translating circuits for coupling to the afferent and efferent nerves. But he could get by with much less equipment by copying nature and utilizing some of the other properties of his neuronal building blocks. As we have seen earlier, he would have to do no more than pass the train of pulses indicating the measured level of retinal illumination to the input of a motor neuron that directly supplies, over its axon, the train of pulses that constricts the pupillary muscle. By a proper adjustment of the firing threshold of this neuron, it could then be made to transmit a constricting signal only when the measured quantity of radiation incident on the retina exceeded the desired value, and the amount of this constricting signal—that is, the frequency of the transmitted effector pulses—would increase with increasing brightness, as desired.

The equipment ratio of the two approaches would not be so large if we were dealing with a more complex intellectual process of the brain, but the essential point would remain. It is unlikely that nature would have provided herself with the capability for versatility and equipment simplification inherent in the properties of the neuron unless she planned to make extensive use of it. Not only logic, but the evidence from EEG and probe measurements, strongly suggest that there are no pure "digital" computing circuits in the brain, that is, circuits employing only the on/off switching capabilities of their components.

Here, finally, we appear to have a major difference between computers and the brain. Yet let us not conclude too quickly that the difference is so profound as to impose narrow limits on the areas of mutual relevance of brain and computer science. Completeness requires that we investigate the possibility that a valid case can be made for the point of view that the adjective "digital" is no more essential than "electronic" to the electronic digital computer. Improbable though it may seem, such a case can indeed be made!

What a computer does, and *all* that it does, is generate patterns of voltage at its output terminals by performing a precisely prescribed set of operations on the patterns of voltage supplied to its input terminals. These operations are simple, but frequently very numerous. In the basic computer that is composed entirely of interconnected electronic switches, each elemental step is a simple switching operation. Connections to the input terminals of one of the switches bring in voltages, either from the computer input data or from the output of earlier switching operations; the switch thus innervated assumes one electrical state or another in accordance with whether its pattern of input voltages meets the conditions for operation determined by its own internal design. The electrical result of each of these simple processing steps joins with the outputs from other similar operations, and perhaps with some of the computer input voltages, to provide the raw material for additional processing steps. Ultimately, the outputs of some of the switch processing elements provide the final answers to the problem being solved—the voltages on the output terminals.

The secret of the power of modern computers resides in the discovery that extraordinarily complex operations can be broken down into steps that can be handled by very simple processing elements. In mathematical calculations, any operation that the mathematician has invented can be broken down into such elemental steps and caused to control the generation of the voltages representing the output numbers. And in logic problems, the computer can deduce new conclusions from given propositions by the application of the rules of logic, which can be broken down into the same simple processing steps as those used in mathematical computations.

Now let us return to the point of this discussion—the properties required of the processing elements, the "neurons" of the computer. In actual computers they are usually purely digital elements—on/off switches. This contributes to the simplicity, increases the reliability, and lowers the cost of the computer components. Furthermore, the theory has been thoroughly worked out only for computers based upon such yes/no devices. This is a new field and a difficult one. It is natural that the early development of the field should be characterized by exploitation of the simpler principles of logical processes. Much of the theory to date emphasizes true/false choices as the elemental steps out of which complex problem-solving can be synthesized. The on/off alternatives of a simple switch nicely match the true/false alternatives of the steps of such theory. This is, in fact, the source of the "digital" operating characteristics of most modern computers.

However, there are other ways of solving logical problems. There is, for example, probabilistic logic, in which the basic elements are not positive yes/no answers, but estimates of the probability that the answer is yes or no. Simple on/off switches can be used as the components of computers based upon such logical schemes, but they are inefficient—much as devices such as variable-weight-factor summing amplifiers are inefficient when used as components of a computer designed around two-valued logic.

When we are wiser about these matters, it seems certain that we shall want processing elements for our computers that provide greater versatility in their performance characteristics than do simple on/off devices. In fact, the exploratory work now under way in various laboratories on different types of "electronic neurons" with variable-summing and adjustable-threshold features is probably a forerunner of this ultimate broadening of the spectrum of the elemental processing components that will be used by the computer circuit designer.

This brings us to the conclusion we were after: *the narrowly digital nature of its processing elements is not here to stay and hence is not a really essential characteristic of the electronic digital computer.*

But if the essence of the modern computer is not to be found either in the term "electronic" or in "digital," where does it lie? Are we engaged in a meaningless exercise in semantics, or is there some characteristic of electronic digital computers, not evident in the name, that possesses fundamental significance? There is indeed one such characteristic. It was referred to earlier as the secret of the power of modern computers—the discovery that complex computational and logical operations can be broken down into steps that can be handled by very simple processing elements. The individual processing steps, we have just seen, may be expected to develop with time. What will not change, what is really fundamental about the general types of machines that have been too narrowly described as "electronic digital computers," is that they get their amazing results by the performance of a very large number of very simple processing steps. *This would also appear to be a valid description of the essence of brain function.*

Thus our argument has finally led us to the conclusion that computers and the brain do not simply display superficial similarities in some of their operational characteristics. Instead, they are mechanisms of the same kind, in the sense that they obtain their similar results by essentially similar means. If this is true, then it is clear that the computer scientist and the brain scientist need one another badly for the future development of their respective fields. Consider the differences between the physical and biological approaches and how beautifully they supplement each other. We have seen that computer science is dominated by theory. The most intensive work is under way aimed at learning how intellectual processes can be broken down into simple steps. Computer programs have been worked out for the playing of games like checkers and chess, and for the automatic production of new theorems of geometry and the propositional calculus. Better understanding of the principles of learning is being gained continually by the physical scientists, who are developing techniques of programming existing machines, and of building new ones, that can do an increasingly effective job of learning from experience and modifying their performance accordingly. Progress is also being made in the theory of general problem-solving —the reduction to precisely specified sequences of simple steps of the processes that are described, when humans employ them, by such words as "originality" and "ingenuity."

It is from the work of these physical scientists that the theoretical techniques must come for explaining how the elemental processing steps of the neurons in the brain are capable of combining to produce the performance attributes of intelligence. Problems of the complexity of those arising in the brain cannot be solved by experiment alone; theory will be essential to point the way to meaningful experiments and to help interpret the results when they are performed. Since the biologist has neither the training nor the tradition for this kind of theoretical work, he needs the physical scientist—he cannot do the job without him.

But it works both ways. The task that has been undertaken by the physical scientist—that of developing quantitative and precise theoretical models of intellectual processes—is one that is too difficult for him to handle without clues from the life sciences. Any hint that "nature may do it this way" can be of inestimable value to the theoretical research worker in helping him choose a promising approach for his speculations from among the many blind alleys that confront him.

Fortunately, collaboration is under way and is increasing. From such interdisciplinary effort we may confidently expect great progress to be made in the coming years in our understanding of the operation of the brain. The human implications can be tremendous, in terms of relief of suffering from brain injury and disease, the better physical and psychological management of our mental health, and, ultimately perhaps, the development of electrical, chemical, and operative techniques for the practical enhancement of our intellectual capabilities.

Computer technology will be similarly rewarded. Increased understanding of the theory and practice of intellectual processes will lead inevitably to a steady evolutionary upgrading in the "intelligence quotient" of successive generations of computing devices. The application of lessons from the life sciences may be more effective than anything else in speeding the day when, by the availability of machines that truly "think," humanity will finally be able to enjoy the real fruits of automation.

These are foreseeable practical consequences of the cross-fertilization of computer and brain research. There is also a philosophic by-product of first magnitude that may well come out of this kind of activity. The convergence of computer and brain sciences will render untenable the studied avoidance of the phenomenon of consciousness that has characterized the science of the last fifty years. When it is established that there is a continuous gradation between the design features and performance characteristics of man-made machines and the intelligent living products of nature, scientists will be forced to come to terms in some way with this most vivid and real property of human experience.

To be sure, in the last chapter, in considering consciousness, we defined a postulate, generally similar to that which underlies much modern thinking, that permitted us to get on with our physically based speculation. But our working hypothesis constituted no more than an untidy patching up of the hole in our logical structure that we hoped would permit it to hold together until we could finish our planned exploration of some of the current frontiers of brain research. We have evaded the main issue: why a philosophy with the spectacular and growing successes of mechanism should fail so completely to provide any means of dealing with the very real phenomenon of consciousness. Questions are already arising in increasing numbers, the answers to which now appear to require a completely unsatisfactory blending of physics and metaphysics. Consider, for example, Sperry's split-brain animals, which respond differently to external stimuli depending upon which half of the brain they are using. Have they been provided with two different senses of consciousness that are turned on or off in accordance with which eye they look through? If an affirmative answer is not yet required by the evidence, what will we say if Sperry succeeds in extending the split-brain technique all the way down through the brainstem and thereby makes possible the development of two clearly different personalities in the same body? And what is the significance of the remarkable fact, discovered by Magoun and coworkers, that the sense of consciousness is turned on or off by the presence or absence of suitable electric currents in the reticular activating system of the brainstem? What about the peculiar phenomenon of "double consciousness" experienced by Penfield's patients under temporal-lobe stimulation, in which they had the subjective sensation of living concurrently in the past and the present?

Questions arising out of a blending of physical and biological developments are even more compelling. Consider the following line of speculation: It is now known that there is no essential difference between living and nonliving matter. Living matter either has, or has almost, been synthesized in the laboratory out of inert ingredients, the statement depending upon just where the line is drawn in the very fuzzy region that separates life from nonlife. Rapid progress is also being made in breaking the genetic code; it is no longer purely science fiction to speculate that one day man may be able to synthesize the chromosomic content of cell nuclei and, by providing a suitable growth environment, thereby "build" living organisms of considerable complexity. Now, if the resulting animal is similar to a naturally created higher animal, will it be conscious? It would be hard to doubt that it will. What then if a creature of similar behavior and intelligence were to be fabricated from components of quite a different kind—with a nervous system and brain based on electronic components instead of neurons, for example? Would it too possess consciousness and the subjective feelings that go along with it? For all we know today, surely this has to be considered to be a possibility. And how about existing electronic digital computers? Is it possible that, somewhere among their wires and transistors, there already stirs the dim glimmering of the same kind of sense of awareness that has become, for man, his most personal and precious possession? Fantastic? Perhaps.

Such speculation is no longer pointless. It leads to what may well be the only sound procedure for permanently plugging the hole in the logical structure of the mechanistic philosophy: *to accept the sense of consciousness itself as a natural phenomenon suited to being described by and dealt with by the body of laws and methods of the physical sciences.*

This suggestion is really not particularly revolutionary. The immediate human reaction—that consciousness is by its very nature a mysterious and unexplainable phenomenon—is not very pertinent. All the laws and properties of nature are fundamentally mysterious and unexplainable; science can no more explain gravitational attraction or electric charge than it can the sense of consciousness. "Explanation" of the laws and fundamental particles of physics would involve exactly the same kind of crossing of the boundary into the realm of metaphysics as would "explanation" of the subjective sensations and feelings that constitute our personal sense of awareness.

All that is really required, for the sense of consciousness to constitute a reasonable candidate for admission into the structure of physics, is that it be orderly and lawful in its operation, and that techniques be conceivable for determining the relationships between its properties and the physical environment in which it occurs. Admittedly, the observations involved in any attempt to make consciousness scientifically respectable will have to depend mainly on variations in the personal sensations of human subjects, rather than on the objective readings of oscilloscopes and meters. This will make the matter more difficult, but certainly not impossible. We may never know just what is meant by a level of consciousness that is twice as intense as another, but there need be no ambiguity about the determination that all human subjects report themselves to feel conscious or unconscious in accordance with whether the electric potential at a certain point in a specific nucleus of the brainstem is greater or less than, say, 0.025 volt. Similarly specific relationships are already hinted at by some of the experiments connecting the electrical conditions of definite brain structures with such attributes of consciousness as fear and pleasure. Of course, this observation also underlines the fact that consciousness is not a simple property but possesses several attributes corresponding to the various sensations, perhaps in somewhat the same way as a fundamental particle of physics may possess not only mass but also charge and spin.

In interpreting consciousness as a physical property of matter, we do not really need to go back 300 years to the time of Spinoza. We have no reason to associate consciousness with all matter—only with the brain. And only with part of the brain, part of the time. We have learned that most of the work of the brain is done completely unconsciously, and we have come to have a healthy respect for the quality and the complexity of the computing/control functions that are carried out in this way. Even in what we consider to be our conscious mental activity, we are actually aware of only a part of what is going on in the brain. There must be intricate switching and scanning processes underway that move related thoughts successively into our consciousness; we are aware of the thoughts, but not of how they get there. Such unconscious activity sometimes appears to extend to complicated logical thinking—how else can we account for the sudden insight or solution of a difficult problem that sometimes comes to us when least expected? Even when it seems to us that our conscious processes are completely responsible for our mental activities, we may be wrong; the real work of the brain may be that which is going on quietly behind the scenes. The evidence of Chapter 8 as to the automatic, mechanical character of basic learning processes should have left the reader with a real question as to whether what his sense of awareness tells him he is doing in a learning situation is entirely to be trusted.

What is required to fit the facts, therefore, is not a theory that assigns a tiny bit of consciousness to every atom of matter. It does not even appear that consciousness is an inevitable property of complex computing/logic-processing structures. Instead, the evidence suggests that the property of consciousness is possessed only by very special organizations of matter (of types yet to be determined) when placed in a suitable electrochemical state (that is still unknown).

The relative rareness of the conditions necessary for the conscious state may, of course, be matched by its relative unimportance. No useful purpose has yet been established for the sense of awareness that illumines a small fraction of the mental activities of a few species of higher animals. It is not clear that the behavior of any individual or the course of world history would have been affected in any way if awareness were nonexistent. But this is a cosmic rather than a personal point of view. To a conscious person, anything pertaining to the property of consciousness must always seem of overriding importance. Of the greatest human significance, therefore, is the probability that our subjective sensations are ruled in a regular and predictable way by the processes of natural law. It will become progressively more difficult for this probability to be ignored as the matter is thrown into increased prominence by the convergence of the computer and brain sciences. The result may well be the transfer of the phenomenon of consciousness out of metaphysics and into the realm described by the physical laws of nature. It would be hard to imagine a development of more far-reaching importance to science and philosophy. Yet it could come as a consequence of increased collaborative research on computers and the brain.

Truly the convergence of the disciplines of computer research and brain research is a movement of the greatest importance. It is doubtful whether the history of science provides any example in which the merging of two technical fields provided a superior opportunity for major accomplishment. Although the collaborative effort is making good progress, it is still in its infancy. One prediction can be safely made: as understanding develops, promising new avenues of research will open up at a rapidly increasing rate. Whether or not the interdisciplinary effort is adequately manned today, it is very likely to be undermanned tomorrow, in relation to the importance and opportunities of the field.

This book has been written in the hope that, by calling attention to some of the interesting adventures available to those who explore the mysteries of the brain, it might help a few computer scientists make the decision to join the movement. There can be considerable doubt as to its attainment of the objective, but there can be no question as to the importance of the goal. The cause is a worthy one.

index

Frontal lobes, 145–153
    damage to, 147–148
    and emotion, 151, 153
    and intelligence, 152–153
    plasticity and redundancy, 162
    traditional view of, 145
Frontal lobotomy, on chimpanzees, 148–149
    on humans, 149–150
    relief of pain by, 150
Fulton, J. F., 17

Gage, Phineas, strange case of, 146–147
Gajdusek, D. C., 97
Galambos, Robert, viii, 17, 195, 213–214, 217
Galeano, C., 218
Galvani, Luigi, 1–2
Gamma-efferent mechanism, 65–66
Garcia-Austt, E., 217
Genes, 87–96
Genetically directed "wiring" of nervous system, 19–22, 33–35
Genetic control of behavior, 91–95
    evidence, 95
    evolutionary hypothesis, 91–95
Genetics, 86–95
    general features, 89–91
    library of specifications, 87, 89–90
        individual variations in, 90
    molecular mechanisms, 86–91
    mutations, 91
Gerard, R. W., 195, 217
Gifford, E. M., Jr., 89, 97
Giurgea, C., 217
Glial cells as memory elements, 192
Gonadotrophin, 70
Goode, M., 139, 143
Goose flesh reflex, 56
Grand mal epilepsy, 105
Grasshopper, 80
Gray matter, in brain, 25
    composition, 28
    in spinal cord, 19

Habituation, 213
Hagiwara, S., 73
Hallucinations in epilepsy, 136–137
Hamlin, H., 143
Hance, A. J., 216
Harlow, H. F., 217
Harvard cats, 50–53

Hassenstein, Bernard, 39
Heath, R. G., 144
Hebb, D. O., viii, 147–148n., 165, 195–196, 217, 228
Hendrix, C. E., 216
Hernandez-Peon, R., 140, 144, 206, 217
Hess, Eckhardt H., 211, 218
Hess, W. R., viii, 124, 144
Higher intellectual processes, 226–227
Hippocrates, 105
Histone as deactivator of RNA, 88–89
Homunculus, 31
Hormone, adrenocorticotrophic (ACTH), 69
    gonadotrophic, 70
    thyroid-stimulating (TSH), 68
Horowitz, N. H., 97
Huang, R. C., 96–97
Hubel, D. H., 50, 54
Hudgins, C. V., 200, 218
Huxley, J. S., 17, 97, 144, 218
Hypnosis, learning under, 202
Hypothalamus, electric measurements in, 124–125
    electric rhythms in, 134
    multiple programs stored in, 69
    pituitary gland control by, 69–71
    temperature control by, 59–60
    in ulcer formation, 130–131
    visceral control by, 125

Imprinting (see Learning)
Inherited behavior patterns, 79–83
    bee, 83
    birds, 79–81
    caterpillar, 81
    crab, 80
    grasshopper, 80
    octopus, 80, 82
    squid, 80
    wasp, 82–83
Inhibitory post-synaptic potential, 11
Input devices, nature's, 7
Input/output cable, 18
Input/output devices, nature's, 13–17
Insects, intelligence, 82–85
Insensitivity of thought mechanisms to brain damage, 225
Intellectual processes, higher, 226–227

Memorization (see Learning)
Memory, 166–196
  attention focusing in, 183–184
  brain-wave signature, 214–216
  decay, 190–191
  double consciousness, 167
  electroshock interference with, 185–187
  fraction of experience recorded in, 190
  mechanisms underlying temporal lobes, 184
  multiple mechanisms of, 181–186
    evidence from brain concussion, 183–184
    long-term, 182
    medium-term, 184–185
    short-term, 182
    transfer to long-term memory blocked by lesion, 184
  old, strength of, 186–188
  of past events, location of, 179–180
    sensory qualities in, 180
    time scale preservation in, 180
  recording, RNA changes during, 193
  storage capacity needed, 188–193, 223
  storage element, 191–192
  trace, duplication, 175–176, 178
    localization, 168–180
      in brainstem, 169, 179
      in cortex, 169–180
      for learned response, 176–179
      for past event, 179–180
  triggering, by cortical stimulation, 166–168
    epileptic lowering of threshold for, 168
  (See also Concept; Concept formation)
Mental illness, brain-wave activity in, 137
  treatment by electric stimulation, 133
Menzies, R., 200, 218
Michie, Donald, viii
Mickle, W. A., 144
Miller, G. A., 196
Mind/brain concept, dualistic, 229–230

Miniaturized construction, nature's techniques of, 86–96
MIT frogs, 46–50
Molecular mechanisms of genetics, 86–91
Moniz, Egaz, 149, 165
Monkey, conditioning of, 203
  executive, 131
  split-brain, 175, 178–179
Morrell, F., 196, 218
Moth, tropism, 77–78
Motor neurons, 7
Motor strip in cortex, 34
Moving-edge detectors in eye of frog, 47–48
Muller, H. J., 94n., 97
Multiple memory mechanisms (see Memory)
Multiplexing of receptors, 38
Muscle, neuron control of, 16
  patterns of activity, 60–62
  response, gamma-efferent mechanism, 65–66
  tone, reticular activating system control of, 66
Mutations, 91–94
Myelin, 18
Myers, R. E., 170n., 196

Nerve impulse, all-or-nothing nature, 4, 8
  direction, 9
  discovery of electrical nature, 1
  frequency, 9
  lack of degradation, 9
  saturation, 5
  speed, 8
  in stretch receptor, 4
  summation, 11
  threshold, 4
  transmission, 19–21
  (See also Neuron)
Nerves, 18
  regeneration, 20–22
  types, 3
  (See also Neuron)
Nervous system, economy of design, 37–38
Net convexity detectors in eye of frog, 47–49
Net dimming detectors in eye of frog, 47–48
Networks of interneurons, 38–49

Neurology, father of, 1
Neuromuscular junction, 16
Neuron, 5–13
  afferent, 3
  chains, 11
  changes in memory recording, 193
  as computer component, 12
  depolarization, 8
  dimensions, 18, 28
  effector, 7, 15–17
  efferent, 3
  functioning of, 7–17
  inter-, 7
  as memory storage element, 191–192
  as more than on/off switch, 233
  motor, 7
  myelinated, 18
  networks, 38–49
  parts, 7
  post-synaptic potential, 11
  receptor, 13–17
  saturation, 5
  sensory, 7
  spontaneous firing by, 4
  structure, 5
  threshold, 4, 12
  types, 7
  (See also Nerve impulse)
North, H. Q., viii
Nucleotides, 87

Occipital lobes, 34
Olds, James, 127, 144
Ommatidia, 40
One-eyed cats, case of, 170–179
On/off switch, nature's, 5–13
Optic chiasma, cutting, 171
Optomotor response, 39–46
Oscillators in nervous system, 56–57
  cicada, 57
  Eigenmannia, 57
  lobster, 56
  lower animals, 57
  Torpedo fish, 57
Oscilloscope, cathode-ray, 3
Output devices, nature's, 7

Pacinian corpuscle, 14
Pain relief, in dental chair by tape recordings, 141–142
  by electric stimulation in brain, 133

Pain relief, by frontal lobotomy, 150
Paramecia, learning by, 207
Parameter adjustment by reticular activating system, 65–67
Pattern interconnection principle, automatic, 203–204
  in concept formation, 224–226
Pavlov, I. P., 197–199, 201, 210
Penfield, Wilder, viii, 36, 144, 154–162, 165–168, 188–189, 194, 196, 238
Perception invariance, 49, 51–52
  in memorization, 222
Peripheral data processing in nervous system, 37–54
Permanently wired-in behavior patterns, 74–97
Personality, changes caused by frontal lobe damage, 146–148
  split, in split-brain animals, 181
Pfeiffer, J., 112
Phase properties of brain waves, 215–216
Phenylketonuria, 95
Philosophy, of brain/mind relationship, 219–220, 229–230
  of consciousness, 219–220, 237–241
Photic driving of alpha rhythm, 104
Physical quantities, receptor measurement of, 13–17
Physical science, convergence with biology, 236–237
Pittendrigh, C. S., 97
Pitts, W. H., 46, 54
Pituitary gland, 69–71
  role in stored program selection, 67–71
Placement of electrodes by stereotaxis, 122
Plasticity, of cortical areas, 160–162
  of thought mechanisms, 226
Pleasure centers, 127–129
  discovery, 127
  do-it-yourself experiments on, 127–128
  in humans, 133
  insatiable aspects, 128–129
  kinds, 128–129
  locations, 129
  in monkeys, 129
  proximity to punishment centers, 131–133